BOOKS  ABRIDGED

Sayonara
JAMES A. MICHENER

◆

Fire in the Ashes
THEODORE H. WHITE

◆

Adventure Happy
JULE MANNIX

◆

Cress Delahanty
JESSAMYN WEST

BOOKS ABRIDGED, INC. *New York*

Sayonara

JAMES A. MICHENER

SAYONARA—James A. Michener
Published by Random House at $3.50
Copyright, 1953, 1954, by James A. Michener

CHAPTER I

ON APRIL 4, 1952, I shot down my sixth and seventh MIGs. It happened up near the Yalu River and when I returned to base at J-10 I was excited. The Air Force doctor took one look at me and said, "Gruver, you've had it."

Boy, they were sweet words. They meant I was through flying for a while. But since I'm a West Point man I felt obligated to appear eager before the flight surgeon who had been called back from civilian life, pot belly and all. So I frowned and said, "Nothing wrong with me, Doc. A bottle of beer'll fix me up."

"That's right," the doc agreed.

He had taken my eagerness seriously and for a minute I felt a little sick inside. I didn't want to fly any more. Not just then. I wanted to appear rough and ready but I also wanted some solid chairborne duty.

But the doc was smart. He laughed and said, "Don't turn pale, Gruver. I was only kidding. I never take this hero stuff seriously. You're going back to Japan!"

From the way he said this you knew he thought Japan was paradise, but I'd been through the place and it never impressed me much. Dirty streets, little paper houses, squat men and fat round women. I had never understood why some Air Force people got so steamed up about Japan.

I said, "If you go for Japan, I suppose it's good news. I'd just as soon rest up right here at J-10."

Doc said, "You mean you never tangled with any of those beautiful Japanese dolls at Tachikawa?"

I said, "I'm a four-star general's son. I don't tangle with Japanese dolls, beautiful or not."

Doc looked at me sorrowfully and said, "Chum, you're sicker than I thought."

7

I hadn't meant to sound stuffy, but when you know your outfit sort of has you ticketed for fast promotion right through to colonel and maybe one-star general by the time you're thirty-five, a lot of the ordinary razzle-dazzle connected with military life doesn't impress you. On the other hand, I had always tried not to act superior to reserve officers just because they were civilians at heart.

I said, "I'll think of you, Doc, when I hit those clean Tokyo sheets and that Tokyo beer."

He shook his head with a tricky little leer and said, "For you, Chum, it ain't gonna be Tokyo. For you . . . special orders."

Like a warning flash and without my actually thinking the word I blurted, "Kobe?"

"Yep, Chum! You made it."

Instinctively I put my left hand on my hip and felt for my wallet. I said, "About these special orders? Were they from General Webster?"

"Yep, Chum! You're in." He gripped his hands in a tight little ball and winked at me. "Why wouldn't one general look after another general's son? Kelly has your orders."

"I'll go see Kelly," I said, glad to get away from this know-it-all civilian.

But as I left the medical tent and started down the gravel path to squadron headquarters, another civilian called me: "Gruver, could I speak with you?"

I turned and saw the chaplain and since he almost never spoke to anyone except about trouble I stopped short and asked, "Kelly again?"

"Yes," he said almost sorrowfully. "This time it's serious." He led me to his tent, a beat-up affair with Bibles, crucifixes and the special silver gadgets for conducting Jewish ceremonies.

"Kelly face another court-martial?" I asked.

"Worse. He's appealed to his Congressman."

I'd always been disgusted with enlisted men who write letters to Congressmen. The Air Force had a sensible and just way to handle any problem. Congressmen weren't needed. So I asked, "Why don't you advise the colonel to throw this guy out of the service?"

"Under the new rules . . ."

The new rules! I was always forgetting the new rules. Starting in 1945 a lot of soft-headed do-gooders in Washington had revised the basic rules for military conduct and as a result you now saw enlisted men writing to Congressmen.

"So under the new rules, what happens?" I asked.

"So Kelly gets his way. He goes back to Japan. And when he gets back to Japan, he marries the girl."

This was too much. I sat down in one of the padre's rickety chairs and asked, "You mean that in spite of all you and the colonel have said to this kid he still gets permission to marry the girl?"

"That's right."

"Why doesn't somebody bust him in the head?"

"That's no solution. I want you to talk with him."

"Nothing more I can say. Look, Padre. Kelly belongs to your church. You're the guy who's got to save him."

Chaplain Feeney became very serious and took my hands in his. It was a trick he used when he wanted to make a point and it accounted for much of his success with the squadron. He was never afraid to plead with a man. "You must believe me when I say I'm not trying to save Kelly for my church. I'm trying to save him for himself. If he marries this Japanese girl it can lead only to tragedy. In ordinary times such a marriage would be unwise, but under the new law . . . when he can't even take her with him to America . . . What's to happen, Gruver?"

He spoke so passionately that I had to give in. "All right. What do you want me to do?"

He was embarrassed at what he was about to suggest and hesitated a moment. Then he said, "You're engaged to a fine, good-looking American girl. You showed me her picture one night." He smiled as I reached for my wallet pocket. "If the opportunity presents itself, show Kelly your girl's picture. Let him remember what a fine American girl looks like."

I said, "I'm not selling anything."

The padre was a smart man. "Who asked you to?" he said. "When he says he's determined to get married tell him you understand. Tell him you've seen some really wonderful Japanese girls."

"Trouble is, Padre, I haven't. They're all so dumpy and round-faced. How can our men—good average guys—how can they marry these yellow girls? In '45 I was fighting the Japs. Now my men are marrying them."

"I've never understood it. Such marriages are doomed and it's my job to prevent them."

"I agree."

"Then you'll speak to Kelly?"

"Wouldn't it be simpler for the colonel just to order him not to get married?" I asked.

Chaplain Feeney laughed. "Some things can't be handled that way. We've investigated the girl Kelly wants to marry. She's not a prostitute. She's not subversive. As a matter of fact, she got a good recommendation from our investigators. Used to work in a library. Kelly has a right to marry her."

The word *marry* caught me strangely and I was swept back four years to a spring week-end in Texas when a gang of us left Randolph Field for a big time in San Antonio. We were walking down some stone steps to an open-air theater by the river that runs through the middle of San Antonio, when suddenly I saw this beautiful girl coming up. I did a double take and cried, "Aren't you General Webster's daughter?" And she gave me a dazzling smile and said she was and I stood right there staring at her and asking, "Why didn't you look like this when you lived across from me in Fort Bragg?" and she said she'd always looked like this but I had been too busy going away to the Point to notice. I tried to recall but couldn't even remember her clearly from those days so I said, "You must have been a long-legged kid of eleven when we were at Fort Bragg." Then she said something which stopped me cold. She ignored the other Air Force men standing beside me and said, "I'm still a long-legged kid." And she was right and eighteen days later we sort of made up our minds to get married. But Eileen's mother and Korea took care of that.

So I brought myself back to Korea and told Chaplain Feeney, "I'll do what I can."

"Thanks, Gruver." As I started to go he asked, "Mind if I speak to the colonel about you?"

"What for?"

"You're as tense as a watch spring, son. I'm going to tell the old man you ought to be grounded."

I laughed and said, "The doc beat you to it. I'm on my way to Japan."

"Wonderful," he said. "Tokyo?"

"No, Kobe. My girl's father is general down there."

"That's fortunate."

"It has its drawbacks."

"I mean Kelly is going to Kobe, too. You can keep an eye on him."

I was disgusted. "You mean you're flying him back to where the girl is?"

"His Congressman insists on it."

I started to say what I thought of Congressmen who butt into military affairs like this but the padre said, "You might save the boy."

I thought of mean, sawed-off Joe Kelly and said as I left, "Nothing could save that bum."

CHAPTER II

I T WAS a curious day in Korea. Our air base at J-10 wasn't
what you'd call warm, but there was a shot of spring in the air
and the ground was beginning to thaw and even Korea felt pretty
much the way any part of the world feels in spring. I took a
couple of good deep lungfuls of air and walked down headquarters street, a dismal drag even with spring nibbling at its
edges, and I said to myself, "Skip Kelly. Let him take care of
himself."

I headed for my bunk, where there would be some beer and
a poker game, but then I realized that Kelly had the hot dope
on my orders, so I went into the squadron tent where I found
this mutt sitting behind a hand-painted sign big enough for a
general: AIRMAN KELLY.

He was a runty kid in his teens. I was twenty-eight and everybody younger than that seemed immature, but Kelly really was.
He'd come up through a tough section of Chicago and had sandy
hair and an up-with-your-dukes Irish face. He was against the
world and against all officers in particular. He had the weird
record of having been promoted to corporal four times—and
busted back each time. He was bitter and always in trouble and
the last man in our outfit you would expect to get involved seriously with any girl.

He shoved my orders at me and said, "Pays to have friends."

I had been responsible for one of Kelly's court-martials, but
he had astonished me on the second by requesting me as his
counsel. He respected no one, but he did like men who flew the
jets. When he jammed the papers at me I was going to haul him
up again, but he grinned and said, "Hear you bagged two more
today. How was it up there, Ace?"

"Never gets easier."

"You know what's in your orders?" he asked in a snide way that a gangster might use in asking about a pay-off.

"Kobe," I said, picking them up.

"Yeah, but I mean how you happened to get them?"

"I've never discussed things like orders with enlisted men," I said, turning for the door.

Kelly was different. He said, "What I mean is, did you know about General Webster writin' to the colonel about you?"

"Me?"

"Yeah, General Webster started all his letters, 'Of course I don't intend to intrude on your handlin' of the squadron but . . .' He always got the *but* in."

"But what?"

"But he would sure like to have Major Lloyd Gruver come right the hell down to Kobe."

I stuffed the papers into my pocket and said, "I didn't ask for orders like that."

Kelly laughed in an ugly way and said, "You ain't heard nothin' yet, Ace. General Webster's had you assigned to the Interservice Aviation Board, which means you sit on your parachute all day long and do nothin'." Then he grinned and added, "Why do you suppose you're gettin' orders to Kobe? And a cushy job? And a priority flight?"

I sensed that I was getting in too deep with Kelly and changed the subject. "Chaplain tells me you're heading for Kobe, too."

"Yep. Chaplain said no. Colonel said no. You said no. But the Congressman said yes."

I let him know by my manner that I was disgusted with such procedures and asked with some irony, "And I hear you're getting married."

"Yep. I hear you're gettin' married too."

"What do you mean?" I asked.

"The general's daughter is arrivin' in Kobe. Tomorrow."

Kelly stared up at me with a nasty grin and when I asked if this was true he said, "Yep. General Webster arranges it so you can marry his daughter. My Congressman arranges it for me. Generals for the officers. Congressmen for the peasants."

Kelly and I looked at each other in one of those odd moments when you seem to see life in absolutely clear cold light. You see another human being without uniform, without past or future. There he is with his own problems and ambitions that are miles apart from yours but which at the same time are part of yours. I could respect Kelly. He was trying to get my goat and he was an evil little twerp, but I could respect him.

I took out my wallet and asked, "Have I ever shown you a picture of the general's daughter?" I think Kelly must have been looking at me in that same cold clear light for he leaned forward like a human being and said no.

But I got mixed up—I'd never before bagged two MIGs in one day—and the picture I grabbed was not my prize shot but one of Eileen and her mother. Kelly studied the picture and asked, "Is the battle-axe your mother-in-law?"

I recovered the picture and said, "This is the one I meant to show you."

Kelly whistled and said, "Wow! She's a dish. Even for a general's daughter, she's a dish."

I said, "It's pretty exciting to think of a girl like that waiting for you in Kobe. Thanks for the good news, Kelly."

He said, "You ever seen Katsumi?"

"Where's Katsumi?" I asked.

"The girl I'm marryin'."

"I'm sorry. I don't know Japanese names."

"Think nothin' of it," he said brashly.

He produced a small P.X. picture of his girl. I was embarrassed because this Katsumi was certainly no Madame Butterfly. She had a big round face, prominent cheeks and what looked like oil-black hair. If you'd never been in Japan you'd probably have taken her for an Indian or an Eskimo maybe. But if you've ever seen Tokyo you'd recognize Katsumi at once. She was one of the millions of girls who could never be pretty, who did all

14

the heavy work and who dressed as if the only clothes in Japan were made from old flour sacks.

I had to say something and by the grace of God I remembered about her working in a library. I said, "She sure looks intelligent."

Kelly said, "She's a lot brighter than me."

I was about to leave when I recalled my promise to the padre. I asked, "Aren't you taking a big risk?"

"Risks don't scare me any more," Kelly said defiantly.

"I mean about not being able to take her home?"

"That's what don't scare me," he said.

"How old are you, Kelly?"

"Nineteen."

"You're only a kid. Why don't you think this over?"

"I have. The Army and the Air Force and the State Department have ganged up to keep me from gettin' married. Only makes me more determined."

"What do you mean, ganged up?" I don't like people who feel sorry for themselves.

"When my Kobe skipper saw I was really gettin' serious about Katsumi he gave me the bum's rush to Korea. Then the double-domes in Washington set a deadline. 'If you marry a Jap girl after then,' they said, 'we won't let you bring her back Stateside.' So I drew a court-martial for demandin' that I be sent back to Japan to marry the girl before the new law. I never made it. And now each week Father Feeney looks me up and hands me a pamphlet provin' how stupid I am even to be thinkin' about such a thing."

He ripped open a drawer and slammed down some mimeographed sheets widely used in our area to bring young kids to their senses. The one on top was titled, "But Will Your Family Accept Her?" Kelly grabbed it in his hairy hand, crumpled it up and pitched it into the basket.

"They've tried everything to stop us, but do you know what I'm gonna do, Ace?"

"Something stupid, I'm sure."

15

"That's right. I'm stupid enough to be in love. It happens that I love this girl. And if I have to give up my American citizenship to marry her, that's O.K. with me." He was trembling mad and put his girl's picture back in his desk.

I was outraged to think that any American man would dare to talk like that. Give up his citizenship! I wanted to grab the young idiot and knock some sense into him, tell him that anyone who even thought of surrendering his American citizenship for a Japanese girl ought . . . He turned his back on me and started on some paper work, as if to dismiss me.

I don't take that from anyone. I got sore. I reached out, grabbed him by the shirt and spun him around. "Who in hell do you think you are?" I cried.

To my amazement he cocked his fist and threatened me. "I'll let you have it, Ace."

For one brief moment I wanted to mix with this squirt and pin his ears back, but I realized that would be murder. I could have massacred him any day in the week. So I dropped my hand and said, pretty well shaken up, "You get to be a hophead with these damn jet planes."

Kelly was completely at ease. He laughed and said, "We could use some more men like you."

I said, "Excuse me, Joe. But you sounded crazy when you said you'd give up your citizenship—for a girl."

"I am crazy," he said. "I'm in love—crazy."

I felt a little dizzy and said, "Let's go over to my bunk and split a beer."

"Wonderful!" he cried, slamming his desk shut. As we walked through the late afternoon sunshine with the hint of spring warmth about us he said, "You know, Ace, back there I wasn't afraid to sock you. Because I know that if I did you'd knock my block off fair and square and you wouldn't yell for a cheap court-martial."

"Oh, brother! How wrong can you be? I just finished arguing with the chaplain that you ought to be court-martialed for having written to your Congressman."

"I mean, you wouldn't turn me in over a personal grudge."
I thought a minute and said, "I guess you're right."

"That's what I mean," he said.

We went into my bunk and promoted a fifth of Suntory. I said to Joe, "The Japs must make this out of farmers' socks." But Joe took a murderous gulp and cried approvingly, "Wow, that's man's stuff."

It was obvious that he wanted to talk with someone. He asked, "You really do think I'm nuts, don't you? The guys at the mess hall do too. That is . . ." He paused, looked at me carefully and said, "That is, some of them do. But you know a strange thing, Ace? In the bunks at night you never hear one man who married a Japanese wife complain. You hear a lot of other guys complain about their women. Men with wives back in the States talk about Junior's braces and country-club dances and what kind of car their wife bought. But the men with Japanese wives tell you one thing only. What wonderful wives they have. They're in love. It's that simple."

This flustered me because he might have been talking about my own family. My father was a four-star general with a tremendous reputation as a result of what he accomplished in Guadalcanal and the Philippines, and my mother had written a couple of stories that had appeared in the *Atlantic Monthly*. They were excellent people, they were exciting people, but they had never been in love.

I said, "There's a better explanation. The guys with Japanese wives are younger. They don't have kids to talk about."

Joe thought that one over, took another swig, and said, "You could be right Ace. But I ain't takin' no chance. Because when I see Katsumi I see a dame who could fill my heart for the rest of my life." He looked down the tent as if pondering his next comment, then went ahead and made it. "Tell me, Ace, do you feel that way about your girl?"

He had me again because I was a professional soldier. My future was all cut out and I knew that I would never find any one girl whose presence filled my heart forever and ever. Among

17

the young officers in my gang love wasn't like that. You looked the field over and found a good-looking solid citizen who could stomach you for the rest of your life and if she came from a military family, like Eileen, so much the better. I couldn't explain to Kelly that Eileen would be the finest wife an Air Force officer could have and yet not be the way he was describing.

I said, "You come see me in ten years and you'll see a happy citizen!"

Joe took a final slug and cried, "I believe you, Ace. Boy, Ace, you're one in a million. Ace, you're one officer in a million I could talk to." He shook my hand clumsily and banged his way out into the dusty company street. Then he looked back and cried, "Boy, Ace! We got it made! We're gonna get married!" and he staggered off to the mess hall.

CHAPTER III

O N MONDAY Pvt. Kelly and I flew over to Japan on the same plane and as I watched him strap himself into his bucket seat with real joy at the idea of getting home to his girl I thought how different our two journeys were. He was heading for dumpy, round Katsumi and a future that no one could guess, while I was heading for the big surprise that General Webster had arranged for me: a safe desk job, marriage to his beautiful daughter Eileen, and before too many years a promotion surely to colonel and maybe to general.

I didn't talk with Kelly on the trip over because there were some colonels aboard and it seemed wiser for me to sit up front with them and exchange ideas about the Russian pilots we were meeting over Korea. But when we reached Japan the medics came aboard to disinfect the plane, and while I was standing in the aisle Kelly whispered, "Ace, you're the only friend I know here, and you bein' with the squadron I was wonderin' if you'd be my best man. Saturday?"

The colonels started moving out and I couldn't stand there arguing. My whole inclination—everything I had ever been taught—led me to say no, but I blurted out, "O.K."

"Thanks," he said, and as he trudged across the field, bow-legged and with a gangster slouch, I thought that this square-headed, sandy-haired kid was not the kind you read about in books when they describe the great lovers. Somehow you didn't think of Pvt. Joe Kelly fighting through walls of flame to win the princess. But he was off to marry an Asiatic girl in a strange land and I had to admit that he had guts.

I was watching him when General Webster called my name and when I looked his way there stood Mrs. Webster, too. I shouted, "Surprise! When did you get here?"

Mrs. Webster was a handsome woman—the kind who appear

19

in ads wearing tailored suits and white hair and telling the young bride why one cleaner is better than the other—and it was widely understood in Army circles that Mark Webster owed most of his success to this energetic woman. I once heard my father say, when some of his classmates from '22 were visiting, "Mark Webster at the Point was an inevitable colonel. Absolutely impossible for him to go further. But a first-class wife came along and made him a general."

When Mrs. Webster saw me she hurried forward to kiss me on the cheek. I had to make believe I didn't know where Eileen was so I asked, "What's the news from Eileen?"

The conspirators looked at each other archly. "She's still at work in the oil company," Mrs. Webster said. "But she finds Tulsa dull without you around."

"Boy, did I find Korea dull without her!"

General Webster said, "I hope you didn't mind my dragging you away from the Russians."

"Frankly, sir, I approved. I was getting a bit jittery."

"Well, we'll drive you in to Kobe and let you see what the setup is. You're on the Interservice Aviation Board, you know, but you don't start work for a week."

He led me to a black Cadillac with one bright red star on the license plate. He had always been something of a dandy, ten pounds underweight, extra-sharp uniforms and a smart headquarters company to make him look good. He was what enlisted men call chicken because he demanded all the military courtesies, straight caps, shined shoes. Having known my own father well and having discovered in him a real general who cut right through to the hard core of every problem, leaving glossy shoes and snappy salutes to others, I often suspected that Mark Webster was merely playing at being a general. Once I remarked on this to my father, who grew very angry. He said, "Look, Know-it-all! The Army needs many different kinds of generals. Mark Webster can do a dozen things I can't do." Then he scowled and said, "Not that I would want to do them. But don't underestimate the men who keep the organization running."

But on this ride in from the airport General Webster was way off stride. He wasn't his urbane self at all. In fact, he was downright uncomfortable, but it wasn't until we neared the center of Kobe that I found out what was eating him.

We were passing a corner at which half a dozen enlisted men —we had orders not to call them G.I.'s any more—were loafing. They were in Kobe for Rest and Recuperation from the front in Korea. Five Japanese girls were standing with them and as we drove by, one of the soldiers slapped a girl on the bottom.

"That's what I mean," Mrs. Webster said.

"Kobe's a recreation center," the general said grimly. "I can't change it."

"It's disgraceful. It degrades the military uniform."

"There seem to be no rules against it," General Webster mumbled, leaning back in a disgruntled slouch.

Mrs. Webster, seeing she could get no further with the general, asked me, "What do you think about it, Lloyd?"

"Don't try to make me argue against a general," I pleaded.

General Webster sat up. "Seriously, Gruver, what do you younger officers think?"

I had just started to say, "I've never understood how any self-respecting officer can go with a Japanese girl" when I stopped sharp. For straight ahead of our Cadillac was a tall Marine lieutenant coming out of a nylon-underwear shop accompanied by the first beautiful Japanese girl I had ever seen. She was slim and black haired and her eyes didn't slant. And she laughed. Somehow I had never thought of Japanese girls as laughing. But this extraordinarily beautiful girl laughed and tucked her parcel of nylon underwear beneath her left arm. Then, like any American wife at a busy corner, she grasped her Marine's hand warmly and smiled up at him.

Mrs. Webster leaned forward. "Why, he's a handsome young man," she gasped. "Probably from a very good family. What's he doing with a Japanese girl?"

I had a smart-aleck reply to that question but stifled it and then caught the general's eye and saw clearly that he had thought

21

of the same reply and had killed his, too. Mrs. Webster looked at us and asked, "Is it true, Mark, that some of our young men have actually married such girls?"

"About 10,000 of them," he replied gruffly.

I said, "I spent all afternoon last Friday arguing with a kid nineteen who's determined to marry one of them."

"How deplorable!" Mrs. Webster sighed. It was apparent that she honestly felt sorry for any nineteen-year-old boy who, far from home, had got himself mixed up with a Japanese girl.

At that moment a fat Army major, obviously a civilian, came ambling down the street, window-shopping as he might have done in San Francisco, and on his arm was a Japanese girl.

"You must do something about such behavior," Mrs. Webster said grimly. "At least on the officer level."

Our Cadillac stopped at Camp Kobe and General Webster bounded out of the car and said, "I have one disagreeable job to do. Nancy, you go on back to the club. Lloyd and I'll meet you there soon."

Mrs. Webster smiled at me archly and said, "They're having a special luncheon for us today. I might almost say an extraordinary one."

The general showed me a davenport in his outer office—paneled in Japanese pine and very handsome—and told his aide, "All right, I'll see him now." A colonel disappeared into an inner room and said crisply, "General Webster will see you now."

Through the door came sawed-off Airman Kelly. Playing the Air Force game, he never acknowledged he knew me but stared straight ahead, but as he disappeared through the door leading to General Webster's inner office, he shrugged his shoulders.

I browsed through a copy of the *Infantry Journal,* but my reading was disrupted by the general shouting, "Why in hell do you want to marry her, anyway?"

Then I heard the colonel argue more persuasively, "But, Private Kelly, if you do marry her you can't take her back to the States."

Kelly's response was muffled but judging from what happened

next the kid must have said, "I don't want to go back to the States," because the general shouted, "By God, I'll send you back whether you want to go or not!"

That was when I first heard Kelly's voice. He said, "I won't go."

The general exploded. "You won't go!"

Kelly said, "That's right, because Congressman Shimmark has arranged it for me to get married."

I have found that no matter where you are in the military— Army, Air Force, Navy, it doesn't matter—things quiet down when somebody mentions Congress. I remember hearing about the time my father was stuck in the Philippines without supplies. It was during the battle when he got his fourth star and Mac-Arthur could drop dead and Nimitz was a bum and he would bust Roosevelt in the nose. But a five-foot-four-inch Congressman appeared and Father became as smooth as butter. Because he knew that Congressmen run the military. They approve the budget.

So General Webster retreated before the name of Congressman Shimmark. "All right," he blustered, "go ahead and ruin your life. I've done my duty. I've tried to stop you." Then he apparently turned to the colonel, for he snapped, "Arrange the young fool's wedding."

The colonel was grim-lipped as he led Kelly back into the waiting room. "Who do you think you are," he muttered savagely, "speaking to a general that way?"

Kelly said with great finality, "I ain't takin' no more pushin' around. I'm gettin' married."

The colonel showed him to the door and said, "You'll regret it as long as you live."

Kelly looked at the colonel and laughed. Then he saw me and shrugged his shoulders again. "Saturday," he said through the corner of his mouth.

When he had gone the general appeared. He was red in the face and mumbling. "By God, in the old days we'd have thrown an insolent moron like that into the stockade." Then he saw me

23

and, taking me by the arm, said, "Lloyd, I certainly do wish the imbeciles I have under me were sensible like you. But then you've been reared in a tradition of service to the nation. You understand what a uniform means." He looked for his Cadillac, which hadn't yet returned, and called for a Buick instead. As soon as we got inside he said, "Speaking of Eileen, let's eat."

"I wasn't speaking of Eileen." I laughed.

"I was," he said. "Because . . . I mean . . . it's inconceivable that these officers you see parading Japanese girls could ever have known clean, decent American girls like Eileen. . . ."

We drove up to the de-luxe Japanese hotel which housed the officers club and I could sense the general becoming excited at the prospect of surprising me with Eileen. As a matter of fact, I got pretty steamed up myself because I hadn't seen Eileen for more than a year.

A Japanese bellhop greeted the general. A Japanese bell captain handed him some papers. A Japanese elevator operator took us briskly up to the general's suite and a Japanese chambermaid hurried down the hall ahead of us. A Japanese butler opened the door for us, grinning happily, and a Japanese housemaid bowed almost to the floor, honoring the general.

I stood at attention, waiting for the tall library doors to open, and I remember saying to myself, "Now look, squarehead, you've got to act surprised." But I didn't need the coaching, for Eileen appeared unexpectedly from the hallway and she was twice as lovely as I had remembered.

She hurried to meet me and we kissed and I said, "Wow! what a wonderful way to bring a man back from Korea!" and she said, "I wanted to cable you the minute the Army said I could come, but Mother said, 'We'll surprise him.' "

Mrs. Webster interrupted, "We didn't want to take your mind off your flying," she said.

I held her two hands tightly and stepped back to study her. "Hair fixed differently, eh? Oh, that beautiful blonde hair when everyone out here has black. And your dress . . . It seems to go in and out a lot—nice."

"It's meant to go in and out." Eileen laughed. "I go in and out. Last summer I weighed eight pounds more than I do now—and I really did go in and out."

General Webster coughed and said, "Do you suppose we could go down and eat?"

But Mrs. Webster was enjoying the romantic scene she had arranged and said, "First we'll drink to the young lovers." She produced a set of shimmering wine glasses and explained, "From the P.X. The little Japanese salesclerk said they were made right here in Kobe."

General Webster poured the sherry and declaimed dramatically, "To the lovers!" Then he looked at his wife and complained, "What an ugly phrase! Aren't lovers French people who live in an attic and never get married?"

"No!" Eileen cried. "Lovers are people in an English movie who live in a grass cottage and the vicar's wife condemns them."

"Very unpleasant word, anyway." He poured fresh sherry and said, "To Major Lloyd Gruver and Eileen Webster, United States Air Force. That sounds a damned sight more American and a damned sight more healthy."

Mrs. Webster laughed. "You're right, Mark, but *lovers* has another perfectly good meaning too. Average American people whatever their ages who love each other—even when they've been married twenty-six years." She went over and kissed the general warmly.

My own father and mother had never gotten along together too well and from about ten on I realized that no matter what great advancements my father received and no matter how ordinary Mark Webster's career turned out, my parents envied the Websters because Mark and Nancy were in love while my father and mother were not. Sometimes Father would betray his contempt for Mark Webster's willingness to be pushed around by his wife, and my mother, who came from a famous German family in Lancaster, Pennsylvania, usually stayed there with her circle of friends and spoke sadly of Nancy Webster, "chasing about the world like a camp follower."

At this moment in Kobe, when the senior Websters were kissing, I shared my parents' feelings and for the first time I realized with a certain degree of shock that when I married their beautiful daughter Eileen I would more likely resemble my father than become a second Mark Webster. There would always be some restraint upon me; yet standing there before Eileen and seeing her so radiantly lovely I concluded that I was deeply in love—in my way and my father's way, and I thought in that hesitating moment that my partial love, as you might term it, could lead to the creation of a solid family like Father's, to my promotion in the Air Force like his promotion in the Army, and to a substantial position in society like the one my mother enjoyed in Lancaster. I said to myself, "This is a soldier's way of loving."

We went down to the dining room, where the Japanese headwaiter had arranged a pretty dazzling table with flowers and a church carved out of ice. Three Japanese waiters held our chairs and a three-piece Japanese orchestra hammered out a jive version of "Here Comes the Bride." The officers at nearby tables rose and applauded, but the luncheon was spoiled because right next to our table sat the Marine lieutenant with his beautiful Japanese girl, while next to the orchestra were the fat major and his window-shopping girl.

Mrs. Webster fidgeted with her napkin and said, "If I knew it wouldn't humiliate you I'd leave. Who won the war, anyway?"

Eileen grasped her mother's arm and whispered, "They're fine girls. Please don't create a scene." Mrs. Webster subsided and started to splash her spoon in her cup but soon stopped. "I simply have no appetite," she said firmly.

The luncheon was a calamity and as soon as he could decently do so General Webster dragged me back to his office where he shouted at his aide, "Go out and haul in Major Bartlett." Then he called his secretary and dictated a sharp note: "Effective immediately no Japanese nationals shall participate in any functions of the Kobe Officers Club, including specifically but not exclusively eating in the Club dining room."

"Post it conspicuously!" he said. "Be especially sure there's one in every elevator."

When Major Bartlett appeared the general really ate him out. The fat major, one of those particularly exasperating civilians who won't take military life seriously, didn't even bother to snap to attention.

"Your behavior is a disgrace."

"I understand."

"You can't understand, or you wouldn't go lollygagging down a public street holding hands with a Japanese girl."

"I understand."

"Damn it all, these people were our enemies a short time ago. You understand that you're not to bring that girl into the Club again?"

"I understand."

This infuriated the general, who said sharply, "And you're not to be seen on the public streets with her."

The major looked at me, raised his eyebrows and said, "I understand."

This was too much for the general. He said sharply, "Major Bartlett, I've been ordered to send a levy to Korea. You'd better go along."

"Certainly."

Now I'd had enough. I cried, "Certainly, sir. You know there's such a charge as insolence through manner."

"Certainly, sir," the fat man said to me, nodding slightly.

"Stay out of this, Gruver," the general commanded. "Bartlett, the levy moves out tomorrow."

"Certainly, sir!" he said with the greatest military precision, throwing us each an extra-snappy salute.

When he had left the general said, "The perpetual civilian. Well, there's no use court-martialing a man like that. Maybe Korea'll knock some sense into him."

That evening when we returned to the Club and entered the elevator, the general noted with satisfaction that his memorandum had been posted. But dinner that evening was a chilly

27

affair. Eileen and I sat in silence and absorbed the hateful stares of the officers who normally brought Japanese girls in to dinner. Major Bartlett appeared, bowed my way and sat right where the general would have to see him, chatting with some cronies. But the principal target of the icy stares that night was Mrs. Webster, who didn't seem to mind at all. She brazenly pointed at a table where three American schoolteachers were dining with some civilian men employed by the Army to run the gasoline-supply system. In a voice just loud enough to be heard by eavesdroppers she said, "Isn't it charming to see those pretty American girls at that table?"

Somebody had to say something, so I offered, "After you've been in Korea, it's wonderful to see an American girl."

I realized immediately that this sounded pretty awful, and I was sure of it when Major Bartlett suddenly picked up his spoon and started polishing it like mad. I glared at him but he simply looked at the spoon, breathed on it the way you do when you're polishing apples and polished some more.

Any trouble between me and the fat major was averted by the appearance of the young Marine lieutenant and his lovely Japanese girl. He had apparently not seen the notice, for he headed toward a vacant table and everyone in the room looked up to see what would happen.

The headwaiter pounced on the couple, explained the situation to the girl in rifle-hot Japanese and the obviously well-bred girl turned away in an agony of embarrassment. The Marine wouldn't take this. Calmly he grabbed his beautiful girl by the hand and led her against her will to the table. The headwaiter was furious. He hissed instructions at the girl and he had the bad luck to use some words which the Marine understood, for the American let go the chair he was holding for the girl, hauled his fist back and launched a haymaker.

Another Marine anticipated this and deftly caught his friend's hand. Then he explained the new rule and joshed the troublemaker into leaving, but the first Marine now realized that General Webster and his party were in the room. He was

28

aghast. Quickly he shooed the slim Japanese girl out the door and came over to our table and said briskly, "I'm extremely sorry, sir. I thought they were kidding me."

"It's all right," the general laughed.

"I'm extremely sorry, Mrs. Webster."

She was most gracious and the general felt good. He said, "Lieutenant Bailey, may I introduce Major Gruver. He joins your board next week."

The Marine said, "We've heard about you. Seven MIGs?"

I winked and he said, "We could use you." He bowed and left and the general said, "Somehow or other you've got to respect the Marines. They're publicity hounds but they know what discipline means."

Mrs. Webster said, "It's not that I dislike Japanese. Goodness, they're wonderful people. So clever and all that. Even in the short time I've been here they've shown me unusual courtesies. But a conquering army must retain its dignity. We must remember our position and be firm." Ignoring the fat major, she proceeded to eat her dinner with relish.

CHAPTER IV

O N FRIDAY Mrs. Webster gave striking proof that she really did like the Japanese—if they kept their place. She and Eileen called for me about noon and drove me a short distance out into the country in the black Cadillac. Mrs. Webster said, "I have a real treat for you, Lloyd. We're going to Takarazuka."

"Where?" I asked.

"Takarazuka," she repeated slowly.

"What's that?"

"For one thing it's a village with a delightful zoo. But it's also something especially Japanese."

In a few minutes we entered the Japanese village of Takarazuka. At the head of an extremely narrow lane we got out and walked into a kind of fairyland. For it was now mid-April and the path ahead of us was lined with cherry trees and I had never seen such trees before. The blossoms were extraordinarily profuse, a kind of grayish, sandy purple, rich and delicate. Laden branches dipped down over us and the blue sky of spring showed through. The walk was filled with people hurrying beneath the blossoms to some destination I couldn't see. There were women in kimonos, young girls in bobbysocks, old men in black, babies in bright clothes and half a dozen brilliantly beautiful girls in a kind of green dress that swirled about their ankles as they walked.

"Who are they?" I gasped.

"Those are the Takarazuka girls," Mrs. Webster explained. "The most famous collection of girls in Japan."

"What do they do?"

"That's the big surprise."

We had gone only a short distance when a thin young man in black joined us and bowed very low, drawing breath in through his teeth. "Many, many pardons," he said. "I was waiting for you at the main office." He took us to the zoo, where there were beautiful lakes and flower beds and charming benches on which you could sit beneath the cherry blossoms and watch children play.

The young man asked in good English, "Are you the pilot who shot down seven MIGs?" He was impressed and said, "I used to be a flier. Now I work here."

"What is this place?" I asked in a low whisper.

"You don't know?"

"Never heard of it."

Mrs. Webster saw us talking and cried, "Oh, Lloyd! Don't spoil the fun!"

She and the thin young man took us out of the zoo and up to an enormous building which looked like an armory in Kansas City. It was a theater. We went to our special seats in the very first row and there we faced one of the largest stages in the world on which was enacted the most amazing performance I had ever seen.

I can't say I understood the play. It was called, the young man said, *Sarutobi Sasuke,* meaning *Little Monkey Sasuke,* and Sasuke is a boy's name. It dealt with some children who accidentally conjure up a wizard who helps them save a castle from the enemy. Who the enemy was or what the castle I never understood because at Takarazuka it wasn't the story that counted. It was the overwhelming effect of size.

The play started at one and ran till six. It had thirty-four different scenes, each the biggest and most lavish you could imagine. There was music, there was dancing, there were songs. In fact, there was everything. In this one show there were two gorillas, a jeep, two live pigs, a wizard, three different trios singing three different kinds of songs, a ballet, a football game, a live goat, a motion-picture sequence showing the wizard at work, a passage from an opera and a cave whose trees moved about. But most of all there were girls.

There were more than a hundred girls on stage, and they

31

were all real dazzlers. I thought to myself, "And you were the guy who said he'd never seen a good-looking Japanese girl! Wow!" But at the same time there was something ridiculous about this excess of beauty, for there were no men actors. The most striking girls played men's roles, and I whispered to Eileen, "This show could use a few Clark Gables."

Mrs. Webster heard me and laughed. "In Tokyo there's another theater which has no women. There men play all the parts."

I soon tired of the show—one enormous set after another and beautiful girls making believe they were men. I said I was willing to leave whenever the others had had enough. Eileen said, "I'm ready," and as we walked up the darkened aisle I began to appreciate the enormous size of this theater. It must have seated more than 3,000 people. I asked our guide, "Is it always filled this way?" for there wasn't a vacant seat. He sucked his breath in proudly and said, "Every day in the year. Twice on Saturday and Sunday." I didn't tell him so, but I figured there must be something in a Takarazuka show no American could understand because I was bored by this one and so were Eileen and her mother. But the Japanese loved it. They sat on the edges of their seats, their round faces transfixed with intense pleasure.

We started to return to our car but the guide stopped us and said, "The Supervisor has invited you to attend a special rehearsal of our next month's show."

"Have you two companies?" Eileen asked, a bit bedazzled by the 115 girls she had just seen.

"We have four," the guide said proudly. "One plays here, one in Tokyo, one tours, and one is in rehearsal."

He led us to a huge empty stage where some young girls in green skirts were walking through an intricate dance, while a man at the piano hammered out a tune that sounded like Schubert.

Then suddenly he came to attention and the girls at the piano stopped singing. Everyone looked at the door where an elderly man with a white beard stood for a moment, discovered Mrs. Webster and hastened toward her, bowing very low and saying, "Mrs. General Webster! It is a superb honor." He waved his hand deprecatingly and said, "Rehearsal only."

As he turned he disclosed behind him a most lovely slender actress in a plaid skirt, brown vest, and cocky green tam o'shanter set saucily over one eye. I did a sort of double take and whispered to Eileen, "That's the girl who was with the Marine lieutenant." Eileen studied her and said, "Of course it is."

The Supervisor saw us staring at the remarkable girl and said, "Mrs. General Webster and honored guests, may I present Fumiko-san, one of our finest actresses?" Although I am certain the girl recognized us, she did not betray that fact but stepped sedately forward and bowed low before Mrs. Webster. When she reached me I held out my hand, but she started to bow again, whereupon I withdrew my hand and saw that she was looking up at me with immense gratitude for my not having recognized her in front of the Supervisor. Eileen saw this too and had the presence of mind to say, "We did not see you on stage, did we?" The girl replied in a soft voice, "I not play this week. I . . . Moon . . . Troupe."

Hastily the guide explained, "The four troupes each have a name. Moon, Star, Snow and Flower."

With extraordinary grace Miss Fumiko walked over to a piano, but I didn't hear her sing, for just as she began we left for the flower path leading back to our Cadillac. As we walked beneath the swaying cherry blossoms Mrs. Webster played her trump card. "I'm having dinner with the Supervisor —that sweet old man with the beard," she said. "He's very important. You two drive along home."

And she looked at me with that perfectly frank stare as if to say, "You're twenty-eight, Lloyd. You should have married Eileen four years ago. Grow up." And she was, as always, 100 per cent right. Even though I could use the Korean war as an excuse, we both knew that whenever the big moment of actually

33

getting married approached, I shied away. With jet airplanes I was comfortable. With women I wasn't. I guess that watching Mrs. Webster had made me gun shy.

One night I heard one of our medical doctors talking in a bar. He'd been a big shot in civilian life and he was saying, "We find that if a man comes from a broken home he's apt not to marry early. It's as if he had to be introduced to love. If he doesn't meet love in his own family he could, conceivably, go through an entire life without ever meeting it. Of course," he had added, "at any time almost any girl could provide the introduction if she wanted to take the trouble. But spoiled men who don't marry before they're forty—the men who have never been introduced to love—are hardly worth any girl's trouble. So we can say that some men actually do pass through an entire lifetime without ever meeting so simple a thing as love. No one bothered to introduce them." I often recalled the doctor's words but I was satisfied I wasn't like that, not in all respects. True, my parents had failed to introduce me either to their own love or to the idea of having a home with some girl's love as the central pillar. I think that explains why I was twenty-eight and vaguely in love with Eileen and unmarried. And I think Mrs. Webster knew it and now she was pushing us together.

"I'll see you in the hotel," she cried and left us, towering a good four inches over the little Japanese man who was leading her back to the Supervisor.

I had been hoping for a chance to talk with Eileen alone and as soon as Mrs. Webster left I pulled her into a corner of the Cadillac and gave her a big kiss. She said, "All the way out on the plane I dreamed of meeting you in a romantic spot like this." She pointed out of the car to where we were passing little rice fields pressed close to the road and tiny houses set back among the trees. There was a sweet heaviness of spring in the air as we watched the little workmen of Japan trudging along the footpaths at dusk we felt very much a part of this strange country.

34

Eileen whispered, "I didn't want to leave America. The idea of . . ." she hesitated, then added, "getting married in a foreign land didn't appeal. But now . . ."

I pretended not to have heard her remark about marriage and said, "I was proud of you today."

"About what?"

"That girl."

"The actress?"

"Yes. You knew she was the one your father threw out of the dining room. But you didn't embarrass her."

"Why should I? She came to the Club as a guest and she seemed a very pleasant girl."

"But your mother . . ."

"Mother's all right. She just has to feel that she's running everything."

I asked, "Would she be frightfully sore if we didn't show up at the Club dinner?"

"She knows we're courting."

"What a quaint word for a Vassar girl!"

"I'm not always a Vassar girl. Don't let the tag fool you. Pardner, I been a-livin' in Tulsa, where folks go a-courtin'."

"Let's court."

"What had you in mind?"

"A Japanese night club."

She thought a moment, then smiled and said, "Let's court!"

The driver dropped us at a corner and reluctantly indicated how we could go halfway up an alley and find the Fuji Nights, which turned out to be a tiny room specializing in beer and fried fish. A geisha girl, her face white with cornstarch, came and sat with us and showed us how to order. Soon four other white-faced geishas came up to admire Eileen's blonde hair. One who could speak English placed a strand of Eileen's against her own jet black hair and sighed, "How beautifur!"

Eileen said, "Isn't it fascinating, the way they can't say *l*."

I asked the geisha, "How do you say *lovely lady?*"

She laughed and said, "You tease."

35

"Please!" I begged.

She put her slim fingers under Eileen's chin and said, "You have one ruvrey radie."

Eileen clapped her hands and said, "Your kimono is lovely, too." The girls talked for a while and then the radio was turned on and we danced. The geisha who could speak English said to Eileen, "May I dance with your officer? Very important we know American dancing." Eileen said, "Sure," and for the first time in my life I danced with a foreign girl.

It was pretty dull. The geisha had something sticky on her hair and so much cloth about her middle that I couldn't hold onto her anywhere. She had apparently run into this problem before, for she took my hand and slipped it securely under a particularly huge bundle of cloth and in that way we danced. I asked her why geishas wore so many clothes and she said shyly, "I not real geisha. I only après-guerre geisha." I thought she had used a Japanese phrase and asked her what it meant. "Après-guerre," she said. "Maybe French. In here we only make-believe geisha. (She pronounced it *onry make-berieve*.) To be real geisha need many year study. Many kimonos. We poor girls. We buy one kimono, make believe for Americans. We got to make money."

When she led me back to the table two of the other make-believe geishas started talking in a real jabber and finally one of them ran to the back. In a moment she appeared with a Japanese newspaper and there, about the size of an American penny, was my picture. This excited the five geishas and they made me stand up so they could inspect my uniform. One held up seven fingers and I nodded, whereupon the girls gasped and the first geisha said to Eileen, "You must be very proud."

"I am," Eileen said, and later that night, as we drove home she kissed me warmly and whispered, "I like courtin' with you."

I remember that I thought to myself: "This is it, square-head. Either you get this woman problem settled now or quit for good." So I took the plunge and said, "Where I come from, Podner, courtin' means marryin'. When?"

Eileen smiled gently, as if something very right had happened, and said, "I want to get married . . . if . . ."

I had dived in and the water wasn't as frightening as I had expected so I struck out and said something pretty polished for me, "I've been flying where seconds mean hours of ordinary time. I don't want to wait a single day."

It was then that I first saw she actually was perplexed. She was honestly in doubt. She fumbled a moment and said, "It's difficult for me to explain, but several times here in Japan I've wondered whether you would ever make a better husband than your father."

"What do you mean?" I gasped. "You think there's something wrong with my father?"

"Frankly, I do," she replied. "The way he's content to leave your mother walled up within a circle of a few close friends, there in Lancaster, while he plunges off to the wars. That isn't good enough for me. I came to Japan because I wanted our marriage to start right. I want to be with you . . . in all kinds of weather."

"I don't get what you're talking about," I pleaded.

"About us. Lloyd dear, half a marriage isn't good enough for either you or me. I've got to have a man who loves me with his whole heart. Go ahead and become the greatest general in Air Force history. But love me too."

"Damn it, I do love you," I protested.

"Sure you do, in a cold, partial little way. Let's think about this for a few days."

Suddenly I was fighting to get married and I said, "I thought you came to Japan for a wedding."

"I did, but I've got to marry a complete man. Not just the shreds that are left over after he's led the important part of his life somewhere else."

I was infuriated, not because of what she had said, but because she had seen so clearly. Eileen was beautiful and, as she had proved tonight, plenty smart and courageous. She would be a catch for any man and I wanted her, but she was right

37

when she said that I did not come to her with a whole heart. I knew what she was talking about, for I knew that I had never loved her in the absorbing way that sawed-off Joe Kelly loved his Japanese girl.

But this was the big point: I wanted to learn. In my heart I knew that my parents' way wasn't good enough and I wanted Eileen to help me find something better.

So I took her in my arms and gave her what we called "The Unconditional Surrender," a kiss so long she had to beat on my arms for air. When I let her go she laughed that wonderful golden grin of hers and said softly, "For the first time I have the feeling we'll work this thing out." Then she kissed me in the ear and whispered, "You act a lot better than you talk." And I do believe everything would have turned out all right if it hadn't been for what happened the very next morning.

CHAPTER V

B EFORE I got out of bed Private Joe Kelly called me and
    said, "Well, Ace, this is Saturday! I'm gettin' married!"
I couldn't focus for a minute. Then I said, "Well, congratula-
tions."

"Ace," the little gangster shouted. "Don't you remember?
You're gonna be my best man."

I started to say, "Gee, Kelly, I have an appointment . . ."
but he was on my team. Wreck that he was, he belonged to
my squadron. So I said, "I'll break the appointment, Kelly.
Where's the big event take place?"

I walked down to the grubby building in which our consul
had his offices and was amazed to find four G.I.-Japanese
couples waiting to be married. Katsumi, Joe's girl, looked exactly like her picture: big round face, high cheeks, thick black
hair and small eyes. When she smiled during the introductions
I saw that like most Japanese girls she had in front a big gold
tooth.

"We're gettin' that changed," Joe said with some embarrassment.

Katsumi was uncertain whether she should offer to shake
my hand or not, so when I extended mine she collapsed in
agonizing giggles and popped her left fist over her mouth. Her
knuckles were bright red from chapping.

It was a dismal morning. Since Joe's marriage was third in
line I watched with mounting disgust the spectacle of American soldiers marrying whatever girls they had been able to
pick up. I was ashamed at having been drawn into this sordid
spectacle and was looking down at my fingernails when a bright
voice called, "Are you Major Ace Gruver?" I looked up and
breathed relief, for it was an American girl. She was oversize,

39

but I was glad to know there were some American girls still alive.

She whispered, "I'm a secretary here."

"Interesting job, I bet."

She shook her head. "One marriage after another."

"Don't they know they can't take the girls home?"

"Sure they know. But what I wanted to see you about is that I have a kid brother who is crazy about airplanes. He told me if I ever meet a real jet pilot, to get his ottograft. I want your ottograft!"

She led me into her inner office where she gave me a sheet of paper to sign then added another. "Maybe the kid'll be able to sell this one at a fancy price—like a baseball glove."

"What I don't get," I said, "is why the Government allows these marriages in the first place."

"The Government is smart. Public pressure back home insists the men be permitted to marry, so the Government does permit it, then washes its hands of the whole affair." She showed me a form which each G.I. had to sign, on top of all the others, and it was about the frankest and most brutally cruel I had ever seen. Kelly, for example, acknowledged that he was outside the law, waived his legal rights, said he would look after the girl on his own account and stated in writing that the Air Force was in no way responsible for his wife. At the bottom he swore that he was in right mind and that he had signed before witnesses.

"But these guys go right on?"

"Day after day."

"Why?"

"That's not a fair question to ask me," she said somewhat sharply.

"You work here."

"All right!" she said. "Would you call me pretty? No, nobody would call me pretty. I'm a plain Jane who couldn't get married in America so I came out here where there were plenty of men." She laughed at herself in a delightful, horsy sort of way and said bitterly, "They stamp us 'Stateside rejects'! Sure, there were lots of men when I got here. But the damned Japanese girls had them all."

"I still don't get it."

"Like a soldier told me," she explained. "He kept saying, 'You American girls wouldn't understand.' "

"Understand what?"

She showed me a wedding ring and said, "Look, the man I finally got had been in love with a Japanese girl for two years. Said frankly he knew I'd never be half the wife she would have been."

"Then why did he marry you?"

"Said I'd fit in better in Denver."

She went to her purse and pulled out a wrinkled photograph. "My rival!" she said in obvious amazement. Before looking at the picture I could guess that the girl probably looked a lot like Katsumi. Red face, round features. The American secretary stared at the picture and said, "To me she looks absolutely ugly. I stole this picture when my husband burned the others. I keep it as a reminder that I must be a good wife."

"Where's the girl now?"

"She committed suicide." She placed the damaged photograph back among her junk and assured me, "It all happened before I met Gus. I had nothing to do with the suicide."

The door opened and the consul hurried through. "We'll be ready for the next one in a couple of minutes," he said. "You the witness, Major? Go on in."

The girl led me into the office from which he had come. It was bleak with a writing table, a Bible, a portrait of President Truman and a coat rack. "This is where the foul deed takes place." She laughed. "I'm always one of the witnesses and it's beginning to tear me apart because every G.I. who comes into this room has the same look in his face that my husband gets when he speaks of his Japanese girl." She hammered the table and cried, "Damn them all! They all have the same secret."

"What?"

"They make their men feel important. I try to build my husband up—as a wife should. But with me it's a game. With these ugly little round-faced girls it isn't a game. It's life."

The door opened and the consul came in, followed by Joe Kelly and Katsumi.

The consul was a young man with balding hair and a strained look.

He lined the couple up before the desk, had them sign still more papers, then conducted a brief ceremony. He was mad at Pvt. Kelly, dismayed by Katsumi and fed up with the whole affair. It was an ugly ceremony performed with grudging spirit and I was ashamed at having been witness to it.

But as I looked up from my embarrassment I happened to see Kelly's face as he bent down to kiss Katsumi and in that instant the ugliness in the room vanished and I had to bite my lip. The horsy American secretary wrote something in a book and wiped her eyes, while the consul said to Kelly, "You understand that you have surrendered numerous rights in this matter?"

Kelly couldn't take any more. He looked at the consul and his nose twitched. "You son . . ." he began and I knew that the consul was about to get the full Kelly treatment, which is about as profane as anyone can get. But Katsumi, already the wife, quietly took her husband's hand and said, "We go now, Joe."

Joe collapsed like a ruptured balloon. He looked at me and said, "It's hell to be married. Take it from me, Ace." Then he asked, "Ain't you gonna kiss the bride?"

I was unprepared for this and must have betrayed some shock for I could see Joe cringe. I, in turn, wanted to drop through the floor for having insulted a member of my own squadron at such a time.

I took Katsumi's big face in my hands and said, "The secretary told me Japanese girls make wonderful wives. You be a good wife to Joe." Then I kissed her. "Good luck, kids," I said.

"Thanks, Ace," Joe replied.

SAYONARA

When they left the consul said, "Such marriages are dreadful mistakes. We do our best to prevent them."

"Do you succeed—very often?"

"You'd be surprised. We make the paper work so cumbersome a good many of the young hotheads lose steam. Actually we've helped forestall some inevitable tragedies."

"You didn't have much success with Joe."

"We see everything here. Fights, tears. But if a boy's had the gumption to write his Congressman we know he's determined to go ahead. Now all Joe has to do is get his Congressman to pass a special bill and he'll get Mrs. Joe into the States. Frankly, between you and me, I hope he succeeds. But it's my job to paint a gloomy picture."

It was this same well-meaning consul who got me into my big trouble, for when he turned in his weekly report on G.I. marriages to General Webster he must have mentioned his surprise at seeing me as Joe's witness. At any rate the general called me into his office and stormed, "I'm astounded that you should lend yourself to such a thing—especially since you know Mrs. Webster's and my objection to fraternization."

"This wasn't fraternization, sir. It was marriage," I said. "The kid's from my outfit in Korea, sir."

"Carstairs tells me you even kissed the girl!"

"I did. Kelly asked me to."

The general was outraged. He banged out of his chair and stood looking at a map. Finally he exploded. "I'm damned if I can understand how a man like you, brought up in the best traditions of the service, can outrage military propriety in this way. Such marriages are sordid, disgraceful things. We have to tolerate them because Washington says so, but we don't have to polish our buttons and go down to kiss the bride!"

"I . . ."

"Nauseating. The whole thing's nauseating, but it's especially sickening to have a member of your own staff—you might say your own immediate family . . ."

The bawling out I got from the general was nothing com-

43

pared to the one I took from his wife. She was sweet as butter during dinner but after the general and Eileen had left on prearranged signals she said bluntly, "Do I understand, Lloyd, that you actually encouraged a Japanese marriage this morning?"

"One of the men from my outfit."

"But you surely didn't attend—not officially?"

"He asked me to help him out, Mrs. Webster. It was a guy from our outfit. How could I have refused to attend the wedding . . ."

"Don't call it a wedding! It was a mean little surreptitious ceremony on the most sordid level. It was permitted only because some lily-livered idiots in Washington have no courage to face facts."

"I agree with you, Mrs. Webster."

She didn't want agreement. She wanted to knock me into shape, once and for all. When I saw her closing in on me, trying to make me apologize for what I had done in good faith, I sensed pretty clearly that she saw herself fighting her daughter's marriage battle. Years before she had taken on young Mark Webster in just such a fight and she had been victorious and the entire Army knew she had won and from that time forth she had molded and marched Mark Webster into a one-star generalship that he could never have attained by himself. Now she was going to teach her daughter how to march me into four or five stars.

She frowned and said, "If you expect to make a name for yourself in service, Lloyd, you can't offend the proprieties. You can't insult generals."

I didn't say anything. Instead I looked at her very carefully and when I saw her clean, handsome, hard face with not a wrinkle out of place I thought of Joe Kelly's Japanese girl whom I had kissed that morning, and all at once I caught a glimmering of what the American secretary must have meant when she said, "These damned Japanese girls have a secret." I had an intimation of their secret: they loved somebody—just simply loved him. They weren't going to make him a four-star general or they weren't going to humiliate him over some trivial affair for which he had already apologized. They just got hold of a man and they loved him.

Mrs. Webster said acidly, "Eileen asked me to tell you she'd be at the hairdresser's."

I thanked her, held her chair as she rose and showed her to the elevator. I think she knew that she had presented a dismal picture during our talk, for she said, "I do hope you won't embarrass the general again." I promised her that I wouldn't irritate the general and refrained from pointing out that we had been talking about something quite different: my irritating her.

I went down to a lower floor of the hotel where there was a hairdresser for the American girls who worked with our Army in Japan, and there I saw Eileen coming out more brilliant and lovely than I had ever seen her before. She had what *Life* magazine once called the well-scrubbed look and was absolutely adorable with the fresh bright charm that only American girls ever seem to have. I was disgusted with myself for having quarreled with her the night before and suggested that we sit in a corner of the elegant lounge, where a Japanese boy in bright blue bar-boy's uniform served us drinks.

I said, "If you looked so adorable all the time no one would ever be able to fight with you."

"We weren't fighting last night," she teased.

"I'm glad," I said, "because I've got to keep in the good graces of at least one of the Websters."

She frowned and asked, "Mum give you a bad time at lunch?"

"Very bad," I said.

"Mother's a special case, Lloyd. The Army's her whole life. She watches over father like a mother hen and she's been very good for him. Frankly, I don't think Father approves of all the orders he's had to issue because traditionally the Army is pretty adult about men and women getting together—any women. But he's learned that in the long run Mother is usually right."

"Is she?"

"Yes."

"Now it's my turn to be scared."

"What do you mean?"

"You're afraid I'll be like my father. I'm really scared you'll be like your mother."

"What's so bad with that?" she asked.

"I can't stand being pushed around."

Eileen lifted her glass and made circles on the marble table. She said slowly, "I don't think I'd be bossy the way Mother is because you're much stronger than Father ever was. But mostly I wouldn't hurt you because I love you so much."

That was what I wanted to hear and I said, "I'm twenty-eight now and I've been going around with too many airplanes. What I want now is a wife and a family." She sneaked in a kiss and I said, "Whenever I've thought about a family it's with someone like you—a girl with an Army background like my own. . . ."

She became gently irritated and protested, "That's just what I mean. Why do you say, 'a girl like me'? I'm not a type. I'm me. Damn it all, Lloyd, haven't you ever wanted to just grab me and haul me away to a shack somewhere?"

Now it was my turn to get on edge and I said, "When you're an officer you meet endless problems of enlisted men who just grabbed something and hauled it away. It doesn't appeal to me."

She said, "Lloyd, a man has to surrender himself sometimes. You're not so important you have to defend yourself like a fort."

From the manner in which Eileen spoke I could tell that she was just as tense as I was and it occurred to me that if I married Eileen we would always be a little bit afraid of each other, a little bit on edge always to be ahead of the other person. Mrs. Webster, frankly, had scared the devil out of me and now I could see the same martial tendencies in her daughter. I could see her organizing my life for me solely on the grounds that she loved me, but the definition of what was love would always be her definition.

I said, "What you said last night turned up a lot of new ideas."

"You make it sound very unpleasant."

"Didn't you intend it that way? Your mother sure intends it when she gives a man hell."

She got out of her chair and said, "I don't think you want to take me to the dance tonight."

I didn't want to answer this so I said, "Some of the things you said last night made sense. We ought to think things out."

"That's fine with me. I suppose you want to do your thinking —tonight—alone?"

I said, "O.K. by me," and she started walking across the lounge. It was late in the afternoon and the place was empty, so I ran after her and said, "Eileen, what are we fighting about?"

And she replied, "The next fifty years," and she looked so cold and so much like her mother that I turned and walked away and caught a ride out to Itami air field, where I astonished everybody by reporting for duty two days early.

CHAPTER VI

YOU could say that Itami is right in the heart of Japan, for it stands in the triangle formed by the three great cities of the south: Kobe, Osaka and Kyoto. Actually the three are one big city, for you can travel all the way from Kobe to Osaka without ever being in the country but for some reason they've been kept apart: Osaka criss-crossed with hundreds of canals, Kobe with its big docks, and Kyoto with endless museums and temples.

As soon as I got to Itami that Saturday night I felt better. I was home. Planes, neat air strips, men I knew. My work there was a dead cinch. General Webster had arranged it as a kind of present to his daughter, so I could be with her. The board I was on met a couple of times a week but the three senior members did all the work and had a bunch of us jet pilots in from Korea for consultation, if needed.

One of these was Lt. Bailey, the Marine who had brought the Japanese actress into the Kobe Officers Club that day. He was a real hot-shot jet man, and since we agreed on most problems the older officers were quite satisfied if we missed meetings because they never liked what we had to say. So Mike Bailey and I really had things squared away and at the end of the first week he said, "We ought to see something of Japan. I finagled it so you can move into the Marine hotel. Proved it was necessary for our consultations. And I promoted a Chevrolet." He loaded my gear into it and we set out for his quarters.

"We live six miles from the air base," he explained. "Extra advantage is that we're not hooked into the Itami phones. They don't bother us much. Son, I got us really fixed up."

He drove so fast that it seemed only a couple of minutes before we came to an interesting town with narrow streets and

48

hundreds of people wandering about. We inched our way down an alley and up a small hill to a big rambling four-story hotel. "Marine Barracks," he said proudly. "Look at that Jap kid come to attention." A bellhop tossed Mike a snappy salute and whispered, "Seven o'clock, Makino's." Mike gave the kid 100 yen and said to me, "Finest people in the world, the Japanese."

I said, "I thought you told me you fought them at Tarawa."

"Who bears a grudge?" He told the boy to show me the room vacated by the Air Force major who had preceded me on the Board and when I got there I found I had an excellent view of the town. Below me was a wide and rocky river which cut the place in half. Up our side of the river came a railroad from Osaka but right below us it cut across to the other side and stopped at the edge of a beautiful park. There were some very large buildings facing me and, as I watched, huge crowds of people left them and started hiking toward the train.

But as I studied these people pressing toward the station I saw another crowd gathering at the rear of the buildings and into this crowd plunged a dozen young girls, arm in arm, each wearing a long green skirt that swished about her ankles.

"Hey, Bailey!" I cried. "What's this town called?"

"Takarazuka," he yelled.

"These girls in green . . ."

Mike rushed into my room and looked across the river. He grabbed me by the arm and shouted, "My god! We're missing the show."

He shoved me out the door and down the steps onto a narrow street along which we hurried to a large and handsome stone bridge bearing the sign in English, MUKO RIVER. CARE PEDES-TRIANS. With a long finger Mike pointed across the bridge and said with drooling relish, "Here they come, the pedestrians."

Then I saw them, the Takarazuka girls coming home to their dormitory after the day's performance. First came the beginning students whose job it was to crowd the back of the stage in big numbers. They were the fifteen- and sixteen-year-olds, and they walked proudly in their long green skirts and cork zori. Bailey nudged me as they passed and asked, "Ever see more beautiful kids in your life?"

I had already seen these dazzling children at the rehearsal and I knew they were beautiful but as I watched them disappear into the evening twilight they seemed to drift away from me with extraordinary grace. They walked in a curious way, one foot set carefully before the other so that their long green skirts swayed noiselessly above the dusty streets. They had now passed so far from me that they were becoming haunting ghosts when Mike nudged me and said, "Watch this one! Imagine General Webster tossing her out of the Officers Club that day."

I looked across the bridge and there came the exquisite girl I had met during my visit to Takarazuka. She was accompanied by two other actresses and they formed such a gracious trio that townspeople who were attending the procession drew back against the sides of the bridge to watch them go by. As they approached us, Mike's girl kept her dark eyes straight ahead.

I asked Bailey, "Aren't you going to say hello?"

"In public?" he cried. "A Takarazuka girl! You must be nuts."

The three girls were now abreast of us and Bailey's girl, without actually turning her head, gave him ever so slight a nod, which Bailey pretended not to have seen. Then, like green shadows over some field at the end of day, the girls passed down the narrow street.

Now the principal actresses appeared, the ones famous throughout Japan, tall, stately girls whose distinguished and memorable faces advertised all kinds of products in the magazines. They moved with special authority and were besieged by mobs of young girls seeking autographs. Among these actresses I noticed several who took men's roles on stage and who now dressed like men in public. That is, they wore slacks and sweaters and berets, yet in doing so they managed to look enticingly feminine.

The formal procession of the Takarazuka goddesses was ended, but on the far end of the bridge appeared one last girl in a soft white stole, gray kimono and rippling green skirt. She had been delayed and was hurrying to overtake her friends. Her green zori tapped out a gentle rhythm as she hastened pin-toed toward us, her body leaning forward in unstated urgency. I never saw this girl again; I never even discovered her name. She may have been only a beginner of no consequence, but as I watched her soft disappearance into the spring night I felt as if I had been brushed across the eyes by some terrible essence of beauty, something of whose existence I had never before been aware.

Mike Bailey tugged at my arm and said, "Well, let's get down to the restaurant."

"What restaurant?" I asked.

"Makino's," he said, and he led me through a jungle of thin and winding streets and I felt that I had never before really seen a Japanese town: the crowded life, the tiny shops, the paper doors with small lights shining through.

We ducked into a restaurant doorway hung with red and white streamers that brushed our faces as we passed. Inside were many Japanese crowded at small tables eating fish, which I have never liked. A Japanese woman greeted us with three low bows, a little maid fell to her knees and took our shoes and two powdered make-believe geishas showed us up a flight of narrow stairs.

We entered onto a top floor where three couples sat quietly at small tables. In a corner, imprisoned by a quarter-circle of a rounded table, stood a fine-looking chunky Japanese man of sixty, watching over a charcoal stove on which bubbled a large deep pan of fat, into which he tossed chunks of fish, swishing them around with long metal chopsticks. This was Makino-san. The après-guerre geishas told us that we were to sit on the floor at the quarter-circle table that cut Makino off from the rest of the room.

Mike said, "This is the best tempura restaurant in Japan."

"What's tempura?" I asked.

"Look." He pointed to a menu painted on the wall in Japa-

51

nese and English. Makino-san had twenty-nine varieties of fish from lobster to eel, including squid, octopus, shrimp, sardines and the excellent Japanese fish, tai.

"This is living, son," Bailey cried, putting his arm about one of the make-believe geishas, who laughed and called him "Mike-san." The other geisha started to arrange my dishes for the meal but Mike said, "All right, girls, beat it." They nodded obediently and went downstairs. I must have looked disappointed, for he said, "It's silly to keep geishas at your table when you have a girl joining you."

"I didn't know a girl was eating with us."

"Didn't you see Fumiko-san say she'd be here?"

"The girl on the bridge?"

"Yeah. Fumiko-san. She gave me the high sign as she passed on the Bitchi-bashi."

"What's this Bitchi-bashi?"

"*Bashi's* Japanese for bridge. We call the one where the girls pass the Bitchi-bashi because there is so much lovely stuff there and you can't touch the merchandise."

"Look, Mike," I said. "I don't get this special approach. You know the girl. Why don't you just go up and ask her for a date?"

Bailey's jaw fell and he said, "A Takarazuka girl isn't allowed to have dates."

"Why not?"

"Well, in the old days theaters had a lousy reputation in Japan, so the railroad decided to keep Takarazuka what you might call impeccable."

"What railroad?" I asked.

"This whole resort grew up as a place for excursion trains from Osaka and Kyoto and Kobe. Started with a hot springs, then a zoo and finally some genius thought up these girl shows. They don't make a nickel on the town or the theater, but they do a fabulous business on the railroad. Everybody comes out to see the show. Fifty lavish scenes, a hundred beautiful girls—" He stopped suddenly, scrambled to his feet and hurried to the door. "Fumiko!" he cried with real emotion.

The delicate actress seemed entirely changed from when we had seen her shortly before on the Bitchi-bashi. Her kimono was a powdery blue and at her neck at least five undergarments showed, each folded meticulously upon the next so as to form a handsome frame for her golden face. She wore white tabi socks, white cork zori instead of shoes and an enormous sash tied in a flowing knot in back. When I rose and extended my hand she barely touched it with her own. I was amazed at how graceful she seemed, how young.

Mike Bailey had passed the point of amazement. He was drooling and arranged her cushions and plates as if he were a French headwaiter. Then he pinched her ivory-colored cheek and said, "It's murder trying to see you, baby." She laughed at this and her voice was high and tinkling like that of a child playing with dolls.

When she sat with us the tiny restaurant seemed to thrust back its walls, our talk grew more expansive and Makino, tucked away in his corner, started to fry the fish. Mike said generously, "This American is Ace Gruver, Seven MIGs." He showed her how jets fight and when she started to admire me perhaps a little too much he tried to change the subject, but she said, "I meet Gruver-san already."

Mike did a double take and Fumiko san laughed again. "How you like me in *Swing Butterfly?*" she asked him.

"You were wonderful!" he cried. "But I'll bet if you'd put that show on while MacArthur was here he'd have thrown you all in jail."

I asked why and Fumiko said—I can't explain how she talked or exactly what she did with English and Japanese gestures, but she made me understand—"*Swing Butterfly* make fun of American sailors falling in love with Japanese girls. I geisha. I fight off whole shipload American sailors."

With a deft twist of her shoulders she demonstrated how she played the role and Makino and two men in the restaurant roared and suddenly I didn't like being in that little upstairs room. I didn't appreciate having a fat cook laugh at Americans.

I said to Mike, "You probably want to be alone. I'll blow."
He got very excited and cried, "Hey, you can't, Ace. If any
Takarazuka snoopers broke in here and caught Fumiko alone
with me. Much trouble."

"What good do I do?" I grumbled.

"You are in the way," Mike admitted, "but it would be a lot
easier on Fumiko if it looked like an innocent dinner for three,
wouldn't it, lady?" I turned to see if Fumiko agreed and saw to
my astonishment that she had turned pale and was trembling.

For at the entrance to the room stood three Takarazuka girls,
tall and shatteringly beautiful. Two of them wore the Takarazuka
green-skirted costume but the girl in the middle did not. She
wore gray slacks, a blue-gray sweater, white shirt and tie and
slate-gray cap. She was obviously disgusted at catching Fumiko-
san seated with two Americans.

In three decisive steps she stood over us and spoke harshly to
Fumiko-san who scrambled away in disgrace. I remember looking up at the strong face of this intruder. She was extraordinarily
beautiful, yet strangely cold. I felt curiously insulted by her and
cried, "Are you the boss of this outfit?" but she spoke no English and snapped at me in Japanese. Then brusquely she turned
away and led Fumiko-san to a table where the four actresses
ignored us.

I started to get up but Makino, the cook, grabbed my arm and
translated, "She not angry. Only she say very dangerous Fumiko-
san walk with Americans."

"She wasn't walking," I cried. "She was sitting here."

"Please!" Makino protested. "I not speak good. Please, no
trouble." He whisked away the dishes from which Fumiko-san
had been eating and Mike and I sat glumly staring at our mess
of tempura. It galled me to be sitting on the floor, Japanese style,
while the Takarazuka girls, by whom we had been rebuked, sat
at a table, American style. I said, "Let's get out of here," but
before we could leave, the leader of the girls—the one in slacks
—came over, looked me gently in the eye and spoke softly.

Makino translated, "She have no English. She most sorry but

Fumiko-san young girl from famous family in Japan. Suppose she get fired Takarazuka, everybody lose face."

The lovely actress looked at me beseechingly and said, in Makino's interpretation, "Very difficult to be Takarazuka girl. We got to protect one another."

She smiled at me, bowed graciously and returned to her table. I felt lots better but now Mike began to boil. "What in hell am I?" he demanded. "A man or a mouse?" He pushed Makino's restraining hand away, strode over to the table, reached down, grabbed Fumiko-san by the chin and kissed her until she had to struggle for breath. Then he bowed politely to the girl in slacks and said, "I'm mighty sorry, too. But us boys also have to protect one another."

Then we left, but at the door we looked back to see the four Takarazuka girls sitting primly on the chairs, staring at their plates.

When we got back to the barracks Mike said, "I don't blame the girls. They're under strict rules. If they get caught with an American soldier they're fired. But that snippy babe in slacks sort of got my goat."

I asked, "Why do you bother with them, if you can't date them?"

He looked at me in amazement. "Since when does a man have to have reasons for chasing a pretty girl?"

"But you can't even talk with her!"

"Son!" Mike cried. "Didn't you read when you was young? Didn't you stumble upon them there fairy tales? Where the prince fights his way through the wall of fire? The more rules they put up against you the more fun it is."

We went down to the shower room and while Mike was yammering away I had the stifling premonition that I ought to get out of Japan. When we returned to the hall Mike headed for his own room but I said, "Come on in a second," and we talked for a long time. I said, "I had the strangest feeling just now. I wanted to get out of Japan. I was scared, I think." I started to tell him about my bad luck with Eileen and he interrupted.

55

"Don't tell me! The general's wife started to throw her hooks into you. I sized her up when she tossed a girl like Fumiko-san out of her third-rate club . . ." He shook my hand warmly and said, "Son, when you escaped Mrs. General Webster, you escaped horrors worse than death."

"But I didn't want to escape," I said. "I wanted to marry Eileen and have a wife I could be proud of and a home somewhere and a good life in the Air Force. Everything was arranged and I liked it all."

"So now what?"

"I had the craziest feeling, Mike, that I was back in St. Leonard's."

"Where's that?"

"Prep school. I went to St. Leonard's. I was all set to take the exams for West Point, but there was a teacher there who loved English literature and he got me a part in the school play. It was by a Hungarian called Molnar, and all of a sudden I didn't want to go to West Point. I didn't want any part of it and my mother, who's written a couple of damned fine stories for the *Atlantic,* came to school and said, 'We've always expected you would go to the Point, like your father and his father.' I said, 'Suddenly I feel as if I'd had a vision of a completely different world.' At that she started to cry and talked pretty incoherently, but what I got was that if you ever once experienced that vision don't let anything stop you. She wouldn't come right out and say I shouldn't go to the Point, because her own father went there and became a pretty famous general. But I could see that that's what she meant.

"For the next two weeks I went through hell. Everybody at the school was just swell. They didn't rave at me and say I was ruining my life if I gave up the appointment to West Point, and the English teacher wouldn't say that if I did go to the Point I was selling out. But then Father flew up from Texas and he was like a breath of sea air in a Kansas drought."

"He put you straight, eh?"

"No. Father never rants."

56

"He's a general isn't he? Then he rants."

"You Marines get the wrong idea sometimes. If you ever meet my father you'll meet the man who justifies having generals. He looked at me that day and said, 'If you don't want to go to the Point, Lloyd, don't. Unhappiest men I know are those who've been forced into something they have no inner aptitude for.' "

"That was a noble start," Mike said, "but what did he use for the clincher? How did he force you to go to the Point?"

"He didn't. We just talked and he flew back to Texas and I went on to the Point. And up to this very night I've never once been sorry. But tonight that old sick feeling came over me and I had the distinct impression that maybe I didn't want to stay in the Air Force and buck for a star. Maybe I didn't want to marry Eileen and mess around with her silly old man and cantankerous mother." I put my hand against my forehead and said, "Maybe I felt my whole world crumbling under me."

Mike grew serious and said, "Boy, do I know! I watched my old man go through the depression. I watched a world really crumble. That's why I don't put much stock in the permanent security of worlds—of any kind. But what hit you? You don't just decide a thing like that for the hell of it."

"Well . . . I'm almost ashamed to tell you what hit me."

Mike had a very quick mind and he said loudly, "Fumiko-san! You took a good look at Fumiko-san close up. Well, son, she'd put anyone off his rocker—anyone, that is, but an old hand at l'amour like me."

I laughed and said, "I wish it were so simple. I could duel you for Fumiko-san in F-86's at 40,000 feet. But the other day I was best man at a marriage between a G.I. and a Japanese girl. Boy, she was no Fumiko-san, but she impressed me powerfully. Like a chunk of earth in the middle of a cheese soufflé. And tonight, seeing that other part of Japan I wondered . . ."

"You wondered what?" Mike asked. "You certainly don't want to snatch the enlisted man's wife."

"This sounds silly but I flew down here ready to marry Eileen. When she and I started to hesitate about that, I started to wonder about everything else—even about staying in the Air Force. I know it's ridiculous but that G.I. and his dumpy Japanese girl . . ."

Mike stared at me in slack-jawed horror and asked in a hushed voice, "You mean you're ponderin' life?" He mussed his hair down over his eyes and sobbed, "Oh, what does it all mean—the eternal struggle—sex—the New York Yankees!"

"All right, louse it up. But suddenly I felt as if I were in a world of swirling darkness where the only reality was this earth —this earth of Japan."

"My God!" Mike cried, clutching his head. "A new Sigmund Freud!"

I had to laugh, and while Mike phoned down for some cold beer I asked, "Don't you ever get crazy ideas like that?"

"A million of 'em. They never hurt anybody."

"But to have an idea like that suddenly bust open your whole world . . . I thought I was back in prep school again."

"I think it's easy to explain," Mike said after his second bottle of beer, which gave him added authority. "You've been fighting like crazy up in Korea and you get this big idea about comin' down to Japan and getting married . . ."

"She didn't even tell me she was coming to Japan."

"Don't let details mess up my theory. Then when you see the battle-axe her mother is . . ."

"She's not really a battle-axe."

"Who threw me out of the Club with Fumiko-san?" The question awakened all of Mike's animosities and launched him into a tirade against generals' wives and he never did finish his explanation.

But next night we were at the Bitchi-bashi watching the stately procession of Takarazuka girls as they approached us through the evening dusk to vanish into the deep shadows. I was deeply moved by the passage of these quiet figures and they appeared to me as members of a military group dedicated to their rituals and promotions the way I was tied to mine. They were not free and I was not free, for I believe that no man who flies a plane against the enemy or steers a ship into enemy waters is a free man. He is bound by certain convictions and restraints that other men never know.

I was pondering this when Fumiko-san came by. She was accompanied by the actress in men's clothes who had reprimanded us the night before and when the bobby soxers on the Bitchi-bashi saw this tall girl they made a wild dash to surround her and demand autographs.

I said to Mike, "She must be somebody."

He asked a Japanese girl who the actress was and the girl broke into horribly confused giggles and said, "She—is—Hana-ogi-san. Number one girl!"

The beautiful actress stopped for a moment on the bridge and looked our way. Mike bowed very low and blew a kiss off his thumb to Fumiko-san but both actresses ignored him and resumed their way into the night shadows.

CHAPTER VII

I HAD to miss the Monday night Procession at the Bitchi-bashi because General Webster sent a message ordering me in to Kobe to report on how my work was going. I knew what he really wanted was to ask me why I hadn't been around the Club. No doubt Mrs. Webster had commanded him to find out and I wondered what I would tell him. It was difficult for me to explain even to myself.

In his office the general asked me a lot of trivial questions he couldn't possibly have been interested in and then led me down to the Cadillac. At dinner I looked for Eileen but he said she was in Kyoto visiting a museum and wouldn't be able to join us. I looked at Mrs. Webster eating her shrimp cocktail and lost my appetite.

It was a chilly meal and after dessert the general excused himself to do some paper work and I observed silently, "If my father ever becomes Chief-of-Staff I'll warn him not to put Mark Webster in charge of intelligence, because he sure telegraphs his hand."

Mrs. Webster didn't bother to telegraph hers. When we got to her apartment she asked bluntly, "What's wrong between you and Eileen?"

"I'm sure she must have told you."

"Lloyd, don't be evasive. You haven't seen her in more than a week."

It was obvious that this was one time when I'd better stick to the truth. I said, "We had a quarrel. She told me . . ."

"A quarrel? Whatever about?"

I gulped and said, "She's afraid I'm too much like my father." Mrs. Webster started at my honesty but made no move to stop me so I finished. "And I think she's—too bossy." There was something in the inflection of this sentence that betrayed clearly the fact that I thought Eileen was too damned much like her mother. But Mrs. Webster never batted an eye.

So I added, "And then I've been working."

"Ridiculous," she snapped. "Mark found you this job because there wasn't any work attached to it."

"If that's why I got it . . ." I began with standard dignity.

". . . you'd sooner be back in Korea?" she concluded.

"Yes."

"Lloyd, don't be silly. It's obvious to everyone in Kobe that you are an extremely brave young man whom General Webster brought back to Japan so that you could be with Eileen. There's nothing dishonest about that—if you plan to get married."

"We planned that for a long time—sort of."

"How do people get married—sort of?" She was sitting on an expensive lounge purchased in Paris and she leaned forward, repeating the offensive words: "Sort of?"

"I mean there's nothing definite. Has Eileen said there was anything definite?"

"Of course she hasn't. She hasn't talked with me about this but I can see how humiliating it is for her. The whole hotel . . ."

I knew Eileen pretty well and I was sure she didn't give a hoot what the hotel thought. But Mrs. Webster did because if we didn't get married it would make her look ridiculous. I said, "We wonder if we're the right people for each other."

"At this stage? Why, you've known Eileen for years. Lloyd, this is just a lovers' quarrel and it has no more significance than that."

"Maybe it didn't at the start but Eileen's questions and some of the thinking I've done made me wonder if perhaps my whole idea of life isn't wrong."

Now I had struck something serious and Mrs. Webster accepted it so. She spoke very deliberately and at the same time fidgeted nervously with a lace handkerchief. She said, "If an Army man ever questions the big idea of military service he's lost. Believe me, Lloyd, I've seen it many times and it's the worst thing that can happen to you. From your baby days you were cut out for the service. You've never known anything else."

I could have contradicted her and said that for two weeks I had imagined another way of life but that would have raised too many questions which I couldn't have answered.

I said, "Wouldn't it be better all around if your husband sent me back to my outfit?"

"In Korea?"

"Yes. That would settle my doubts."

To my surprise, she agreed. "It does seem better now. But it would be wrong for two reasons. It would make Eileen seem ridiculous. Couldn't hold her man. And it would be the cowardly thing for you to do."

"Eileen doesn't need me," I said.

"You're absolutely right, Lloyd. She's asked to parties every night. But not by Army men. By civilians in Army suits. Suppose she falls in love with one of these civilians? She'll settle down as a druggist's wife in Chicago and that's not for Eileen, believe me."

I found Mrs. Webster a lot too tough for an airman twenty-eight years old to handle. I said, "I'll drop in and say good night to the general."

But this woman kept hold of you like a steel trap. She said, "And there's a third reason why going back to Korea would be wrong. Because you would be running away from your fundamental problem."

I wanted to shout, "What I want to run away from is you. I'm running away from your daughter because she's so much like you." But a man can shoot down Russians and still be afraid to shoot down his commanding officer's wife. I said, "I'll call Eileen tomorrow."

She said, "Good. I know Eileen and I know she wants to marry you. Don't let lovers' quarrels keep you apart. That would be foolish." She tucked the handkerchief into her sleeve and added with powerful emphasis, "And don't let a temporary uncertainty tease you into thinking you've made a mistake on your whole life. You're an Army man, Lloyd. You were bred to it."

I found General Webster in a workroom lined with books. He indicated them with a wide sweep of his hand and said, "The colonel who had this suite three years ago got these books together. Practically any subject you might be interested in."

I said, "I suppose you know what Mrs. Webster and I were talking about. I think it would be better all around if you sent me back to Korea."

The general drummed his fingers and said, "Better, maybe, but it would be so damned obvious. That's what's wrong with military life. Every move can be so easily interpreted by the enemy. But damn it all, Lloyd, what's wrong between you and Eileen?"

"Nothing's wrong, sir. It's just that we both feel uncertain about our getting along—ultimately."

"Very sensible." He poured me a stiff drink and said, "You're not much of a man unless you're scared silly by the prospect of marriage. Take me. Night before my wedding your father had to get me blind drunk to keep me from sending a Western Union messenger to my wife's house. . . ."

He related in his rambling way the case histories of half a dozen military marriages and of how all the men at some time before the wedding or after had wanted to funk out on the deal. "But in the long run," he assured me, "marriage is the best thing for any man. It was the making of me. And j'your father ever tell you about his classic wedding? He was engaged to your mother, Lieutenant-General Himmelwright's daughter, and two days before the wedding he fell in love with another girl. Just about went mad from indecision. But suppose he had gone off his rocker and said he wasn't cut out to be a general. By God, twenty years later America might of lost Guadalcanal."

He poured us a couple of more drinks and said, "Look at it this way, Lloyd. What the hell were you put in this world for? Be one of those washed-up old fuddies with no home of his own, sitting in a club somewhere yakkity-yakking about China?"

I guess the whisky made me brave, for I said, "Ask Eileen if she'll have dinner with me tomorrow."

"Good boy!" the general cried, whamming me on the back. "I ordered my wife not to speak to you on such a subject. Humiliating to Eileen and all that. But Nancy said there came a time in every girl's love life . . . Isn't that a horrible word?"

"I'll call Eileen about twelve," I said.

General Webster tossed off an extra one and said, "I feel ten years younger. If you have children, Lloyd, have boys."

As I went down in the elevator I saw a new sign which read, "Officers of this command will not appear on the streets of Kobe walking with girls of the indigenous personnel. This order also applies to officers when on the streets of Osaka and Kyoto. Signed, Mark Webster, Commanding." I thought, "Oh, boy! The general's wife is really determined to clean up all Japan," and then I got to laughing because here the American Army was forbidding its men to be seen with Japanese girls, while the Takarazuka army was forbidding its girls to be seen with American men.

I was still chuckling when the elevator doors opened and I heard my name. It was Pvt. Joe Kelly, wearing a service revolver as big as a cannon. He yelled, "At last the Air Force gave me a break. Transferred me to the Joint Message Center. I got the best job in Osaka." He waited for an officer to sign a receipt for important mail, then joined me. His Ford was at the curb.

"Where can I drop you?" he asked, unstrapping his artillery.

"Look, I work at Itami."

"So what's the difference to me. The Army pays for the gasoline."

"And I live at Takarazuka."

"I'll go that way."

We piled in and he reported on how things were going with him and Katsumi. "We found a nice house. You ought to see it. . . . Say, Ace! It's early. Why not drive into Osaka and visit with us?"

He was so energetic and I was so interested in him in the way I had explained to Mike that I agreed. He barreled the Ford along the Kobe-Osaka road and I tried to observe exactly what this ancient and historic Japanese road was like. I saw the little paper-windowed houses stretching mile after mile, with never a sign of countryside. I saw the open-front stores that did business all night and the thousands of people moving along the road in the twilight.

As we entered Osaka he bore to the south until we came to a road which dropped down beside one of the numerous canals. Soon it petered out and four Japanese kids assumed guard over the Ford while we hiked up a narrow alley down which two men trudged with wicker baskets of enormous size.

At the far end of the alley stood an inconspicuous one-storied shack made of wood long since weatherstained to a blackish gray. In the States we would not have called this a house at all. With its sliding paper doors it would have been a shed, and cows or farm tools would have been kept there, but when Joe slid his doors back, there was Katsumi in a kimono, cooking the evening meal. Promptly she took my shoes and offered me a cup of bitter green tea and said in lovely, stilted English, "It is fine to see you among us to—night."

"She's been takin' English lessons," Joe said proudly, "and I study a little Japanese." He rattled off a few phrases and Katsumi beamed at him as if he had written an encyclopedia.

"It's nice here, Ace," Joe said expansively. "Two rooms, the canal down there, a good job and good food. Ace, I'm livin'. For the first time in my life I feel like a human bein'."

He showed me where to put my shoes and how to prop myself up with pillows as we sat on the tatami mats. He said, "I grew up in an orphanage but I was sort of adopted by a family. They found me disappointin' and deserted me—not that I blame 'em, I was a stinker—so I went back to the orphanage and then reform school and then the Air Force. Now I'm a family man." He looked at Katsumi with glowing approval and asked, "Notice the big change, Ace?"

65

"I like the kimono," I said, for Katsumi was one of those ordinary Japanese girls who in flowing kimonos become almost attractive.

"It ain't the kimono, Ace. Watch her smile!" In Japanese he commanded his wife to smile but when she did so I still didn't catch on, so Joe cried, "The tooth, Ace! The tooth!" Then I saw. The big gold tooth had been removed and in its place some Army dentist had fitted a trim porcelain crown. Katsumi really did look attractive in kimono and tooth.

"It's a reformation," I said.

"It's a miracle," Joe sighed. "And she don't giggle no more, do you, Babe?" He dragged Katsumi toward him and kissed her on the cheek. "Because I told her that if she ever giggled again and stuffed her fist in her mouth I'd break her arm off at the wrist." He gave Katsumi a solid wallop on the bottom and she giggled like mad, stuffing her hand into her mouth.

"Sometimes she forgets, Ace, but this is livin'."

He explained to his wife that I bunked at Takarazuka and she spoke in rapid Japanese which he interpreted for me: "A hell of a fine idea, Ace. We're goin' to Takarazuka tomorrow to see the new show. Join us."

"I'd like to, but I have a dinner date in Kobe."

"So what! Show's over by six and I'll race you right in to Kobe, no stops." He pulled an imaginary cord and made like a train whistle. "It's a deal, Ace, because with Katsumi you'll really enjoy it. She knows all the actresses and can tell you what's goin' on."

He gave Katsumi a command in Japanese and she went to a chest where she kept her prized possessions, appearing shortly with a magazine in bright covers. It started at the back, the way Jap books do, and she showed me the photograph of a dazzling stage set. I asked what the magazine was.

"Fan magazine for the Takarazuka shows," Joe explained. "She subscribes to three of them." He shuffled a pile of colorful magazines and I could tell from the devoted way in which Katsumi put them back in order that she had once been one of the enchanted girls who stood each night by the bridge to watch the great stars pass.

"I suppose she belongs to a fan club," I joked.

"Don't kid!" He spoke in Japanese again and Katsumi returned to the chest from which she handed me a stack of photographs. Apparently they went far back in time to when Katsumi had been a child. I asked, "Does she have the pictures of the girls who were in last month's show?"

Katsumi immediately shuffled through the pictures and assembled the entire cast of principals and explained what each did. She even sang two of the songs and I asked, "Does she know all the shows as well as this one?"

Joe patted her arm affectionately and said, "She never misses one. Hasn't for years."

"Then it's a date for tomorrow. But you promise to get me back to Kobe for dinner."

He didn't have to because when I called Eileen next day she played hard-to-get and told me abruptly, "I'm having dinner with a Marine." I said, "That's too bad, how about Friday?" and she said Friday was booked too, so I said, "Boy, I'm playing in tough luck. I'll call you later." But neither of us would have bet much money on when that later would be.

CHAPTER VIII

A CTUALLY, when I went to the theater that afternoon I was rather relieved. It seemed to me that Eileen and I were pretty well washed up and I didn't have to worry any more about Mrs. Webster. I said to Joe, "I'm sort of steamed up to see this show," but I was hardly prepared for what Takarazuka did to *Madame Butterfly*. At any moment they might run in a scene unconnected with anything that had gone before or would come after. There were old Japanese dances to please the classical fans, jitterbugging to represent 1890 America, mutiny aboard an American ship, twenty stupid Japanese cops and a fire.

But running through this burlesque of a great opera there was one solid thread: ridicule of American military men. I have to admit that Mike Bailey's girl, Fumiko-san, was terrific as a ravishing geisha holding the American fleet at bay. There was nothing really offensive with her pantomime but you felt that all the Japanese in the audience were egging her on because they had had a bellyful of Americans.

But the star's performance was quite different. The girl in slacks who had reprimanded us in the restaurant played this part and her Lieutenant Pinkerton was blatantly ridiculous. Yet at the same time the actress herself seemed more essentially feminine than any of the other girls on stage and it was this that made her version of Pinkerton so devastating. She was all Japanese women making fun of all American men.

One act of such petty nonsense was enough for me. When the Act I curtain fell I got up to go, but Katsumi put her hand on mine and said, "No, no! Now is the best!"

From a side entrance the star appeared dressed in old-style samurai costume, pursued by two villains. They attacked her, and in the highly ritualistic dance which followed I for the first time fell under the spell of Japanese art.

68

I cannot tell you what there was about this dance that captivated me. It might have been the haunting music, for now the Western instruments like violins and oboes were silent and in their place were the hammering of a slack-headed drum, the clicking of wooden blocks and the piercing wail of an Asiatic flute. Or it might have been the dazzling curtain before which she danced, a vast gold-and-blue-and-red affair with eight gigantic embroidered irises standing in solemn Oriental perfection. But mostly it was this remarkable woman, this Hana-ogi. Silently, in the Japanese manner, she wove back and forth between her assailants. Instead of a sword she used the traditional symbol, her right hand held vividly upright, and as I watched this hand it traced a wonderful pattern against the gold curtain.

The scene came to a frenzied close with Hana-ogi stamping an unforgettable rhythm and weaving that bright hand through the darkness. The crowd burst into applause and I whispered to Kelly, "Tell Katsumi I'd like to meet that girl."

To my surprise Kelly said, "That's easy. Katsumi knows 'em all." But when he spoke to his wife she became grave and Joe reported, "Katsumi says that your particular girl wouldn't speak to an American."

Right there I could have avoided all that followed, but then I asked, "How does Katsumi happen to know an actress like that?"

Joe laughed and grabbed his wife's handbag, rummaging through it till he found half a dozen pictures. They were all of the dancer, showing her in some of her famous roles. She was a Spanish bullfighter, a Venetian gondolier, a Broadway playboy and a Japanese samurai. She was always the man and she always looked devastatingly feminine.

Joe explained, "Katsumi organized a fan club. Osaka girls who idolized Hana-ogi."

"What's her last name?"

Joe asked Katsumi and said, "Just Hana-ogi. It's a stage name. My wife is crazy about her. Until Katsumi married me she was a real moron. Used to stand in the rain to see her goddess."

"But why?"

"Look, Ace. Suppose you were fat and dumpy and had to work like a slave all day. Then there's this tall slim beautiful girl who's famous all over the country and makes a lot of dough. One actress like Hana-ogi proves what a girl can become."

Katsumi understood our conversation but said nothing. Quietly she recovered the photographs, restored them to some preferred order and replaced them in her bag.

Act II was an amazing experience, for Hana-ogi proved that she was much more than a mere dancer. She had a fine clear singing voice, striking power for dramatic scenes and a wanton comic sense. I leaned across Katsumi and asked, "Joe! Do you think this girl could get by in New York?" He whispered back, "I never been to New York."

But Katsumi heard my question and she realized even before I did that I was determined to meet Hana-ogi that day, so in the darkness she touched my hand and said, "After, we go on flower walk. I speak you to Hana-ogi-san."

When the final curtain fell on *Butterfly* I started to leave but again Katsumi whispered, "No, Ace-san. Now everybody so beautiful." Quickly the curtain opened and there was the entire cast of 120 standing in glorious kimonos, singing a farewell song. A runway reached out into the audience and the stars came down and posed right above us. Our seats were such that Hana-ogi stood very near me and for the first time I saw her in woman's clothes. Her kimono, I remember, was green and white.

Katsumi now led me through the crowd and we came to the flower walk through which the Takarazuka girls passed on their way to the Bitchi-bashi. A large crowd had assembled to applaud them as they appeared and at last, I saw Hana-ogi. Slowly she moved toward me through the great press of people and I think my mouth fell open slightly, for on this day, fresh from triumph, she was a glorious woman.

Katsumi broke the spell by catching Hana-ogi's hands and gabbling away in Japanese. Finally she said to me, "Hana-ogi-san hope you like her play." The tall actress looked at me over

Katsumi's shoulder and I replied quietly, "I liked the play but not the American sailors."

Katsumi reported this and Hana-ogi blushed and said something which Katsumi was reluctant to translate. "Go ahead!" Joe insisted.

"Hana-ogi-san say Americans to be funny. Not bad."

"It wasn't funny," I said. Hana-ogi caught my meaning and frowned, so I added quickly, "But Hana-ogi-san's dancing was wonderful." I imitated her fight with the villains and she smiled.

Hana-ogi's other fans now pressed in upon us and I said awkwardly, "Why don't we four have dinner?" But when Katsumi translated this, Hana-ogi grew very angry, said something harsh and passed abruptly down the flower walk.

I now entered upon a week of dream sequences. The Korean fighting must have exhausted me more than I knew, for my sudden relaxation on the make-believe job at Itami permitted my nerves to find their own level. It wasn't high.

Sometimes at night I would wake with a start and believe myself to be in a falling jet fighter up at the Yalu River, and I would struggle to regain control both of the plane and of myself. Then, as I lay in the dark Japanese night I would see Hana-ogi-san. I would see her oval face smiling at me, ever so small a Japanese smile, and I would wonder how a man could be so tossed about by the mere idea of a girl. I knew nothing of her character or her personality, but almost willfully I was hypnotizing myself over this strange girl. Much later I would recognize that I was creating for myself the image of love and that without this image a man could well live an entire and empty life.

So each evening I fed my delirium by standing at the Bitchi-bashi to watch Hana-ogi pass by and if, during the preceding hours, I had by chance begun to question whether she really was as lovely as I imagined, one sight of her dispelled that heresy. On Friday I returned to see *Swing Butterfly* and at the final promenade I applauded so loudly that Hana-ogi had to look at me, but she betrayed nothing and looked quickly away. Saturday night I was really jittery and Mike Bailey dragged me along on another secret date he had with Fumiko-san and I spent most of the evening questioning her about the Takarazuka girls.

Fumiko said, "My father famous man but he kill himself when Japan surrender. No money no hope for me. I read in paper Takarazuka seek new girls. I brush my hair each night, study dance, shout with my voice. I chosen and one year I work ten hours each day and think this my one chance. Supervisor like me and I go Moon Troupe with Hana-ogi-san. She kind to me and I act parts good. I live dormitory with other girls but best time when Moon Troupe go Tokyo."

I said, "You in love with someone in Tokyo?"

"Love? How I love someone?"

"Aren't you going to get married?"

She looked at me quizzically. "I Takarazuka girl. What else could I want be?"

Her answer so amazed me that I did an impulsive thing which astonished me as much as it did Fumiko-san. I took her hands in mine and said quietly, "Tonight, when you go back to the dormitory you must speak with Hana-ogi-san. Tell her that I am in love with her and must see her."

Fumiko-san withdrew her hands and said in dismay, "Never hoppen! Hana-ogi-san never speak men. And with American! Never hoppen!"

"You tell her," I repeated.

The next afternoon Joe Kelly drove out to Itami and said abruptly, "Wife says you're to be at our house for supper at seven. Hana-ogi's comin'."

CHAPTER IX

I CANNOT remember how, exactly, I got to Joe Kelly's house that night, but when I finally turned up the alley from the canal, when at last I saw the little wooden building and the sliding paper doors my heart was hammering like thunder. I slammed the doors aside and rushed in expecting to see Hana-ogi standing there. Instead Joe and Katsumi were horsing around and cooking food. They told me to sit on the floor and from that position I watched this couple in love and it occurred to me that I myself had never lived in a house where love was. My parents loved each other in the required way and I am quite sure that General and Mrs. Webster loved each other, but it was always love for some ultimate purpose: army advancement, social position in Lancaster, children. Here I was visiting the house of love itself.

Presently the door opened and Hana-ogi entered. Softly and with infinite grace she slid the doors closed behind her and slipped out of her zori. She was dressed in a gray-blue kimono and her hair was rumpled. She stood so silently that Joe and Katsumi did not realize she was there; so while their backs were still turned I stumbled awkwardly to my feet and said, "I am so glad you came." She did not understand my words but even so she nodded in acknowledgment and I knew that she was twice as beautiful as I had ever seen her on the stage.

Katsumi now hurried forward and embraced the actress while Joe greeted her in broken Japanese, at which she laughed heartily, and I got the distinct impression that she was not at all the remote and glamorous girl I had stared at on the Bitchi-bashi, for her gentle good humor was exactly what you would expect from a good, happy country girl working in the city.

But I had seen only two aspects of Hana-ogi and she was infinite, for when I asked Katsumi what her last name was and when Katsumi blushed and said she wouldn't dare ask that ques-

73

tion I insisted, and when Hana-ogi heard Katsumi translate she
grew extremely angry. I couldn't understand what was happening
but Katsumi, blushing a fiery red which showed through her
yellow cheeks, said, "Takarazuka girl never tell her real name.
More better we eat now."

It was a pretty formal meal. I asked a half dozen questions,
none of which Hana-ogi really answered and it was not until
Katsumi produced an album of Hana-ogi's pictures that there
was any real animation. Then the two girls spoke in rapid Japanese, laughed a lot and sang bits of songs from the famous shows
Hana-ogi had starred in. Finally the ice thawed a bit and I
learned that Hana-ogi came from the north of Japan, where a
woman in a nearby village had once seen a Takarazuka show in
Tokyo. This woman had suggested that Hana-ogi apply for the
examinations. Her father had been killed in the B-29 raids on
Tokyo. Her brother had been hung for what he did to American
soldiers in a prisoner-of-war camp.

Hana-ogi's willingness to tell of her family encouraged me to
speak and I said I had a good start in the Air Force and with
my background I surely ought to become a colonel and from
there on it was the roll of the dice. I said that if I did become
a general I hoped I would be as good a one as my father. She
asked his name and when I said Hot Shot Harry Gruver she
grew silent and Katsumi said, "All Japanese know Gruver-san—
Guadalcanal." The evening grew formal again.

Hana-ogi rose and indicated that she must go. I was deeply
agitated at having seen her, having talked with her—even though
it was in translation—and I did not want to have her go. I said,
"Katsumi, please ask her to stay."

Hana-ogi replied something sharp which Katsumi refused to
translate. When I insisted she stood stubbornly silent, so I appealed to Hana-ogi, who looked at me in a quiet, submissive
Japanese way which betrayed no emotion but which dared me to
budge her one inch. Softly, as if she were a child of seven, she
said, "America . . . no!" I could sense in her gentle reply a
finality of hatred and steel. But long after she had gone I recalled

the graceful way she bent down by the doors to put on her zori, the rare delicacy with which she arranged her kimono, so in spite of persistent apprehension that I was headed for trouble, I determined that no matter what she thought of Americans, no matter what orders Camp Kobe handed down regarding Japanese girls, I was going to see her again.

For the next two nights nothing happened. I posted myself at the Bitchi-bashi to watch the procession of girls and when I saw Hana-ogi step upon the bridge at the opposite end, my heart hammered like one of those riveting machines you fix airplane wings with. She was like a medieval princess walking out from the palace. She was so straight and proud and sure of herself.

"Son, you got it bad!" Mike Bailey warned me on the second night.

"I'm going to see that girl. Tomorrow," I said. "Tomorrow night I'm going to storm that Bitchi-bashi and I'm going to have a date with that girl."

Mike stayed away from the bridge that third night and as the first Takarazuka girls crossed I felt my heart hammering again and soon there was Hana-ogi, accompanied by three other stars, and I stepped right into the middle of them and took Hana-ogi's hand and kissed it. Then I said, "I have got to see you," but none of the girls spoke English and Hana-ogi drew her hand away and started to leave, but I no longer gave a damn so I grabbed her by the shoulder and swung her around and kissed her on the lips. We kept our eyes open and I remember that in this crazy moment I could not tell whether her eyes were slanted or not, but they were very black, like the sky at night.

She pushed me away and crossed the bridge and I heard behind me the muttering of Japanese men and I thought, "Oh, damn, a public mess and I'll be court-martialed," but when I turned there was no animosity. The men were laughing and one old fellow with a load of wood on his back pointed at some more Takarazuka girls approaching on the bridge and made motions encouraging me to kiss them too, but I hurried back to the Marine Barracks, where Mike Bailey greeted me with a pair of field

75

glasses and the crack, "It looked good, son. The subtle approach. Grrrrr."

I said, "I promised to see her tonight. I did."

He said, "Ace, don't let this thing get you. If you want to make a play for a pretty actress—O.K. But don't let it get you. Frankly, you looked silly as hell down there on the bridge."

In a few minutes a Japanese boy appeared with a message for Mike and he said, "Fumi-chan wants to see me in the restaurant. She wants you to come along."

When we got there Makino-san, the cook, had already heard of my behavior and he gave me hell. "Very important in Japan these girls. You do much wrong, Ace-san."

"What did I do?" I demanded. "I kissed a girl."

"A Takarazuka girl," he said with reverence. Before he could argue further Fumiko-san appeared. She did not cry but she did plead with me and said that something like that could ruin a Takarazuka girl and that if Hana-ogi ever lost her job her mother and her younger sisters . . . "She very poor, Hana-ogi," Fumiko told me.

"What do you mean?" I asked.

"You Americans not know what poor is. Hana-ogi never tasted meat until she came Takarazuka. Never had one nice clothes. Ace-san, you not speak her again—please?"

She told me that Hana-ogi's only chance in life—her one opportunity to escape from terrible poverty—was Takarazuka. She said there was already a likelihood that Hana-ogi might become one of the rare lucky ones—kept on at Takarazuka forever "as teacher of the dancing" when her days as an actress were over. "Here is good life for Hana-ogi-san. There is no other."

I asked Fumiko why she risked seeing Mike Bailey and she laughed. "I not great actress. I not poor girl. My family making lots of money again."

Then she pleaded, "Do not come to the bridge again, Ace-san. Please?"

I wanted to see Hana-ogi, I wanted to see her eyes close to

mine and her golden face pressed against my lips, but I said, "I promise."

But although I kept my promise not to haunt the bridge it meant nothing, for the very next morning Joe Kelly wheeled up to Itami Air Field and said with real joy, "Dinner again tonight, Ace!"

My heart must have bled out through my eyes, for he laughed and said, "Yep. Hana-ogi came into Osaka late last night and talked with Katsumi for three hours."

"What did she say?"

"How should I know?" And he rattled off a jumble of Japanese.

I wish that throughout the rest of my life I could occasionally know the excitement that captured me that night. I shaved at Itami, polished my shoes and set out for Osaka. When I reached Joe's house, I thrust back the sliding doors and cried, "Hana-ogi, I . . ." But she was not there. Katsumi was alone, singing to herself as she prepared dinner. I sat on the floor and watched her time-christened movements over the charcoal stoves that Japanese women have used for centuries. For them there were no can openers, no frozen foods. Each item was laboriously prepared by hand and as Katsumi did this ancient work she hummed old songs and it seemed to me that she grew lovelier each day—but how truly lovely I was to learn in a few minutes.

For little Joe Kelly came busting into the house trembling with anger. He threw a package on the floor and cried, "This son-of-a-bitch of a colonel!"

I had heard Joe sound off against officers before and I tried to tone him down, but this time he had real cause. "This bastard, Colonel Calhoun Craford! He rides me. Every damned day he rides me."

I happened to be watching Katsumi at the brazier. She never looked up, but I could see a tenseness come over her entire body, and I knew she was desperately afraid for her man.

For I had heard of this Calhoun Craford, a tough guy who hated colored people. Joe said, "Every guy in that outfit who's

77

married to a Japanese girl goes through hell with this bastard Craford."

Katsumi, aware that Joe's trouble had been caused by her, now left the charcoal brazier and came into the middle of the room. She pushed Joe down onto a pillow and took off his shoes. "You not to come on tatami with shoes, Joe," she said softly. She brought him a tiny cup of hot sake wine and when he had drunk this she led him into the other room where there was a Japanese bath and soon I could hear tensed up little Joe Kelly, the dead-end kid, sloshing about in the tub while his patient wife soused him with cold water and rubbed his back. After a while they joined me and Joe scratched himself under the dark blue kimono Katsumi had made him. He said, "To hell with Colonel Craford. Look what I got!" And he produced a bottle of Italian wine which Katsumi took.

Then, as we heard the soft click of zori on the alley stones, we all fell silent and I think Joe and Katsumi were as excited as I, although their hearts couldn't have been pounding as hard. The paper doors slid back and there was Hana-ogi in a green-and-gold kimono, her lips slightly parted in a smile, her brilliant eyes glowing from her night walk. She started to speak but I caught her in my arms and kissed her. This time we closed our eyes, but when we finally drew apart—for she was kissing me too—she passed the back of her hand across her forehead and I think she knew then that for a girl dedicated to Takarazuka and a man dedicated to American military life love could result only in tragedy, and she pushed my hand away from hers and gently removed her zori and sat down on the tatami and spoke quietly to Katsumi, who spoke to Joe in Japanese, and all three of them fumbled around, not knowing how to translate what Hana-ogi had said, so she held out her hand to me and invited me to sit upon the mats beside her, and finally Katsumi said, "She not mad no more."

After dinner Katsumi said, "Joe, we take walk." Hana-ogi did not protest and as soon as the fragile doors slid shut I took her in my arms.

We sat upon the mats unable to say a word. I put my finger on her wonderful face and said, "Nice," but she could not understand. She gave me some instructions in Japanese but all I could do was shrug my shoulders, so she laughed and grabbed my big toe and pulled my cramped legs out straight and patted my knees, indicating that I must be stiff from sitting Japanese style. Then she made a pillow for my head in her lap and in that way we continued our meaningless conversation on the tatamis.

It was apparent to each of us that we would meet many times, but that when she passed me on the Bitchi-bashi she would look straight ahead and it was also apparent that she intended us to be lovers—but not on this first quiet night—and that as the days went by we would postpone one decision after another until finally some external force, say Takarazuka or General Webster, intervened to make the climactic decisions for us, but as she looked down at me with calm eyes, as her wonderful hands held my face and as her slim, graceful legs stretched out at last beside mine on the tatami mats, one question at least was answered. I had often wondered how a self-respecting American could get excited about a Japanese girl. Now I knew.

When it came time to leave, Hana-ogi refused to be seen with me on the street and caught a train back to Takarazuka. Joe drove me over to Itami, where I took the bus to Takarazuka, but something must have delayed Hana-ogi's train, because when I got to my room and looked out at the Bitchi-bashi, there was Hana-ogi crossing it in the April moonlight. I rushed down to speak with her but she passed proudly by, her cream-colored zori going pin-toed along the railroad track to her dormitory.

I didn't sleep much that night because when I got back to my room I found a letter which had been delivered by special messenger. It contained a routine reminder of recent orders issued by Camp Kobe and along the foot in capital letters I read: ANY PUBLIC DISPLAY WHATEVER OF AFFECTION FOR A JAPANESE NATIONAL BY A MEMBER OF THIS COMMAND IS FORBIDDEN. OFFICERS SHOULD NOT EVEN APPEAR ON PUBLIC STREETS ACCOMPANIED BY WOMEN OF THE INDIGENOUS PERSONNEL.

I knew that I was entangled in a ridiculous situation, for I could not walk with Hana-ogi in the city and she could not walk with me in the town. If General Webster caught me dating a Japanese girl I would be disciplined and if the Takarazuka people heard of Hana-ogi dating an American she would be fired from the Moon Troupe.

For about two hours that morning as I lay awake—from three to five—I decided the whole affair was too damned silly, but toward dawn I began to see Hana-ogi dancing along the wall of my room and her classical postures, the stamping of her feet and the gestures of her right hand allured me so that I could think only of her tight and disciplined body. My thoughts were filled with the grace of her movement and as the sun rose I fell asleep knowing that somewhere within the triangle of the three cities we would meet.

CHAPTER X

I T CAME unexpectedly. On a warm day in May I waited for
Hana-ogi at the Bitchi-bashi but she did not appear and dis-
consolately I wandered down to the railroad station to purchase a ticket back to Itami, but as I approached the cage I
saw Hana-ogi standing off to one side, holding a ticket in her
hand and impulsively, even though we were in the heart of
Takarazuka, she came to me and we went to the ticket cage
together and we bought two tickets for a small town at the end
of the line, and on this lovely day we walked for the first time
through the ancient Japanese countryside.

Wherever we went the land was crowded. Where in Texas
there would be one farmer here there were forty. Where the
footpath in New Hampshire might be crowded with three
people, here it was overwhelmed with fifty. There were no
vacant fields, no woodlots, no mossy banks beside the wandering streams. On every foot of land there were people and no
matter how far we walked into the countryside there were
always more people. More than any day I ever lived in my
life I treasure this day because I discovered not only Hana-ogi's
enormous love but I also discovered her land, the tragic, doomed
land of Japan.

In Korea we used to joke about enlisted men who bought
Japanese girls of sixteen or seventeen—a man could buy a
young girl anywhere in Japan—and we thought it a horrible
reflection on Japan, but today I saw that it would always be
possible to find some Japanese farmer who would be eager to
sell his daughter to a kind man, for if she stayed at home and
had to fight for her share of the skimpy rice in the family
bowl she could never do as well as if she went off with a man
who could buy rice for her. All the problems we used to laugh
about as being so strange—so unlike America—I saw explained

this afternoon. The Japanese were no different from us. Their farmers loved their daughters exactly as Iowa farmers love theirs. But there was not enough land. There was never enough food.

I thank God for that May evening walking among the rice fields while the crickets droned at us, for if I had not seen this one particular old man tending his field I am sure that when I finally learned the terrifying truth about Hana-ogi I could no longer have loved her; but having seen this old man and his particles of soil I loved her the more.

He stood where a trail turned off from the main road, leaving in the joint a thin sliver of useless land that in America would have been allowed to grow up in burdock. In Japan this tragic triangle was the sustenance of one man's large family. On this May night he was bent over the field, digging it to a depth of fourteen inches. The dug soil he placed reverently to one side until his tiny field was excavated. Then, as we watched, he took each handful of soil and gently pulverized it, allowing it to return to its bed. Pebbles he tossed aside and sticks and foreign things, and in the two days that followed this man would finger each item of his soil. Not for him a plow or a harrow, but the gnarled fingers and the bending back.

It is difficult for me to report these things, for I cannot explain how Hana-ogi explained them to me. By pointing, by gestures, by little pantomimes with the old man she explained that he was like her father except that her father's field—before the American bombs killed him—was slightly bigger. But her father had nine children.

It was breathlessly apparent to us as the sun sank below the distant hills that in terribly crowded Japan Hana-ogi and I were seeking a place in which to make love. There was now no thought of Japanese or American. We were timeless human beings without nation or speech or different color.

At last we came to a structure that was familiar to me, two inclined massive poles with two more set across them at the top like an enormous capital A, flat at the point. It was the timeless symbol of a Shinto shrine and here there were trees, but as always there were people too. We watched them come through the towering A, stand silently before the shrine, clap their hands three times, bow and depart, the torn white paper and the rice ropes of their religion fluttering quietly in the wind above them.

Hana-ogi led me past the shrine until we came to a grassy bank partially protected by four trees. Villagers passed ten feet from us and dogs barked nearby. There was no place where there were not people. But at last we had to ignore them and it seemed to me as I sank beside Hana-ogi in the May twilight that we were being watched by the million eyes of Japan.

I remember vividly two things that happened. I had no conception of a kimono and thought it a kind of wrap-around dress but when we embraced and it was clear that Hana-ogi intended that we love completely, I tried to undo this gossamer dress, but it led to another and then another and to still more and although we could not speak we fell to laughing at my astonishment. Then suddenly we laughed no more, for I was faced with the second vast occurrence of the day, for when in the fading light I at last saw Hana-ogi's exquisite body I realized with shock—even though I was prepared to accept it —that I was with a girl of Asia. I was with a girl whose complete body was golden and not white and there was a terrible moment of fear and I think Hana-ogi shared this fear, for she caught my white arm and held it across her golden breasts and studied it and looked away and then as quickly caught me to her whole heart and accepted the white man from America.

We returned at last to Takarazuka and as we approached that lovely place we went into separate cars and I waited long till Hana-ogi had disappeared across the Bitchi-bashi before I appeared on the streets, heading for the Marine Barracks. Mike Bailey was in the shower and when he heard me go by he yelled and brought me back to military life with a bang.

He said, "Mrs. Webster saw me in Kobe today and asked me a lot of questions."

"About you and Fumi-chan?" I asked, nonchalantly.

"Don't play coy, son. About you and Eileen."

"What'd'j tell her?"

"It isn't so much what I told her as what she asked." He waited for me to press the point, but I called downstairs for some cold beer and he said, "She asked me if you were going with a Japanese girl."

I sort of gulped on my beer and Mike said promptly, "Of course I said no. You aren't, are you?"

I took another drink of beer and pondered a long time what I ought to say. Then the pressing desire to talk with someone overcame me and I said, "I've been walking with Hana-ogi. We must have walked for five miles and I'm so deep in love . . ."

Mike was a fine character to talk with at a time like this. He laughed and said, "I feel like a traitor, Ace, getting you into this. Hell, I'm the one who's supposed to be in love."

I said, "It hit me like a propeller zinging around when you aren't looking. Jesus, Mike, I tell you the truth, I'm a desperate man."

Mike laughed again and said, "No need for a guy to be desperate in Japan. If you can't cuddle up to Hana-ogi because she's an actress, there's always the Tiger of Takarazuka. Better men than you . . ."

I started to say boldly, "But we . . ." My voice trailed off and I ended lamely, "The stars came right down and knocked me out."

Mike looked at me quizzically, then said without joking, "Look, Ace, I know better than most men around here how sweet a Japanese girl can be. But don't get involved. For the love of God, Ace, don't get involved."

"I am involved."

"Mrs. Webster said the M.P.'s have instructions to pick up officers seen holding hands with indigenous personnel. That's a lovely phrase, isn't it?"

"I just don't give a damn, Mike. To hell with the M.P.'s and to hell with Mrs. Webster."

"I agree with you, Ace. But while I was talking with the general's main tank division her daughter came up. Ace, that girl's a ravin' beauty! Why do you have to mess around with a Japanese actress if this Eileen is on tap?"

I put the beer down and stared at the floor. That was the question I had not wanted Mike to ask. I saw Eileen as I had known her at Vassar, bright, eager, a wonderful sport. I saw her that winter in Texas when her father was a colonel at San Antonio and I was at Randolph Field. Why hadn't I married her then? Why had she turned down the other young officers and insisted upon waiting for me? I felt like the announcer who asks the burning questions at the end of each radio program about breaking hearts, but I knew that you could turn my radio on the next day and still not get the answers.

I looked up at Mike and said, "I don't know."

He asked me directly, "Are you afraid of American women?"

I said, "I hadn't thought of it."

He said, "I've been over here a long time, what with one thing and another. I've watched lots of our men go for these Japanese girls . . . Hell, I won't be superior about it. I do myself. But frankly and all kidding aside, Ace, the Air Force would never let you marry a Japanese girl. You're one of their bright young men and they'd bring all sorts of pressures to bear. . . ."

"Who's talking about marriage?"

Mike sighed. "That's better. The way you started, you were talking about marriage." He grew thoughtful and added, "It's very strange. I'd never have picked Hana-ogi. She's always so mannish. Come to think of it, I've never seen her in girl's clothes. Have you?"

I thought of her rare charm and started to speak reverently but this scared Mike and he said, "Ace, I know damn well you're thinking about marriage and it's going to be tough. Son, it's going to be tough."

I insisted that I didn't know what I was thinking about, but my problem was solved for me in an unforeseen manner.

85

Katsumi and Joe dropped by the air base the next afternoon and Katsumi took care of everything. Haltingly she said, "We have find house for you, Ace."

"A house!" I drew her toward a wall where no one could listen. "What do I want with a house?"

"Where else you and Hana-ogi-san stay?"

"Wait a . . ."

"You not love Hana-ogi?"

"Sure I love her, but . . ." I appealed to Joe, who grinned and said, "When a Japanese girl loves you, Ace, it's solid."

I said to them, "Hana-ogi could get into trouble. . . ."

Katsumi looked at me incredulously and said, "When Hana-ogi come our house to see you it mean she love you. When she walk to Shinto shrine it mean same thing. Where you two make love? Here at Itami? I don't think so. (She pronounced it, "I don' sink so.") Officers Club Kobe? I don't think so. Takarazuka? No!"

I was about to call the whole affair off when Katsumi handed me a map showing that the house was not far from hers. Then she said, gravely, "Today Hana-ogi-san number one girl at Takarazuka. She work very hard for this. You be good man not tell anyone you love Hana-ogi. She come your new house tonight seven o'clock."

I was now overboard in the slipstream where things happen so fast you never get your parachute open. I was tumbling about and all thought of General Webster's orders, my promotion in service and my early ideas about the Japanese enemy were swirling in confusion. But of one thing I was determined. I would go to that house in Osaka early in the afternoon and I would clean it and I would stock the shelves with food and I would make it a home.

But at three-thirty I was called into an urgent meeting and it was nearly seven when I reached Osaka. I hurried up the main street to where my canal ran off to the right and I passed along the narrow footpath until I came to a little store, where I bought an armful of things to eat.

As I approached my house I saw that the sliding doors were open and from them came a bright light and a sight I shall never forget: a tiny cloud of dust followed by the merest flick of a broom. Hana-ogi had hurried to the new house to clean it for my arrival.

I dashed into the room, threw the food on the floor and took her in my arms. I kissed her wildly and pressed her golden cheek next to mine, but instead of the flood of kisses I anticipated she pushed me away, pointed to my shoes and cried, "Oh, Rroyd-san!" For a moment I was bewildered and then she knelt down and started to untie my offending shoes. Quickly I prevented her from doing this, so she picked up the food I had dropped and when she placed it on the shelf I saw that with her own money she had already stocked the kitchen.

There was a pot cooking over the brazier and I looked in, then turned quickly to find Hana-ogi cleaning my shoes and placing them in the corner. I took three steps, lifted her away from my shoes and carried her into the middle of the room, where I stood looking about me helplessly till Hana-ogi laughed and with her expressive head indicated a closet which I kicked open, releasing the bed roll. I spread it as well as I could with my feet and gently placed Hana-ogi upon it. She closed her slanted eyes for a moment, then looked up and smiled.

CHAPTER XI

IN THE days that followed I often recalled the stories I had read about American and English sailors who had fallen in love with island girls and of how idyllic it was. But these stories invariably ended with the big kiss and it had not occurred to me that after the big kiss these island lovers must have had things they wanted to talk about.

I knew exactly four Japanese phrases. *Ichi ban* meant *number one* and I used this interminably. When I first saw Hana-ogi undressed I gasped at her amazing beauty and cried, "Ichi ban!" When she cooked a good meal it was "Ichi ban." When she saw President Truman's picture in the paper I said, "America ichi ban."

I also knew *Domo arigato gozaimasu,* which meant *thank you.* I used it all the time and it was curious how this phrase of courtesy came to mean so much to us. We were deeply indebted to each other, for we had undertaken unusual risks, so there was an extra tenderness about all we did. When I spread the bed roll I would say, "Dom' arigato" but more often I used the full phrase. I was in a land of courtesy where great courtesy had been extended me.

Of course I knew the universal Japanese words *takusan* and *sukoshi* for *much* and *little.* Every American in Japan used these words as his final comment upon an infinity of subjects. I remember once when I was moved to great depths by something Hana-ogi had done and I pointed to my heart, put her golden hand above it and cried, "Takusan, takusan!" And I indicated that it was for her that it had become takusan after having been sukoshi for so many years.

And finally I knew that strangest of Japanese phrases, *Ah, so desu-ka!* It was usually abbreviated into *Ah, so!* and meant exactly what it would mean in English. It was also shortened to *Soka, Soda,* and *Deska* and I used it for everything. Often I would hear Hana-ogi and Katsumi talking and one of them would be narrating something and the other would repeat over and over in the most mournful way, "Ah, so desu-ka! Ah, so desu-ka!" We all laughed hilariously when Joe found an American newspaper item in which a famous woman journalist from New York said that even the Empress of Japan was becoming Americanized because she spoke a little English. "All the time I talked with the Empress she nodded her head and whenever she agreed with me she said clearly, 'Ah, so!'"

Hana-ogi, on her part, had acquired just about as much English. Like all Japanese girls her favorite phrase was *Never hoppen!* She could say this with the most ravishing wit and effectively kill any high-blown idea I might be trying to make, but once when I said that some day she would see New York she said with great finality, "Never hoppen."

A second phrase she used a great deal was one she picked up from Katsumi and it too was common all over Japan: *I don't think so.* Hana-ogi had trouble with *th* and this phrase of classic doubt usually came out, "I don' sink so."

But if Hana-ogi had difficulty with *th,* her conflict with *l*'s and *v*'s and *f*'s was unending. She had acquired, from her Takarazuka shows, a few American phrases which she loved to use on me at unexpected moments, but they were so mangled because of the limited alphabet of sound in the Japanese tongue that I often had to think twice to detect her meaning. Once, at the end of a long night when we stayed up to clean our tiny house she caught me in her arms and cried, "Oh Rroyd, I rub you berry sweet." I was unprepared both for her emotion and her pronunciation and for one dreadful moment I almost laughed and then I looked down at her dear sweet slanted eyes and saw that they were filled with tears and we sat down on the tatami as morning broke and she told me in signs and kisses and strange half-words that she had never thought that she, Hana-ogi— dedicated to Takarazuka and knowing nothing else—would ever discover what it was to . . . She stopped and we had no words

89

to finish the thought. Then she jumped up and cried, "I make you cawhee." And she took down the coffee pot.

It was true that not being able to talk made our physical love, there on the tatimi mats, more powerful, but when that was past, when you lay there on the dark floor and heard feet along the canal path, you yearned desperately to talk of ordinary things, and once I thought of what Joe had said and I wished to God that I might be able to talk with Hana-ogi about the country club or the braces on junior's teeth or anything trivial at all—like the news that Katsumi-san was going to have a baby. I wanted to talk about that baby, what it would be like, would its eyes be Japanese, would it live well in America, but all I could do was to place my hand on Hana-ogi's hard flat stomach and whisper, "Katsumi-san takusan—takusan."

The matter of praying gave us some trouble, as it did Joe and Katsumi. Joe, being a good Catholic, was repelled when Katsumi established in their home a Shinto shrine, complete with symbols to be prayed to. There were some heated words and the shrine came down, but I don't think Hana-ogi would have agreed to surrendering her Shinto faith, for one day I came home and found that she had erected in our home three separate shrines: Shinto, Buddhist and Catholic. I tried to explain that I wasn't any of the three, but she said she was willing to be all of them for me. I asked her why she honored both Shinto and Buddhism and she said that many Japanese were both and that some were Christians as well, and she found nothing curious in tending the three shrines faithfully and I noticed that she paid just as fair attention to my one as she did to her two.

It became so imperative that we converse with each other that we looked forward with sheer delight to the visits of Joe and Katsumi and I was glad whenever Katsumi sneaked away from Joe's surveillance and came to our house to pray to her Shinto gods for her baby to be a boy and strong. Whenever she appeared Hana-ogi and I would unleash an accumulation of questions about the most trivial things. I would say, "Tell Hana-

ogi I like more salt in all my vegetables." Imagine, I had been
unable to convey that simple idea accurately. And Katsumi
would reply, "Hana-ogi want know, you ever eat octopus?" and
I would cry, "Is that what she was trying to ask?" and I would
repeat the word *octopus* and Hana-ogi would tell me what it
was in Japanese and thus we would possess one more word to
share.

But the hoard of meanings grew so slowly that as the days
passed and as we fell more hopelessly in love we discovered
that it was impossible to exist as passionately as we insisted
without better communication of ideas, so I started to learn a
little Japanese and Hana-ogi—who despised Americans and
what they had done to Japan—reluctantly joined an English
class. She bought a little conversation book which she studied
each day on the train back and forth to Takarazuka and one
night she volunteered her first complete sentence in English.
Screwing up her courage like a schoolgirl reciting Milton, she
swallowed, smiled at me and declaimed, "Lo, the postillion has
been struck by lightning."

The shock of these words was so great that I burst into uncontrolled laughter and I saw Hana-ogi slowly freeze with
hatred. I had laughed at her best intentions. I too was an
American.

I rose quickly from the floor to apologize, but when she saw
me move toward her she ran away. Grabbing her English book
she tore it to pieces and threw them at me. Those pages which
fell at her feet she trampled upon and screamed in Japanese as
she did so.

Finally I caught her hands and kissed her. I held her head
to mine and when she started to sob I could have torn my
tongue out. This cruel inability to speak was killing us and
we were becoming lost people in a void of ideas. . . . We
were lovers who could not love and when Hana-ogi had sought
to bridge this gap—humiliating herself and surrendering her
hatred of the enemy—I had laughed at her.

I realized then that words must no longer be permitted to

keep us apart. I held her head close to my heart and burst into my own words, whether she could understand them or not. "Hana-ogi, Hana-ogi!" I said "I love you with all the heart and mind within me. I've been a barren desert . . . I've been a man flying a lost plane far in the sky and I have never before known a human being. Now I've come to an alien land among people I once hated and I've met you and taken you away from these people and brought you to a tiny house and you have made a shred of heaven here. Hana-ogi, if I've hurt you through my ignorance you ought to lash me through the streets of Osaka, for my heart is in your care and if I were to hurt you I would be destroying myself. Whether you understand or not, these words are for you." And I kissed her.

I believe she comprehended what I said, for with her face now pressed to mine she spoke softly in Japanese and I think she unburdened herself of the accumulated passions that had been tormenting her word-stricken heart. I closed my eyes and listened to the wonderful sound of her voice as she uttered the strange, angular syllables of her native language. She did not use one word I understood, but the meaning of her thoughts somehow seeped through and we knew that we were more deeply in love than ever before.

From that night on Hana-ogi and I talked with each other a great deal and we discovered that in love what is said is far less important to the person spoken to than to the one who speaks. If I wanted to tell her that the days were growing longer and that I first noticed this during the year when I was a young boy on an Army base in Montana, I said just that, and it was marvelous for me, for then I remembered how I felt as a boy—the great cleanness of life and the bigness—and I had a larger heart with which to love. And Hana-ogi spoke to me of her childhood and of how she dreamed of going to Tokyo and of how, when she got there, it seemed so much smaller than she had imagined. I understood only a little of what she intended, but one thing I understood with amazing clarity: when she had talked of these things for a long time she was lovelier than I had ever imagined a woman could be. In those long nights of talking, there in the bed roll on the tatami mats, I think we came closer to sharing with complete finality two human lives than will ever be possible for me again. Forbidden the use of words, we drove our hearts to understanding, and we understood.

In the morning after Hana-ogi tore up the English book I gathered the mutilated pages to burn them, but in doing so I noticed that her book had been published in 1879 by a brilliant Japanese scholar who had apparently been bowled over by English during those first wonderful days when Japan was opening her gates to Western learning. This gentleman's first sentence "for young ladies to use when starting a conversation in public" was Hana-ogi's epic "Lo, the postillion has been struck by lightning," and although I am sure the ancient scholar never intended it so, that sentence became the gag line of an American-Japanese home. Whenever trouble appeared in any form Hana-ogi would declaim, "Lo, the postillion!"

CHAPTER XII

SINCE I now knew that the secret of love is communication, I wish I could tell you exactly how Hana-ogi and I learned to talk in those exquisite days of early love, but I cannot recall how it was done. I do remember the evening when I tried to ask Hana-ogi what her name meant. I was barefooted and wearing the cheap blue-and-white kimono so common in Japan. I sat with my back against the fragile wall, my feet awkwardly out upon the tatami. I tried to convey the idea: "What does Hana-ogi mean?" but I did not succeed for the only two words she understood were *what* and her own name and she naturally suspected that I wanted to know what she wanted. So with tiny gestures and much pointing she indicated our small house of great love and said that all she wanted was to be here with me, and that when she slid the paper doors shut in the evening she wanted to lock us in and the world out.

Quietly I sat against the wall and tucked my kimono tighter about me, relishing the delicate thoughts she had expressed for both of us. But then I tried again and this time she cried, "Ah, so desu-ka! The other Hana-ogi! Yes, Rroyd-san. I tell."

It is here that I wish I could explain, but I can't. Knowing almost nothing of my language this extraordinary girl nevertheless told me the following story. Some of the passages she danced, some of them she pantomimed, and some she spoke in such expressive Japanese that I could fairly guess their meaning. And this is the story she told me:

Once upon a time in a small village near Tokyo there was a girl of great beauty. No one knows her name, but she was to become Hana-ogi, the most renowned prostitute in the entire history of Japan. As a child she lived with her widowed mother but it soon became apparent that her only possible future lay in the green houses of Yoshiwara, the ancient walled quarter

94

by the marshes of Tokyo, where the unwanted young girls of farmer families were trained to become courtesans.

The old mother sold Hana-ogi when the rare child was seven, and for eight years this girl, always more beautiful, waited on the established courtesans of Ogi-ya, the green house which she would later make the most famous in all Japan. While she still wore her obi tied behind with its long ends signifying that she was virgin, the older girls taught her the skills of their trade and on her fifteenth birthday Hana-ogi discarded forever her real name, tied her obi in front, and took her first customer.

He was a young man from Odawara and he fell so desperately in love with Hana-ogi that he used to haunt the steps of Ogi-ya even when he had not the money to come inside. In perplexity he watched Hana-ogi become the most prized woman in Yoshi-wara, and there were more than four thousand there at the time. She became famous for her poems, exquisite sighings of the heart and delicate memories of farm life when the early dew was on the rice fields. Priests in the temples sometimes told the worshippers of this saintly girl who took no thought of buying her own freedom from the green houses but who sent all her money home to her old mother. On holy days Hana-ogi went to a Buddhist temple that was known as the silent temple because it had no bell to record the great days and one evening Hana-ogi led a procession of thousands from the Yoshiwara bearing a bronze bell for this silent temple. It was her gift to the priests who were poorer than she.

Her fame became so great that visitors from China came to see this glory of Nihon. (My Hana-ogi rarely called her country Japan, never Nippon.) Poets wrote famous songs about her. Men close to the Shogun came to talk with her, and above all the painters of the passing world, the wood-block artists who lived along the edge of the Yoshiwara, made many portraits of her. Today, in the museum at Kyoto, you can see maybe three dozen famous paintings of Hana-ogi. When I see them, said my Hana-ogi, I think that this immortal woman is speaking to me across the years and I take courage.

Now all the time that the great men of the Shogun's palace and the world-famous painters were with Hana-ogi, the young lover from Odawara was watching, too, and one spring as the cherry blossoms were about to bloom he abducted Hana-ogi from the green houses. Where they hid themselves, these two happy people, no one knows. Whether they had children of their love no one can say. The years passed and bad luck fell on the house of Ogi-ya. No more did the rich men and the painters come there and no more did the priests of the nearby temples receive gifts from Hana-ogi. The portraits of this unforgettable girl were sold in great quantity, for everyone wished some memento of the loveliest woman Japan had ever produced.

Then one day there was a burst of glory. (Here the real Hana-ogi, my living grace, assumed a kind of cathedral beauty as she simulated an incredible procession.) Hana-ogi had come back to the green houses. She was thirty-four years old, more beautiful than she had ever been. Young girls walked before her, bearing flowers. A minister of state walked proudly behind her. Two men held umbrellas over her head, and she was dressed in an exquisite blue kimono with rich flowing robes of purple and the geta upon her feet were eleven inches high. Within five days the greatest artists of Japan had issued magnificent pictures of her joyous return, and we can see them still, the stately processions, the rare, wonderful woman coming back to her strange world.

It was the golden age! In those days there was singing and long talks and beautiful pictures and fine women and Nihon was never so joyous. And queen of the golden age was this country girl, Hana-ogi. She never explained her absence, she never told what had happened to her lover, but people guessed that like all Japanese men he had grown tired of her and had abused her. She lived at the Ogi-ya for many years and when she was too old to serve the visitors any longer she disappeared one day and no one ever again heard of Hana-ogi.

My living Hana-ogi folded her hands and sank upon the floor.

I was aghast at such an ending to so powerful a story and I

cried, jumping to my feet, "No! No! What happened to Hana-ogi?"

It took some time for me to explain myself and then my beautiful Japanese narrator stared up at me in blank surprise and said, "In Nihon many girls. Every time new girls in Ogi-ya."

I shouted that I knew that, but what had become of Hana-ogi? My adorable oval-face on the floor looked up in confusion and said, "Hana-ogi become old girl." (She pulled down the lines of her face and indicated that a tooth was missing.) "She old, she go."

"But where? Where did she go?"

My living Hana-ogi shrugged her shoulders. Then, sensing my disappointment, she formed the sign of a Buddhist temple and made believe to ring the bell which the ancient Hana-ogi had bought with her few coins and she indicated that no doubt this most glorious woman of Japanese history had been thrown out of the Ogi-ya when her teeth were broken and that she had possibly taken a position near the steps of the temple to beg alms.

There was an overwhelming ache upon my heart and I knelt upon the floor beside my Hana-ogi, who had fled her prison for her lover and whose future was as uncertain as her predecessor's. There was an enormous bond of tenderness between us and that was the definable beginning of my determination never to surrender this rare woman, this tender and gracious miracle.

The consequences of such a determination I did not then foresee, but they were explained to me in part by an event which occurred three nights later. Like any husband and wife we ultimately felt even our perfect home confining and we wanted to go to a movie, but this was no easy trick. Hana-ogi knew that I might be arrested if I appeared on the streets with her and I knew that she would get into serious trouble if she were seen with me, so she left our paper doors first and in five minutes I followed and we met inside the darkened theater and held hands like any beginning lovers, congratulating ourselves on having evaded the chaperones. But our luck didn't hold because two women had recognized Hana-ogi when she entered as the great star at Takarazuka, so that when the lights went up these women choked the aisle and begged an autograph and soon Hana-ogi was surrounded by young girls.

We hurried out a side door and she fled alone down a back street and I ambled up the main street and when I got home I found her sitting dumb on the floor, her head bowed. She told me that she had always known that some time we would be found out and that she was not frightened. She would have to leave Takarazuka but she might find a job in pictures. Or there were certain theaters in Tokyo which might offer her work. She said, "I not scare. But Takarazuka I like very very much." (She said, "I rike berry berry much.")

I suggested at once that perhaps she should leave me and return to Takarazuka dormitory and endanger no longer a brilliant career but she kept staring at the floor and said quietly words which meant this: "I always planned to act till I was past forty, and when my days as an actress were over I intended to take the place of Teruko-san, who was the greatest dancer Takarazuka ever had and who now teaches us the classical steps. But when I came here, Rroyd-san, I knew the danger I ran and if tomorrow were yesterday I would come here again."

I think that's what she intended to say and I was deeply troubled by the responsibility I had undertaken and by the resolve I had made never to desert her, but when she saw my silent fears she put her soft hand upon my face and said, "This time only time I be in love. I not stop our love one day before . . ." She made a great explosion with her hands as if the world had fallen in. She embraced me and we fell back upon the bed roll. She started to whimper and said, "I not speak true. Oh, Rroyd-san, I afraid. I not want to leave Takarazuka. I not want to sit by temple—begging—old woman—teeth broken away. But if I go you now, I never find courage to come back. I never love nobody no more. Never, never. (She pronounced it, "I nebber rub nobody, nebber, nebber.") I not want to be alone.

98

I want to sleep here, with you." Beside my head she placed her hard, tiny pillow stuffed with rice bran and we talked no more, for we were finding, as so many people must, that the ways of love are often terrifying when the day is done and one can no longer avoid studying the prospects of the future.

But next day she gave me proof of the courage she said she did not have. We were eating cold fish and rice when our doors slid back and disclosed beautiful Fumiko-san. A curious change came over Hana-ogi and it seemed that she was no longer in our little house but back on the stage at Takarazuka and I appreciated how desperately a part of her that theater was. Fumiko had come, she said, to warn us. An Osaka newspaperman had seen us at the movies and had informed the Supervisor, who had not reprimanded Hana-ogi that afternoon because he hoped she would come to her senses before he was forced to take official action. Fumiko-san implied that he had asked her to speak with the brilliant star who had so much to lose if she persisted in her indiscretion.

Hana-ogi was deeply disturbed by this news and I became aware that these two girls had long ago formed a team of mutual protection and that they had always stood together as a team against the difficulties and defeats of their profession. Earlier Fumiko had found an American who had imperiled her career by kissing her in public and Hana-ogi had protested. Now it was Fumiko's turn to sound the warning. The two exquisite girls talked for a long time in Japanese and I judged they were assessing the various risks in the situation but Fumiko's arguments did not prevail and she left with tears in her eyes. When she had closed the doors Hana-ogi said simply, "I stay."

I discussed with her the possible results of this choice, even at times coming close to arguing on Fumiko's side, so that Hana-ogi stopped short, stood facing me, and demanded, "More better I go?" When I cried no and kissed her, she closed the discussion by saying, "I stay."

There was a firmness about her mouth when she said this and I was surprised, for I had come to look upon her as the radiant symbol of all that was best in the Japanese woman: the patient accepter, the tender companion, the rich lover, but when Hana-ogi displayed her iron will I reflected that throughout the generations of Japanese women there had also been endlessly upon them this necessity to be firm, not to cry, not to show pain. They had to do a man's work, they had to bear cruel privations, yet they remained the most feminine women in the world. Now that I knew them, these strange Japanese women, I saw the contradiction everywhere. Katsumi was having a baby when she hadn't the slightest idea how it would be cared for or under what flag, yet it was she who bolstered up the spirits of her family. Hana-ogi had placed her career in jeopardy for a few months in a tiny house with a man who could never marry her. The young girls I saw with their American soldiers, the little women bent double carrying bricks and mortar to finish the ninth story of a new building, the old women in rags who pulled plows better than horses, and the young wives with three children, one at breast, one strapped on the back, one toddling at her heels. I concluded that no man could comprehend women until he had known the women of Japan with their unbelievable combination of unremitting work, endless suffering and boundless warmth—just as I could never have known even the outlines of love had I not lived in this little house.

CHAPTER XIII

O N THIS night I could not sleep. I was agitated by Hana-ogi's problem although as events turned out, I should have been concerned about my own. I was aware that I had found that one woman whose mere presence beside me in the dark night made me both complete and courageous. Toward four in the morning I hammered my pillow in confusion and Hana-ogi wakened and felt my forehead and said, "Rroyd-san, you sick!" And she leaped up from our bed and tended me as if I were a child and I hadn't the fortitude to tell her that I was in a trembling fever because her picture of an old woman huddling beside a Buddhist temple had made me nightmarish.

She cooled my head and wrapped dry sheets about us and I went to sleep assured that somehow we would escape from the inevitable consequences of our acts. But when I woke I was shivering again, not from fever but from outrage. For Lt.Col. Calhoun Craford, a paunchy red-faced man who hated every human being in the world except certain Methodists from his corner of a hill county in Georgia, stood over our bed.

"Well," he drawled infuriatingly. "You doin' mighty fine, Major Gruver. The Giniral's gonna hear about this. Fine spectacle you are. A giniral's son, shackin' up with a nigger."

With an almost premonitory sense I recalled Joe Kelly's threat one night when he had come home beat: "Some day I'll kill that fat bastard." I felt that if Lt.Col. Craford said one more thing in that room I'd beat Kelly to the job. I think the colonel sensed this, for he looked contemptuously at Hana-ogi huddled beneath the sheet and stalked through the paper doors.

When Lt.Col. Craford showed me in to General Webster's office in Kobe, the old man minced no words. "A fine, clean, upstanding man like you! The son of a general in the United States Army. You've broken every law of decency. You're under house arrest. Furthermore," the general said, "Ive cabled your father."

I gulped and he saw that that one had hurt, so I recovered by saying, "All right, sir, but I wish you hadn't."

"I wish you hadn't made an ass of yourself. Craford, take him under guard to his quarters."

Lt.Col. Craford enjoyed humiliating me, especially since I was the son of a four-star general. He marched me into the lobby of the Marine Barracks, up the short flight of steps leading to the elevators, and down the hall past all the open doors. "This is it, nigger-lover," he growled.

As soon as he was gone I called the motor pool to see if I could get hold of Joe Kelly. After the fifth call I made contact and he whispered, "Can't talk, Ace, I'll be over." He arrived around noon that morning and slumped into a chair, "Jeez, Ace, the fat's in the fire."

"What happened?"

"Old Blubber-gut sent a bunch of strong-arm boys to search your house. They photographed everything. I hope you didn't have any Air Force papers you shouldn't have. Anyway, they wrecked the joint and boarded it up for good."

"What happened to Hana-ogi?"

"The neighbors say she slipped out right after you were arrested. Katsumi watched Blubber-gut's men tear up the house. Then she hurried out to Takarazuka with the news but Hana-ogi never batted an eye."

"How can people take things so calmly?" I cried.

"You learn," Joe explained. "When you're a Japanese woman or an enlisted man, you learn."

It was that evening that my real torment began, for when the performance of *Swing Butterfly* ended I looked down from my prison and saw graceful Hana-ogi, moving like a goddess down the flower walk and across the Bitchi-bashi. I became more determined than ever that I must not lose her.

On the third evening after my house arrest began, I was sitting before the dismal meal of Marine food brought to my room by the waiter, when Mike Bailey opened my door softly, cased the joint like a detective, then motioned down the hall. In men's clothes, looking like a would-be jaintor, Hana-ogi slipped in to see me. Mike made a hasty sign of benediction and tiptoed out.

I cannot describe how joyous it was to see Hana-ogi in my room. Not only had I been tortured by my longing to have her beside me in the bed roll but—as I realized now—I was even more hungry to hear her soft voice chattering of the day's events and I believe my heart actually grew bigger as she told me of the little things: "Fumiko-san say I crazy. When Colonel Craford smash house two kimonos rost."

I became so incensed over the lost kimonos that I realized that I had reached a new meaning of the word *love*. I was engaged in a heavenly contest with Hana-ogi to see which of us could give most to the other and this experience of surrendering my desires to another human being was something entirely new to me.

Toward morning she dressed and left my room, asking, "You have dinner tonight—Makino's?"

I explained what house arrest meant and said that I had pledged my honor as an officer. She said simply, "I have pledge my honor too. I have pledge the honor of my mother and the food of my two sisters." Then she kissed me and left.

So that night I put my honor way down in the bottom drawer among my socks and crept through the alleys to Makino's. Hana-ogi in green skirt and brown blouse was waiting for me. Old Makino made us tempura and to my surprise I found I was getting to enjoy Japanese food. We talked of many things and Hana-ogi said that soon *Swing Butterfly* would close in Takarazuka. Maybe it would go to Tokyo. The news was terrifying and I hadn't the courage to discuss what it might mean to us but she said, "I no go Tokyo. I stay here and wait for you."

It was incredible to me that she would give up Takarazuka and I said, "Hana-ogi, you can't."

Before she could reply Makino came running in and cried, "M.P.'s!" I crowded into a cupboard and heard the heavy tread of Lt.Col. Craford's polished boots. In that moment I understood what an ugly thing fear was and why we had fought the last war against the Germans: we were fighting the tread of heavy boots. And then like the wind on a stormy day I completely changed and felt disgusted with myself, an Air Force officer breaking my word, hiding in a closet with a Japanese girl who should have hated me. It was the low spot of my life and when Lt.Col. Craford stamped down the stairs I stepped out of the closet and said, "Hana-ogi, I've got to go back."

She looked at me closely and asked, "When M.P. come . . ." She pointed at the closet and asked, "You sorry?" She could not find the right word for *ashamed* but she did bring a blush to her cheeks and she did act out my shame.

"Yes," I said. "I gave my word." But as I turned to go a flood of terrible longing overtook me and I grasped her face in my hands and cried, "Don't go to Tokyo, Hana-ogi. Wait here. I cannot let you go."

Her slim, straight body grew limp and she whispered to me in Japanese, something which meant, "Not Takarazuka or my mother could take me away."

I kissed her hands as I had done that first night. There were a hundred things I wanted to say, but I was choked with confusion. I walked boldly down the stairs, marched openly along the street to the Marine Barracks. Hana-ogi, aware of the deep shame I had felt in the closet and sharing it with me, marched just as brazenly beside me in her distinctive Takarazuka costume and kissed me good-bye at the barracks. "Rroyd-san," she said softly, "I love you takusan much."

CHAPTER XIV

W HEN I entered the barracks, my father and General Webster were waiting. My father looked down the street at Hana-ogi walking bravely back to the dormitory and said, "Pretty girl. Almost pretty enough to justify an officer's breaking his word."

General Webster started to bluster but Father cut him short. He took us into the manager's office and let me have it.

My father is no puling one-star general ordered about by his wife. He said, "You idiot. You poor, bewildered idiot."

I have never heard my father swear. He chews gum when he's mad and makes the muscles in his jaw stand out and right now he looked as if he could beat me up. I stood at attention and looked straight ahead.

"What are you gonna do?" he asked contemptuously. "Dishonor your uniform, humiliate your friends?" He walked around me then snorted. "Some officer!"

General Webster said, "You've broken your word of honor and you're going to be court-martialed."

"Get out of here, Webster," my father snapped. "I'll handle this."

General Webster retreated and while we watched him go, I had a moment to steel myself. When my father turned back to face me I started to speak but he interrupted me and pulled me into a chair beside him and asked, "Son, what's this all about?"

Again I started to explain but he said, "I flew out here from the Presidio to knock some sense into you. But you're not in the market for sense, are you?"

I said, "I don't want any lectures."

He laughed and chewed his gum and said, "Lord knows, son, I hoped you would marry Eileen Webster. Good family, staunch military background. Mother's a bit of a bore but in service you can always get away from her. Say, have you heard the news that really galls Webster? His daughter's serious about a real-estate salesman from Seattle. Major, I think. Webster's furious and is rotating the fellow back to the States."

He sized me up carefully, chewing his gum, and said, "Y'know, son, if you still wanted Eileen you could have her. Wait a minute! Don't underestimate that kind of marriage. Right now you're all boiled up about sex, but a man lives a long life after that fire goes down. Then you appreciate having a woman you can talk to, some one who knows military life. What do you and Madame Butterfly talk about?"

He waited for me to speak but as soon as I started he said, "Let's get back to Eileen. You ever know any officers married to women who disliked the military? Sad lot. Sad business. Your mother and I haven't been what you might call romantic lovers. . . ." He slapped his leg and burst into real laughter. "Could you imagine your mother in a shack along a canal! But anyway we've always been able to talk. We want the same things. We want the same things for you, Lloyd."

He paused and I thought I was back in St. Leonard's on another occasion like this. My father was saying, "Your mother and I want the same things for you, Lloyd," but even then I knew for a certainty that Mother had never wanted those things for me and I had the strange feeling that if she were in Japan right now—if she knew the whole story—she would be on my side and not Father's.

He said, "I suppose you've figured what your present course would mean to things like life plans."

"What do you mean, present course?"

"Well, getting married to a Japanese girl."

"Married!"

"Sure, married." He chewed his gum real fast and then said, "You mean you haven't thought about marriage? Don't you see what's gonna happen, son? You're gonna work yourself into a box. You'll be unable to find a solution. So suddenly you hit on marriage! You'll marry the girl and that'll make everything just dandy. Good God, son! You're twenty-eight years old. Don't take sex too seriously."

I said, "What should you take seriously?"

He said, "A whole life." He chewed his gum furiously and said, "A whole, well-rounded life."

I said, "Promotions and place in society and things like that?"

He looked at me quizzically and said, "You pulling my leg, son?"

I said, "Like the way you married a general's daughter?"

He said very calmly, "I ought to clout you. I just don't understand you sometimes, son. Let's not obscure the facts. Son, I've watched our men marry German girls and French girls and even Russian girls. Invariably, if you know the man, it's a sign of weakness. They're all pantywaists. Strong men have the guts to marry the girls who grew up next door. Such marriages fit into the community. They make the nation strong. In your case and mine such marriages fit into military service. Leave it to the poets and painters and people who turn their back on America because they're afraid of it to go chasing after foreign girls."

He chomped his gum and said, much more slowly, "I ever tell you about Charley Scales? Resigned his commission and joined General Motors. Said he'd make a lot of money and he did. Some years later he came to proposition me about joining him. Lloyd, that was in 1933 when the Army was the garbage can of democracy but I didn't even think twice. I've been tempted in my life but never by Charley Scales. Right now!" He snapped his fingers and said, "Who'd you rather be, Charley Scales or me?"

It was a childish trick but it had a great effect on me. In my mind's eye I could see Charley Scales, a big, happy man of some distinction in Detroit and the world. But to compare him with my father was ridiculous.

Father said, "You talk this over with your Madame Butterfly. You'll find she agrees with me."

I said, "I will."

He said, "By the way, where'd she learn English?"

I said she didn't speak English and he cried, "You mean you've learned Japanese?"

I said, "No."

He stopped chewing his gum and looked at me. "You mean —you have no common language? French, maybe?"

I said, "Well, you see . . ."

"You mean you can't talk together?"

"Well, on a really intricate problem she . . ." I was going to explain that she danced the words for me, but I felt that Father wouldn't understand. But he surprised me.

When he realized that we shared no language he became unusually gentle. I cannot recall his ever having been quite as he was at that moment. He put his arm about my shoulder and said reassuringly, "Son, you'll work this thing out."

He called for General Webster and said gruffly, "Mark, don't blow your top at this kid. You and I know that it was completely silly to issue such an order to a bunch of healthy young men surrounded by pretty girls. But that's beside the point. Don't get sore at Lloyd."

"Why not?"

"Because he's going to be your son-in-law."

"He's what?"

"He doesn't know it yet, and Eileen doesn't know it yet but if you want to do something constructive, keep real-estate salesmen away from your daughter. Because sooner or later she's going to be my daughter, too."

The two generals stamped out of the barracks and in three hours my father was on his way back to the Presidio.

CHAPTER XV

I HAD met a woman I could love forever, and I simply wasn't worried about fathers and generals and Air Force rules. Here on this earth I had found Hana-ogi and by the time my father arrived back in California she and I had things worked out. We made a deal with Joe and Katsumi whereby we took one corner of their house and here we established a life as warm and loving as two human beings have ever known.

I would come home from the airfield to find Joe and Katsumi preparing the evening meal. They would tell me what had happened that day and I would exchange military gossip with Joe. I would be watching the door and finally we would hear Hana-ogi's soft steps coming up the alley and Katsumi and Joe would slip away for a moment. The door would open and there would be Hana-ogi. Like all Japanese she carried her books and bundles wrapped in a bright silk shawl tied cross cornered, and when I think of her at the sliding door of that little house I see her kick off her saddle shoes, drop the silken bundle, and hurry across the tatami to kiss me. At such times I would catch her in my arms, swing her into the air and drop her behind the screen that cut off our portion of the room. There she would slip off her Western clothes and fold herself into a brocaded kimono. She was lovely; beyond words she was lovely.

But I must not imply that the warmth and wonder of that house came solely from Hana-ogi, beautiful and complete as she was, for I think that I have never seen a more satisfactory wife than Katsumi Kelly. She organized her house to perfection and kept it immaculate, even though Hana-ogi and I were apt to be careless. She could cook, she could sew, she could talk on many subjects and as her pregnancy advanced she gave promise of being an even finer mother than she was a wife.

Sometimes I used to watch her and I recalled with embarrass-

109

ment that once in the consul's office I had almost refused to kiss her because she seemed so clodden and repugnant with her giggling and her big gold tooth. Now she seemed to me one of the most perfect women I had ever known, for she had obviously studied her man and had worked out every item of the day's work so that the end result would be a happy husband and a peaceful home.

The longer I lived with Joe Kelly, reared in an orphanage and rejected by his foster parents, the more astonished I was that he could adjust so perfectly to married life. He was a considerate husband, a happy clown around the house and the kind of relaxed and happy family man you see in the advertisements of the *Saturday Evening Post*.

Speaking of the *Post*, it helped me understand a little better what married life is. On May 30th the girls were all whispers and giggles and at dinner they sprang the big surprise! It was an American holiday, so they had pumpkin pie. Where they had finagled the pumpkin we never knew, but the pie was something out of this world, for they had used the pumpkin as you would apples or cherries and had baked it just as it came out of the can and it was really dreadful. I took one look at it and started to say, "What . . ." but Joe cut me short and tasted his piece.

"It's good," he said laconically.

The girls bit into their pieces and you could see them sort of look at each other as if to say, "Americans must be crazy. To eat something like this on holidays." We finished the disgusting dessert in silence and four days later Katsumi, leafing through an old copy of the *Post* saw a picture of real pumpkin pie. She waited till I got home and surreptitiously asked me if that was pumpkin pie. I said yes and she asked me how it stayed so thick and so soft and I told her how you made pumpkin custard and she started to cry and when Joe came home she hugged him and kissed him and told him how ashamed she was and since Hana-ogi wasn't home yet I sat glumly in my corner and thought about the time I had laughed at Hana-ogi for her sentence, "Lo, the postillion has been struck by lightning," and I concluded that Joe's way was better and I wondered how a kid from an orphanage could understand a problem like that while I hadn't had the slightest glimmer.

However, I must not imply that all Japanese women are perfect wives nor were they all the patient, silent creatures I had been told. A trip along our alley would convince anyone that Japanese homes contained every problem to be found in American homes; plus some very special ones. In the narrow house next us lived the Shibatas. He was a minor business official who received practically no pay but had an enviable expense account from which he drew on most nights of the week for expensive geisha parties. He siphoned off part of the expense account to support one of the pretty young geishas on the side. It was rumored that he kept her in a second home near the center of Osaka and traditionally his wife should have accepted such an arrangement with philosophical indifference, but Mrs. Shibata was not traditional. She was modern and tried to stab her husband with a knife.

Across the alley lived the widow Fukada and her twenty-year-old daughter Masako, who had had a G.I. baby without being married. Sometimes at night we could hear the grandmother screaming at Masako that she was a slut, and other women in the alley agreed. The American baby was not wanted and was not allowed to play with pure Japanese babies, and although everyone in the alley loved Joe Kelly and Katsumi and although they were proud to have a great Takarazuka actress living among them with her American flier, there was deep resentment against Masako Fukada, who had disgraced the blood of Japan.

Down the alley were the hilarious Watanabes. His wife was almost as broad as he was tall. They got along together fine except that Watanabe-san had a mistress even more compelling than a geisha: he was mad-crazy to play pachinko. He spent all his money at pachinko and all his spare hours at the pachinko parlor on the corner. When the police closed the parlor each

111

night at eleven he would reluctantly come home and we would hear fat Mrs. Watanabe shouting derisively, "Here comes Pachinko-san! Dead broke!"

Across the alley from the pachinko room was the flower shop. You would have thought there could not be in that entire alley one rusty yen for flowers, but almost everyone who lived along our narrow gutters stopped into the flower shop for some solitary spray of blooms which was carried reverently home for the alcove where the gods lived.

But the true wonders of our alley were the children. I could neither count them nor forget them. They had round faces, very red cheeks, straight black bangs, fat little legs and boundless joy. I don't think I ever heard a Japanese child cry. Certainly I never saw one struck and I came to believe that the most delectable children I had ever seen were these noisy, hilarious children.

Each house in our alley was desperately packed, so that one tiny room often became the equivalent of a full-sized American home and these teeming masses of people lived and worked and had babies and argued politics just like all people across the world. But there was this difference. Not a shred of anything was wasted. I recall certain evenings that spring when I entered this narrow alley at close of day and the front of every house would be open and dozens of children would run, black-bobbed, to greet me and from every open room facing the alley the people of Japan would speak with me and I shared a warmth and goodness that I had never known in Lancaster or the camps where I grew up. I was one of the people and from this alley with the myriad children and the flowers and the unwanted American-Japanese baby I borrowed a strength I had never had before.

CHAPTER XVI

IT EXPRESSED itself in an unforeseen way. I was in my office at Itami Air Base when a sergeant appeared to tell me that Lt.Col. Calhoun Craford was outside. The florid colonel stepped in and got right down to business. "You think you're smart" (he said it: *Yawll thank yore smaht*) "gettin' a four-star giniral to come out and save your neck. You accustomed to hidin' behind your pappy's back?" Then he let me have it. "My men been trailin' you, Gruver. We know you and that tramp are holed up in enlisted man's quarters. But we can't touch you because of your pappy. So we're doin' something better. We're sendin' Joe Kelly back to the States."

"But what'll happen to Katsumi?"

The fat colonel looked at me with disgust. "Who's Kats-what's-his-name?"

"Kelly's wife."

"The Jap girl. Not up to us to worry what happens to her. The girl's a cheap Jap tramp."

I said that Katsumi was a decent girl, that she was studying to become a Catholic, like her husband, but apparently Lt.Col. Craford hated Catholics worse than he hated colored people, for he said, "And when we finish with Kelly we'll figure out some way to handle you. Father or no father."

He left me and I sat for a long time staring at my desk, contemplating the mess I had made of things. I had proved myself a shoddy officer. I had loused up the life of an enlisted man. I had made Eileen look ridiculous and I hadn't done much better with Hana-ogi. Then I began to weigh what I had accomplished in Japan and things looked brighter. I had come to know what a home meant, an unpretentious home where love was. I had found a beautiful girl filled with tenderness and grace and wit. I had learned at last to share my heart with an-

113

other human being. And most of all I had discovered the tremendous passion of turning down the bed roll at night and seeing the slim, perfect body of Hana-ogi. I jumped up and cried, "Gruver-san, if you lose that girl you're nuts. Marry her, stupid. Marry her."

I called Joe Kelly and asked him to meet me at a tiny bar we knew in Osaka where M.P.'s never came. It's impossible to describe such Japanese bars to Americans. How can you explain a bar so small that it has space for only four customers and two hostesses?

"Joe," I said in greeting, "can you keep a secret?"

"Sure, Ace."

"I mean two secrets. Joe, Blubber-gut is laying for you. He's going to ship you home first chance he gets."

"That's no secret. He threatened me openly two days ago. I didn't tell anybody. Didn't want to worry you. What's your other secret?"

I ordered another beer and took a big gulp. "Exactly what papers do you have to sign to marry a Japanese girl?"

Joe whistled and said, "Look, Ace. This ain't for you. I don't believe you could take the bad time they give you."

"What do you mean?"

"They wear you down. Enlisted men get used to bein' worn down but you ain't had the experience of diggin' your heels in real stubborn and resistin'."

"How do you mean?"

"They give you so many papers. The chaplain prays over you. And everything they do they do with crazy smiles, like you was off your rocker and only they could save you. And what's worse, they ask the girl so many heart-burnin' questions. Hana-ogi won't tell you but some night when you kiss her she'll break down and cry for an hour. I don't think you could take it."

I said, "Tomorrow morning I'm starting the paper work."

He said, "Ace, you're a big man. It would make them look silly to lose you to a Japanese girl. So they'll hit you with big stuff."

"I'm ready."

"Ace, they'll hit you with generals and admirals and men who knew your father. The only way you can swing it is to get the help of your Congressman. Who is he?"

"I don't know."

"Where do you live?"

"I don't have . . ."

"Well, where do you vote?"

"I've never voted." For the first time I realized that I was completely a military man. The Air Force was my home.

Joe studied this and said, "Don't worry. Practically any Congressman would love to fight your battle. You want me to take it up with Shimmark? He loves to get his name in the paper."

I thanked Joe and left him saying I'd work it out somehow. Then I went over to the village of Takarazuka, where I waited in a vegetable stall near the Bitchi-bashi. Finally I saw Hana-ogi approaching and I had that rare experience that a man sometimes knows when he sees the girl he loves picking her way along a crowded lane unaware that he is watching, and at such times—when the girls are not on their good behavior, you might say—they are extraordinarily lovely and ratify doubly all thoughts and decisions of preceding days. Hana-ogi was like that. I reached out, grabbed her arm, and drew her in beside me.

"Hanayo!" I cried with a passion I had never before experienced. "I've made up my mind. We're going to be married."

Apparently she didn't understand for she said, "What do you say?"

"I'm going to marry you. Take you back to America."

I remember that the shop was filled along one wall with enormous white Japanese radishes, four feet long and thick as a man. Hana-ogi drew back against them and looked at me for a moment and tears came into her dark eyes.

"We no speak of marriage, Rroyd-san. No. No."

"I know it's a surprise," I said. "But I've thought it all out and I'm willing to give up the Air Force and find some other job."

115

"But Rroyd, I no go America."

"We'll work that out, too," I said. "Some time they'll change this crazy law so a man can take his wife home."

"You no understand, Rroyd-san. I no want to go."

I stepped away from the giant radishes and stared at Hana-ogi. It was incomprehensible to me that any Japanese girl, living in that cramped little land with no conveniences and no future, would refuse America. I said, "I'll explain it all to you tonight."

But she replied most strangely, "Some day you leave Japan, Rroyd-san. Before you go I like you see pictures of real Hana-ogi. In Kyoto."

"I don't want to see any pictures!" I cried. "Damn it, I came here to tell you we're getting married."

"You get auto tomorrow morning—early." She moved quickly toward the door of the shop, then turned to kiss me passionately on the lips. "When you go back America," she said, "I want you remember great beauty of Hana-ogi."

CHAPTER XVII

EARLY next morning we left Osaka in Lt. Bailey's Chevvy and drove along the side of a river which for untold centuries had carried water to the rice fields of this region. It lay far below the level of the road, hemmed in by strong dikes built many generations ago and upon all the land there was the mark of much toil and the footprints of many people.

Our entrance to Kyoto was memorable, for we saw in the distance the soaring towers of great Buddhist temples, their tiers built with corners upswept in the Chinese style. And along one street we caught a glimpse of the famed Heian Shinto shrine, a glorious vermilion thing with enormous blood-red torii guarding it.

But today we were not interested in shrines or temples. We went along a side street burdened with age-old pines, where underneath a canopy of evergreen we stopped to enter a museum. It was built like a temple, with nearly a hundred statues of stone and wood, as if the old heroes of Japan had gathered to greet us, frozen forever in their stiff ceremonial attitudes. The curator hurried up to us and when he learned that I could speak no Japanese he summoned a striking young man. He was in his thirties, I judged, and wore heavy glasses. He had excellent teeth, a frank smile and a rare command of English.

"I studied at Oxford," he explained, "and served for some years in our store on Fifth Avenue and for two years in our store in Boston. What did you wish to see?" It was clear that he did not know Hana-ogi and that he supposed her to be merely some attractive street girl I had picked up for the day. He was therefore somewhat distressed when she spoke to him in Japanese, so I interrupted and said, "I understand you have an unusual collection of prints of Hana-ogi, of Ogi-ya."

Immediately he withdrew deep inside himself and studied me carefully. Then he looked at Hana-ogi and bowed very low.

117

"You are Hana-ogi-san of Takarazuka," he said in precise English. "You are very beautiful. And you, Major, are Lloyd Gruver. Yes, yes. Even in Kyoto we have heard of you. I can truly appreciate your desire to see the famous prints of the other Hana-ogi."

He led us upstairs, past the frowning Japanese heroes, and I felt that I was in hostile land. In this strange building I at last got the feeling of being an invader, surrounded by an alien religion and a strange art many centuries older than my own native land. I experienced the feeling even more deeply when I sat on the floor in front of an easel while the young curator went to a locked cabinet. Hana-ogi must have sensed my uneasy thoughts, for she put her hand in mine and whispered, "Now you see greatest beauty."

I shall never forget the extreme shock of that first print. The young curator said in reverence, "The first one is of Hana-ogi as a young girl, just come to Ogi-ya. It is by one of our finest artists, Shuncho."

It was disgusting. The girl's face was pasty and flat. Her hair was a mass of yellow combs. She was swathed in seven kimonos that gaped at the neck. But worst of all, her eyes were caricatures, mere slants, and her teeth were a horrid black. In this portrait of dead beauty I could not find one shred of loveliness.

I must have betrayed my disappointment for both Hana-ogi and the curator tried to explain that the design was controlled by Japanese artistic tradition, the way a portrait of a woman by Picasso does not appear really beautiful. They took away the first picture and brought in another by an artist whose name I didn't catch. My dismay was greater than before. The famous courtesan had the same pasty face, slit eyes and funereal teeth, but this time her head was twisted into such an angle that I remember thinking, "If she doesn't straighten up she'll strangle."

It was the third picture which caused the argument. I took down the name of the artist, Masayoshi, for he showed Hana-ogi returning to the House of Ogi-ya after her elopement. She was dressed in many kimonos covered by a purple robe and followed by two barefoot servants carrying an umbrella and a massive bouquet of flowers. I studied the picture with dismay, for I recognized it immediately as one that Hana-ogi had described for me that night when she danced the story of her predecessor, but what she had not told me was that this picture of Hana-ogi showed a remarkably ugly woman with a big nose, dirt smears over her eyebrows and paunchy cheeks. "Why she's ugly!" I cried. I felt defrauded.

My Hana-ogi withdrew as if she had been struck and the young man pulled the print away. "I am afraid," he said in clipped syllables, "that you have no appreciation of our art."

"I was told that this Hana-ogi was the most beautiful woman in Japanese history."

"She was," the young man insisted.

"But look at Hana-ogi-san here. This one. She's really beautiful."

The young man did not look at Hana-ogi-san. Instead he took the portrait of the ancient Hana-ogi back to the cabinet and returned with another. Quietly he said, "I am afraid you are blind to the problem, Major. But would you like me to explain in a few words?"

"Indeed I would," I said.

"The picture I'm about to show you is by one of Japan's supreme artists, Utamaro. Have you heard of him?"

"No."

"No bother, but will you believe me when I say his work is prized all over the world? Good. You are going to see one of his loveliest creations. When you look at it don't think of Hana-ogi. Think only of this heavenly yellow."

He flashed the picture before me and the yellow was indeed like a fine sunlight. He continued his narration, pointing out the perfect proportions of the design, the exquisite line, the subdued color harmonies and the suggested textures. I followed him carefully and agreed with what he said. Then brusquely he said, "As for the face of Hana-ogi, we Japanese think it was sent down from heaven."

119

The intensity of his comment caught me unaware and from some distant corner of my brain came the affirmation, "The men who knew this woman thought she was beautiful." And immediately there came another terrible memory—of a time when some of us young offcers were attending a wedding and we saw the bride and there was a moment of awful silence and somebody behind me whispered, "Well, every man thinks the girl he's marrying is pretty." And I could see myself back in America, about to introduce my Hana-ogi to strangers who had never known her and I could feel them cringing away from my Japanese girl—unlovely to them—as I now cringed away from the long-dead Hana-ogi. I looked again at the treasured face, at the curious slanted eyes and the black teeth and from my own humility I said, "I think I understand."

The young man started to take the Utamaro away but I said, "Let me study it some more." I pointed to the colorful printing in the upper corner and asked what it was. During the remarkable discussion that followed the young curator stood crisply at attention with his left hand upon the easel. I have only to close my eyes to see him standing there with his faded echo of the great Hana-ogi.

"It's impossible to say what this printing means, Major. It's a poem, written by some unimportant man who visited Hana-ogi. These symbols are his name: The man from the other side of Yanagiwara. That's all we know about him. But his poem will live among us forever."

"What did he write?"

"I'm sorry but I cannot tell you the meaning."

"You can't translate the symbols?"

"Oh, yes!" he assured me proudly. "But the Japanese language like Japanese beauty and Japanese life can never be truly translated. For example, the name Hana-ogi means *flower* and *fan,* and its symbols are woven into the poem, but what they are intended to mean in this particular poem no one can say."

"How can words have no specific meaning? There's the symbol. Right there. Why can't you read it?"

120

"Ah, but I can, Major. Trouble is, I can read it in so many ways. According to one way the stranger from Yanagiwara is saying, 'Even a mere glimpse in autumn of that night-blooming flower, Hana-ogi, floods my soul with summer.' "

"That's clear enough," I said.

"But it isn't clear, because I'm only guessing that that's what the stranger meant, for the words can also be read, 'Hana-ogi is more beautiful than that evening flower I once laid on a fan for a love of old days and brings no chill of autumn to my heart.' "

I was confused. "You mean those same symbols can mean such different things?"

"They can also mean many other things, Major. Our life in Japan is one of implied means, hidden significances. For example, they say that you have fallen in love with Hana-ogi-san. Which Hana-ogi?"

"Which one? This one. The living one."

"But which of the living ones?"

"This one. Here!"

The young man, who must have hated Americans for taking his art galleries in Boston and London and New York, stood bitterly erect by the easel and said softly, "But there are many Hana-ogi-sans with us today. She is famous in Japan, this girl, and deeply loved. There is the peasant girl who is good to her mother and her six sisters. There is the young courtesan who was in training to be a geisha. Didn't you know that her father had sold her to a green house? There is the famous beauty who was rescued by one of the rich Matsudaira men. The one who committed suicide. His daughter, Fumiko-san, is at Takarazuka now. Or the gracious actress Hana-ogi who always used to be seen with Fumiko-san. Or the ascetic young woman who aspired to be Japan's greatest dancer. Or the reckless girl who ran away with an American flier. You see, we are a very subtle people. Our words mean many things."

On the drive home we were silent until we came to a part of the river bank where three women were tilling a rice field.

Then suddenly Hana-ogi took my hand and kissed it and whispered, "We very poor. My father no want to sell to geisha house. Japanese fathers love their daughters. Same like in America. But . . ." We never said another word about it, not about the Matsudaira man who had bought her nor about his daughter Fumiko-san for whom Hana-ogi now felt responsible. For a few minutes after leaving the museum I had feared that knowing my Hana-ogi's history might make it impossible for me to marry her, but one mention of her father ended such doubts, for I recalled the old Japanese farmer we had watched on that first night we had slept together. That was poverty, when a man sifted each grain of soil by hand to make it yield a little more rice. I knew that if Hana-ogi's father had sold her it was because he had no human alternative. I said with new dedication, "Now we'll get married," but she merely drew closer to me and I believe that she had taken me to Kyoto so that I might know of her childhood and that if the curator had not told me, she would have done so when we studied the pictures. With my right arm I drew her tousled head to mine and drove the car quite slowly beside the ancient, turbulent river.

CHAPTER XVIII

I WAS disturbed, however, that she had not yet actually said that she would come with me to America. I judged that she was hesitating in order to provide me with an escape from my rash promise to leave the Air Force. Then, in a dramatic way, I learned that perhaps she really was determined not to marry me, for an elderly woman showed me Hana-ogi's reasons for staying in Japan.

This gentle mask-faced Japanese woman came to the Marine Barracks in Takarazuka accompanied by a smart young woman who spoke good English and they explained that they wished me to accompany them on a matter of greatest importance. I followed them to the Bitchi-bashi, then through the vegetable stalls and onto the footpath leading to the girls' dormitories.

This was the first time I had been on this path and as I approached the building where Hana-ogi had lived before she met me I grew quite excited but then I saw the dormitory itself and it was forbidding: a plain wooden building covered with bamboo matting and protected by a row of cryptomeria trees planted to make a high hedge.

My guide led me down a narrow path past the cryptomeria trees and up to a small hill that overlooked the river. There she stopped at a curious gate that looked like the miniature entrance to a temple and after opening this she took me into a beautiful garden which surrounded a superior Japanese house made of highly polished wood. It was guarded by an enormous flat stone upon which sat nine young girls wearing the green skirts of the Takarazuka uniform. The girls jumped to their feet and bowed very low until the elderly woman had passed.

She led me to a room covered with exquisite white tatami and containing at one end a raised platform of matched cypress

123

planks polished a golden brown. It was obvious that this was the room of a dancing teacher.

The woman introduced herself as Teruko-san, one of the first great Takarazuka stars. She had been, in her day, a legend and now she handed the legend down to the young girls waiting for her on the rock. They came to her five days a week and submitted themselves to the tyranny of her masklike face.

Teruko-san sat with me on the floor, arranging her kimono with precision, and I saw that her garments were five shades of gray accented by a thin line of blue showing about the neck. Her tabi were white and accentuated the outlines of beautiful and powerful feet. They reminded me of Hana-ogi's superb feet and Teruko-san must have intended this, for she said promptly, "Major Gruver, if you cause Hana-ogi to leave us it is not only the great stage she will lose. It is also this." With a slow motion of her hand, as if she were participating in a dance, she indicated the perfect room. "When I die Hana-ogi is to follow me, for she is our finest dancer. I believe she is to be even greater than I, for when I danced I was alone and stood out like Fuji-san. But today there are many good dancers and Hana-ogi dominates them all. And do you know why they are good?"

I bowed deferentially toward her and she said, "Yes, they are excellent because I teach them as a famous old man taught me. In this way we keep alive the art of Japan."

As Teruko-san droned on I could hear Hana-ogi's bright voice with its sometimes-hoarse edge cutting at my heart, I could see the meticulous manner in which she folded the edges of her kimono to outline her strong neck, and I could see the classic manner in which she danced. Terukosan said, "If you persist, Hana-ogi will never return to this room."

Then she pulled a clever trick. She said, "You must sit here, Major Gruver, for I am to give a lesson," and the interpreter went to fetch the nine young girls. They came in quietly, practiced little steps on the tatami then dropped away their green skirts and climbed onto the low stage in dancing tights.

Teruko-san was transformed. Instead of a gracious elderly

124

lady she became a vigorous, stage-stamping dancer much better than even her best pupil. She led them through one single step for a long time and I detected one or two girls who looked as if they might honestly become dancers and I realized that Teruko-san had intended that I see in these struggling children —they were fifteen I judged—the Hana-ogi of some years back.

When the girls left, Teruko-san said, "I have wanted you to understand exactly what you are doing." She led me to the gate and to my surprise dismissed the interpreter and walked with me back to the dormitory. She took me to a small room, pushed aside the paper door and told me to enter saying, "Hana-ogi."

The room was as beautiful as the girl I loved. Along one wall were the lacquered drawers and trays and chests in which she kept her belongings. The rest of the room was bare and clean and glimmering. There were eight creamy white tatami, so it was not a big room, and six bright cushions around a very old brazier of gold and green ceramic in which charcoal rested on a pile of gleaming white sand. A low table and four jet-black bowls for food completed the furniture except for one shelf which held copies of the plays Hana-ogi had acted in. The only ornamentation was a single Japanese print of a bridge suspended over a rocky gorge with a crescent moon low in the sky.

But this time Teruko-san had been too clever, for it had been her intention that I see this room and lament that I was taking Hana-ogi from it; but it had quite the opposite effect. The room cried out in the late afternoon shadows that I should go ahead and marry its owner. No woman so vital as Hana-ogi could be destined for so narrow a prison. The wood of the room was beautiful, but Hana-ogi was more so. The tatami were neat, the books were important and the Japanese print no doubt represented one of the peaks of art—but so did Hana-ogi, and in addition she was a glorious woman, one who delighted in hurrying through the dark alleys of Osaka to join the man she loved.

We passed down the hall from Hana-ogi's room and at the entrance to the dormitory I bowed very low and said, "Domo

125

arigato gozaimasu, Teruko-san." She was pleased that I spoke even that trivial Japanese, so she bowed equally low and said, "Do itashi mashite, dozo," and I hurried to the train that would take me back to Osaka just as fast as possible.

How can I recall the journey of a young man desperately in love as he moves across the picture-book landscape of Japan to a city of canals where he will meet his beloved?

Now I was in the countryside and I could see the rice fields crowding right up to the last inch of railroad tie. Beyond were the trim clean villages with roofs of red tile and temple roofs of golden tile. In the fields were old men pulling harrows and women digging, while along the village streets children laughed and played loud jumping games.

There was a momentary thrill as the train pulled into the junction town of Nishinomiya, for I knew that when I looked across the station platform I would see a gigantic poster for *Swing Butterfly* with a huge picture of Hana-ogi in the middle. I spent my time waiting for the through express, wondering what the people on that platform would think if they could have known that in a few endless minutes I would be with her.

The express from Kobe roared in. I sought out a back car from which I caught glimpses of the Inland Sea and soon we came to where the river emptied into the sea through great concrete culverts, and promptly we entered Osaka itself, where the train plunged through a canyon of ugly houses hung with laundry and into a tunnel which brought me to the noisy, crowded station. As I approached the canal I was alive with excitement. I was young and I was coming to the end of a journey that I wished I might make each day of my life: from Takarazuka to Osaka, where Hana-ogi was waiting.

CHAPTER XIX

A ND when I reached home there was Hana-ogi waiting for me. I slipped into my blue-and-white cotton kimono and shared cold fish and rice with her. When the meal was over I said, "Terukosan came to see me today. She showed me her dancing school. The one that could be yours some day. Now I know why you want to stay at Takarazuka."

She sighed and said she was glad that I understood why she could not come with me to America, but I added, "And I also saw your little room. With the lovely print." I made my hands fall like the gorge in her solitary picture. At this she blushed and held her hand against the stray-hair sideburns along her cheek. I said, "And when I saw that bare room which holds you like a prisoner—no life—no one to love . . ."

I caught her in my arms and a tremendous surge of love attacked us and later when I lay upon the tatami watching her select her clothes for tomorrow I said, "So we'll be married as soon as possible. You'll love New York. You can see hundreds of shows, some like Takarazuka, but none of the actresses will be beautiful like you."

I was imagining her in New York, so I rose and showed her how she could pull the wanton hair that crept upon her cheeks up into place. She did so and studied herself in a mirror. "Now you look like an American girl," I said. She pulled the hair back down and said, "Japanese way more better."

Then she added an astonishing thing. "You'll go home and marry Eileen . . ."

"Eileen?" I cried. "Where did you hear . . ." I had never spoken her name.

"Yes," she said. "You marry Eileen (she pronounced it *Eireen*) your father tell me."

"My father?"

127

"Yes. General Hot Shot Harry. He come see me late one night."

I could feel my father ordering things again. "What did he tell you?" I demanded.

"He very nice, very kind man. He say if I want to marry you O.K., but he know I never do it. He think you marry Eileen. I think so too."

I was deeply agitated and struggled desperately to get down —for once in my life—to the hard bed rock of living. I said, "Hanayo, you are the hope of my life. If you leave me all the things . . ."

She said in Japanese, "I know, Rroyd. For me you are also the key. With you I could become a woman and a mother and we could travel in London. I could love you and help you . . ."

She became exquisitely tender and I knew then that with her as my wife I could find the solid basis for existence that had so far escaped me; and I was aware that for her, too, I was the only escape she could ever know. If she rejected me now she could become only the glorious outline of a woman, imprisoned in little rooms or on mammoth stages—loved only by other women.

I held her in my arms and cried, "Then we'll be married?"

She stared at me and said, "No."

I kissed her impassive, golden face, thinking bitterly of the stories I had read about white men in strange lands. Always the yellow girl tried to seduce these clean-cut men away from their decent white sweethearts, for everyone knew that yellow girls plotted evil ways to lure white men. And if the yellow girls succeeded the white men sank lower and lower toward barbarism. "Damn it," I cried, "this story's all loused up!" When Hana-ogi looked up in surprise I said, "I'm a West Point honor man. In the story you're supposed to beg me to marry you. Hanayo-chan, please beg me."

She started to laugh at my comic plea, but then I think she glimpsed the empty years that faced her, for she took my hands and held them to her face, confessing in a tone of Japanese doom, "I don't want to become the lonely old woman who teaches dancing." (I recall her words: "I not grad be woman old in house dance teach no man come.")

Her lament burned my heart and I cried, "Then marry me."

This time she answered in a lower voice, still freighted with that inevitable sense of tragedy that seems to haunt the Japanese, "I never intended marrying you, Rroyd-san. Japanese-American marriages are no good. We read about Japanese girls in America—what happened in Cedar Rapids."

"Then why did you come to live with me?" I demanded in anguish.

She pressed her lovely head against mine and said softly in Japanese, "I know it was wrong. But for me it was my only chance in life to love a man. No Japanese man would marry me—what the man in museum told you. Oh, maybe a fish-catch boy or a rice-plant boy, maybe such a man would have me. But Japanese men are very cruel to wives like me. Rroyd-san, in all the world you were the only man I dare love."

It was hellish to be there with her, to hear her committing herself to the inverted world of the Takarazuka girls and the green, flowing skirts and me to airplanes and the management of war. I grasped her hands and cried, "Hanayo-chan! Please! It's our lives you're speaking of. Marry me!"

Limply and in despair she drew her hands away. Then, raising her arms as if to embrace the entire sleeping city of Osaka she said, "I Japanese. I always Japanese. Katsumi-san marry American boy, ne? What happen to her, desho?"

CHAPTER XX

THE answer to that one arrived next day in the form of a special Fourth of July present for Joe Kelly, our overseas hero. We had celebrated the holiday by sneaking out into the country with a couple of picnic baskets. In the distance we had heard fireworks going off in some village near Kyoto and Katsumi had said, "Japanese love to celebrate. Even American holidays we enjoy." But when we got back to Osaka, Joe found the fateful letter tucked under the door. Joe's hands trembled as he read the bad news.

"They sending you home?" I asked.

"Yep," he said weakly.

He showed me the sheet of paper which I at once recognized as one not intended for enlisted men to see, and my West Point training welled up. "How'd you get hold of this?"

"A friend of a friend," he said.

I read the impersonal phrases which two months before would have meant nothing to me. "American military personnel married to Japanese wives will be rotated home immediately lest their allegiance to the United States be eroded." Then there was the usual baloney passage about commanders providing every assistance to men who must make unusual arrangements for wives forced to remain in Japan.

"Joe, I've seen hundreds of orders like this. They all peter out."

"I think they mean it this time, Ace. I had it good here," he said grimly. "Wonderful wife, baby comin', friends, a home." As he surveyed the impending ruin he took refuge in the phrase which our men across Korea had adopted as their reaction to the dismal tricks of war: "That's the way the ball bounces."

For Joe the ball took an evil twist. An implementing letter arrived next day with a cold, hard list of the men who were to

130

be sent home and under the K's Joe found his name. He took the list immediately to Lt.Col. Craford, who said, "I told you you were goin' home. I got four men on that list. Everyone of 'em's been in to cry the blues."

"But my wife is havin' a baby."

"All wives have babies. That's what wives are for."

"Can I be transferred back to Korea?"

The colonel grunted, "You're the fourth guy who would rather go back to war in Korea than go home to the States. You really prefer Korea?"

Joe saw a chance to remain in the area and cried eagerly, "Yes! Can I go?"

"No!" Craford shouted. "You get to hell home. All of you Jap-lovers, get home where you belong." He looked at Joe's papers and asked, "Where is your home?"

Joe said, "Osaka."

Craford banged the desk and shouted, "You get out of here. I oughta court-martial you."

Without thinking Joe caught him up on it. "Would that mean I could stay in Japan?"

Craford became apoplectic and sputtered, "All right, wise guy. All right. When the shipping list comes out you won't have to look. Because your name is gonna be first."

When Joe reported all this I got sore. I've watched my father deal with hundreds of human problems and although he's as tough a general as they come, he always puts men first. In France there was a saying in his outfit: "If your wife is dying, don't bother with the colonel. He'll say no. See General Gruver. He'll say yes." So I told Joe, "You hate the military, kid, but this isn't standard. I'll fight this all the way to General Webster."

I caught the train to Kobe and when we stopped at Nishinomiya there was the poster of Hana-ogi smiling down at me.

General Webster didn't smile. For the first three minutes he never gave me a chance to get a word in. "Who in hell do you think was just in here?" he concluded. "The Supervisor of the Keihanshin Kyuko Railroad!" He waited for this to take effect,

131

but I didn't comprehend, so he said in disgust, "The railroad that runs the theater where you've distinguished yourself—beyond the call of duty."

I waited for the explosion but there was none. General Webster smiled pleasantly and said, "It's all been settled. The Japanese-American scandal has been solved by the Webster-Ishikawa negotiations." He bowed and said, "His name was Ishikawa."

Mimicking a diplomat he continued, "The terms of the Webster-Ishikawa treaty are these." He handed me a sheaf of stapled papers and said, "You fly back to Randolph Field. The actress girl goes to Tokyo."

"When?" I cried.

"Both of you exit these parts on July 10—five days."

Then, to my amazement, he insisted that I have lunch with him, and when we got to the Officers Club Mrs. Webster and Eileen were waiting. We conducted ourselves with the punctilious indifference you give a man who has returned from a leprosarium, but Mrs. Webster was too old a veteran of the social battlefields to play such a game for long. Her opening salvo was, "Have you seen this month's show at Takarazuka? The girl who plays the lead is lovely."

I was still sore about the way Joe Kelly was being treated, so I said to myself, "If all bets are off, here goes," and I said aloud, "I know the girl and she's very talented, but I came to Kobe to try to argue your husband into letting Private Kelly remain in Japan."

"Who's Private Kelly?" Mrs. Webster asked.

"His Japanese wife is having a baby and he's being sent home —without her."

The general grew red in the face and tried to change the subject but Eileen jumped in on my side, "Rotten trick, I'd say. What happens to the baby?"

The general laid down his napkin and said, "I argued with Kelly for half an hour, warning him not to marry a Japanese girl."

This did not satisfy Eileen who asked, "Does the Army force them to desert their wives? Aren't they legally married?"

"Yes, they're legally married," snapped the general. "We have to allow them to get married and then we have to leave the wife stranded."

"This is serious," Eileen protested. "Doesn't anyone try to prevent such inhuman foolishness?"

General Webster addressed Eileen directly, "I argued with this boy. Lloyd argued with him. Where'd it get us?"

But Eileen said, "I'm not talking about what has happened. I'm talking about the injustice of what's going to happen."

Mrs. Webster interrupted and asked, "How are you involved in this, Lloyd?"

I took a deep breath and said, "Kelly's from my outfit in Korea." (From the corner of my eye I saw the general sigh with relief that I had not embarrassed him by mentioning Hana-ogi, but I had no intention of avoiding the issue.) "And you might like to know that it also happens that I'm planning to marry a Japanese girl myself."

I had dropped my napalm. The general gulped. Mrs. Webster blushed an absolute scarlet and Eileen put her hand on mine and said, "I always knew you had guts."

I said, "Thanks, I guess I'd better go now."

Mrs. Webster asked weakly, "The actress?"

"Yes."

The general said, "Lloyd's not marrying any actress. He's being sent home on Thursday."

I started to leave but Eileen insisted upon walking to the door with me, as if I were the girl and she the escort. "I'm proud of you, Lloyd," she said. "I wish you all the luck in the world." We shook hands and I thought of a dozen things to say but none of them made much sense, so I said, "I'm sorry we got things loused up," and she said, "It was mostly my fault," and then as I was leaving she laughed and said, "Remember the time I asked you if you ever felt like just grabbing me and hauling me off to some shack?"

We both smiled awkwardly at this and she said, "That's just about what you did, wasn't it? But with somebody else." She kissed me on the cheek and said good-naturedly, "Well, I'm glad you turned out to be a man and not a mouse."

When I got back home I found Joe and Katsumi alone in a kind of dull panic. "I been all over it with everybody," he said. "Even went to see the consul, but everyone flashes the marriage papers at you and says, 'You signed 'em. You knew you couldn't take her to America.' As if that made everything just dandy."

Since I already knew that his name was at the head of the list I hadn't the courage to ask him what the latest hot dope was, but he came out with it, "I'm first on the first draft."

Katsumi, saying nothing, prepared the meal while I watched the door for Hana-ogi. She arrived about seven and I could tell that she had already been ordered to Tokyo. She had a nervousness about her that I had not seen before and I wondered if she was aware that I was being flown home. We looked at each other for a moment as she kicked off her zori and then neither of us could continue the duplicity. She ran weeping across the tatami and cried, "Rroyd, Rroyd! I Tokyo go five days!"

I caught her in my arms and hugged her as if I intended to crush her then so that she could never escape. "I fly back to Texas right away."

She pushed me away and cried, "You leave Japan?" I nodded and she burst into sobs, calling to Katsumi in Japanese. The two girls stood in the middle of the room and looked at Joe and me and for the four of us the world slowly fell apart.

CHAPTER XXI

THAT was Saturday. On Monday the Air Force officially notified Joe that he would be flown back to America on Wednesday. I found him sitting cross-legged on the floor studying the notice with dull resignation. He looked up grimly. "Why should I be punished? Why should I have to go back to the States?"

Automatically I replied, "The way the ball bounces."

"No!" he shouted. "What's there for me in America?"

I assured him, "You'll get out of the Air Force and find a job and pretty soon Katsumi'll follow you."

He looked at me and said grimly, "I wish it was goin' to be so simple. In Chicago I killed a man. A mixed-up affair—not all my fault. They couldn't pin anything on me. I'm not apologizin', because it could just as well have been my fault. Because I was no damn good. And if I lose Katsumi I'll be no damn good again."

I knew there was something I ought to say, some standard word of courage, but I couldn't think of any. Joe said, "A guy like you, from a good home—you wouldn't understand. For the first time in my life I'm livin'. At night when I hear Katsumi come up the alley shufflin' her wooden shoes—later when she puts that crazy hard, little pillow next to mine—when I see the plain goddamn goodness in that girl . . ." He looked down at the tatami and I guessed that he had tears in his throat.

"Joe, promise me you won't get into trouble with Col. Craford."

He looked up at me as if Craford were already dead. "Him?" he sniffed. "The only time I believe in God is when I think of that fat slob. God must be keepin' score on bastards like that. Otherwise nothin' makes sense."

I said, "Remember, Joe. You promised you'd make no trou-

135

ble with that . . ." I searched for a name and suddenly the total misery of Joe's problem rose in my mouth like bile. I grew purple and cursed Craford for several minutes. I cursed my father and General Webster and Mrs. Webster and every convention that made it impossible for Hana-ogi and me to marry. Then I stopped, but I was still quivering with accumulated fury.

Joe looked up at me and said, "Thanks, Major. I thought you felt that way."

I was still shaking. I said, "Even so I believe things'll work out."

He said, "I don't."

There was nothing to add. He knew I was with him. Maybe I had steered him away from some hot-brained mistake. That's the best I could hope, so I went over to Itami where I was to see the last performance of *Swing Butterfly*.

When I had first seen Hana-ogi I had been insulted by her burlesque of Americans. Now my reaction was different, for I discovered that even against my will I had to laugh at her lampoon of Americans. The reason was simple. She had studied with intimate care my mannerisms and now reproduced them in burlesque form. When she lit a cigarette she mimicked me, when she propositioned Madame Butterfly it was me trying to kiss her on the Bitchibashi.

As her big dance number approached I became apprehensive, for I suspected that her aping of Americanisms would dull her Japanese touch, but I was wrong. Even more than mistress or wife, she was an artist, and if her American jitterbugging was more hilarious for having studied an American at close hand, her Japanese classical dance was stronger.

When intermission came I wanted to rush backstage and embrace her and tell her that no matter if she lived a million years cooped up at Takarazuka, I would be with her every time she danced—but I was not to see her, for I could not get into the dressing-rooms.

136

CHAPTER XXII

SO THE rapture was lost. The great deep rapture I felt when watching Hana-ogi perform was never reported to her, for as I took my seat at the beginning of Act II an M.P. came up to me and asked, "Major Gruver?"

"Yes."

"You'll have to come with us."

The curtain had not yet risen, so Hana-ogi did not see me leave and I was grateful for that. When I got outside and I saw two other M.P.'s with guns I asked, "What's up?"

"Airman Kelly," they said.

"Joe?"

"Yep. Deserted."

"Impossible. I saw him this morning."

Another M.P. broke in and said, "He was called special at 1300. He was scheduled to fly out tomorrow but a special plane came through and Col. Craford said, 'Get him on it.' "

The first M.P. said, "I checked him in at the airport at 1250 but before the plane took off he beat it."

I had a dry ugly taste in my mouth as the siren wailed into Osaka. At Itami I asked, "Did the plane take off?"

"Yep. It's desertion."

I began to sweat. Now Joe Kelly was really done for.

We stopped at the canal and I led the way to the alley, where two M.P.'s tried the door. It seemed to be barred, so they were going to break the paper, but at that moment it seemed like my house and I didn't want the paper broken, so I said, "Maybe a chair's against it. I'll use the window."

I forced open a window and started to crawl in. While my leg was still suspended I saw Joe. He was on the floor with his head blown apart by a .45. Across him, obviously having died later, lay Katsumi with a kitchen knife plunged completely through her neck.

For a moment all I could do was look at the floor—at the two lovers who had needed each other so much. The M.P. came up and looked over my shoulder. Then he called loudly, "You better break the door down, Sharkey."

I watched the frail doors bend and break. I heard the clatter of wood and the tearing of paper and the doors through which Hana-ogi had so often come at dusk, dropping her silken packages on the floor, were gone. Sharkey took one look and said, "Get the camera. You wanna catch this just as it happened."

Sharkey barked to the man at my shoulder, "Eddie, you inform the Jap police." Then he saw me and said, "We'll need you here, Major."

I was numb with helpless anger. Of all the people in the world, Joe and Katsumi Kelly should have been protected and kept alive. I thought of them laughing and helping each other and I got all sick inside, but then I thought of Hana-ogi, who would be coming home soon and I grew panicky for her because the photographers had arrived and were taking pictures like mad.

And then the reporters swarmed at me. They were bright young men, most of whom spoke English, and I had enough sense to keep my mouth shut, for if I had said anything at all I would have blurted out, "They wanted to ship him back to America but he insisted upon staying in Japan."

The reporters saw somebody else and swarmed away but one stayed and asked, "Aren't you Ace Gruver?"

I nodded.

"You the one living with Hana-ogi?"

I wanted to shoot him dead but everything had collapsed now, so I nodded grimly and he pointed up the canal. There at last she was, Hana-ogi. Late afternoon sun played upon her tousled black hair and illuminated the fall of her kimono.

With eager pin-toed steps she hurried toward me down the canal bank but the newspaperman who was standing with me broke away, ran toward her and spoke rapidly. She peered across the crowd, searching for me, and when she failed to find me she broke away from the warning newspaperman to fight her way resolutely toward the very spot where the police waited.

In that moment I could see the collapse of her world and instinctively a shout rose to my lips: "Lo, the postillion!"

She stopped. The smile that had crept upon the edge of her lips vanished. Standing on tiptoe, she peered across the crowd, still seeking me, but I hid myself so that she would have to go back. After a moment she turned away from the crowds that shoved toward the suicide house and I last saw her moving back to the main street. The summer breeze, drifting down the canal, tugged at her kimono and twilight rested on her hair. Then she moved behind a pillar and I never saw her again.

For three hours while I ached to seek out Hana-ogi I had to answer questions and fill out reports as to the death of Katsumi-san. It was after ten o'clock when I was released and I caught a cab whose driver gasped when I said Takarazuka, but he drove me there and at eleven that Sunday night I hurried past the cryptomerias and into the dormitory where Hana-ogi lived.

Apparently I was expected, for old Teruko-san and her grim-faced interpreter were waiting for me. "Hana-ogi-san is not here," they said firmly.

"I know she's here!" I cried.

"Hana-ogi-san is on her way to Tokyo."

"She can't be! I saw her!"

"Please, Major Gruver. Hana-ogi-san is not here."

Unthinkingly, I forced my way past the two women and along the corridor on which Hana-ogi lived. The Takarazuka girls peered at me as I stormed past, then sighed when I reached Hana-ogi's empty room. It was so empty. The little things that made it hers were gone.

CHAPTER XXIII

GENERAL WEBSTER called me in to Kobe next day and said, "That was a dreadful affair last night in Osaka." He asked me if I had heard any rumors that Lt.Col. Craford had handled the affair badly. I wanted to put a blast on the fat blubber-gut who had murdered Kelly, but something old and powerful inside me argued, "Why start a military mess?" I shrugged my shoulders and said, "I guess Craford handled it O.K."

But immediately I knew that I was reverting to the man I had been when I first argued with Kelly against marrying a Japanese girl. I was defending the Army against the man and I felt ashamed of myself. I must have shivered, for General Webster said gruffly, "Lloyd, don't take this so bitterly. Kelly's dead. Nobody can do anything about it. You told me yourself he was a dead-end punk—beyond saving."

I looked at the general. A man under his command had committed suicide rather than return to the United States and he was shrugging it off. I asked, "What about that colonel in Tokyo who shot himself rather than leave his Japanese girl? Or the major in Yokohama? Were they punks?"

"Yes! They were second-class men. I've seen reports on seven such suicides and they were all shoddy material. First-class men sometimes fall in love with native girls, but they get over it. They forget the girls and they go home. They go back to work."

"Damn it!" I shouted. "Why do men like you and my father call them native girls? Can't you believe . . ."

General Webster was remarkably patient. He stopped me by thrusting a yellow paper into my hand. "I suppose a young man's no good if he doesn't have the guts to fight for what he thinks is right," he said. "You've had the courage to fight for Joe Kelly and his native girl, but it wasn't necessary. Read it."

The yellow paper was from Washington and it said a law

140

was being passed to permit men like Joe Kelly to bring their Japanese wives into the States.

I thought of Joe and Katsumi lying in blood and I felt sick. I had to see Hana-ogi. "Sir," I blurted, "I've got to get to Tokyo."

"It's forbidden, Lloyd. You're flying home."

"I don't care what happens. I've got to see Hana-ogi."

The general winced as I used the strange name, then said calmly, "If you disobey another order . . ."

"All right, I'll leave the Air Force. I'll get a . . ."

I expected General Webster to hit the roof, but when he's away from his wife he isn't so bad. He said, "Sit down, Lloyd. I'm not going to throw my weight at you. You're being a stupid idiot and we both know it, but you come by it naturally."

"What do you mean?"

"This seems like 1924."

"I don't understand," I said dully.

"Your father was mixed up with a girl—the one I told you about. There was one member of our class, Chap named Charley Scales. He had a chance in '24 to drop out of service and take a job with General Motors. So your father decided to marry the girl and chuck the Army and go along with Charley, but some of us talked him out of it. Must run in your family."

"My father was going to leave the Army?"

"Yep. He was all broken up." General Webster laughed and scratched his chin. "We thought he was pretty weak to be broken up like that over a waitress. Look at him now."

I said, "I still want to marry this girl."

"Son," General Webster said, "the Supervisor of Takarazuka and I stayed up late last night figuring how to keep his outfit and mine free of bad publicity over the suicides. We protected ourselves and we can't let you ruin things."

"At least give me a chance to say good-bye to her!"

"No, she herself wanted it this way."

"She didn't!"

"I saw her. She said to send you back to America."

141

I said, "I don't believe that." So he handed me a letter which had been written two days before. I knew because Hana-ogi had written it on my stationery and as I read it I could hear her gentle voice groping its way through my language:

Darring,

Pretty soon (That was a phrase I used a lot . . .) *our rast night. I Tokyo go. You America go.* (A passage was scratched out, then . . .) *I not think fire die. Frame not go out. I think you many times.* (Then she added a passage from her phrase book . . .)

Ever your devoted and humble servant,

and the letter was signed with the Chinese characters representing her name. How strange they were, those characters, how beautiful, how hidden from me behind the wall of Asia!

I wanted to fling myself upon the floor and weep as Hana-ogi might have wept had we been at home, but instead there came to me that sad and final Japanese word: Sayonara. Sayonara, Hana-ogi. Sayonara, you beautiful dancer. You've chosen the tough way. I hope your gods give you the courage to follow it. Sayonara, Katsumi, little mother. Forgive me that I once thought you too ugly to kiss. Oh, Katsumi, sayonara. Sayonara, Sukoshi Joe. And you, Japan, you crowded islands, you tragic land—sayonara, you enemy, you friend."

But even as I said these words I knew that I had to put them out of mind, for I was forced to acknowledge that I lived in an age when the only honorable profession was soldiering, when the only acceptable attitude toward strange lands and people of another color must be not love but fear.

Like the voice of my own conscience I heard, as from a great distance, General Webster saying, "I oughtn't to tell you this, Lloyd, because it isn't official yet. But as soon as you get back to Randolph Field they're making you a lieutenant-colonel."

Instinctively I saluted.

The general said, "We'd better move along. Eileen wants to drive us to the airport."

Fire in the Ashes

EUROPE IN MID-CENTURY

THEODORE H. WHITE

BY WAY OF INTRODUCTION
TO EUROPE

EUROPE is more foreign to Americans today than it has ever been in all our history.

Americans before 1914, indeed, Americans almost down to 1938, knew Europe far better and with more instinctive understanding than they do now. Europe lived as we did, was housed as we were, worked as we did. Americans who crossed the ocean went not from one civilization to another but from one home to a second. Europeans and Americans read the same books, were taught the same sciences, saved, planned and lived on a level of material comfort much the same. Within the past thirty years, however, history has thrust Europeans and Americans both as individual human beings and as great communities further and further apart. There have been the revolutionary changes in the American way of life; the amazing growth of arts, cultures and material comforts; the choking off of the immigration which refreshed the European roots of American life with new arrivals for so long. On the other side of the Atlantic have come the wars, the social pounding and jostling that have followed them, the revolutions, the upheavals, most of all the inflations which have made Europeans today so different not only from Americans but from Europeans of yesterday.

This separation of European and American civilizations happens, moreover, at a moment when America is finally more intimately involved in European affairs than ever before in our national history. This is not a theoretical involvement, either. A quarter of a million American soldiers, drafted from home in time of peace, are sprawled across Europe in bivouac and barrack. One hundred thousand of the finest men in America's army are strung out between the Rhine and the Thuringian ridges, on the alert day and night.

These men are the flesh of America's pledge that Europe's

destiny is ours. If a Russian soldier moves to cross the border of Norway, if a Bulgarian fires a shot across the borders of Turkey, if an East German platoon raids a county in West Germany, then every one of these men is committed to battle. With them are committed not only those who dwell in Western Europe, but 150,000,000 Americans wherever they sleep, or work, or play between the Atlantic and the Pacific.

This relationship seems as strange to Europeans as to Americans. While to Americans the relationship has seemed like an ugly burden, sucking taxes, demanding manpower endlessly, the dirty curse of greatness, most Europeans have seen it differently. They see the relationship as a major triumph of American diplomacy—which it is. They see it as a series of shrewdly calculated American mastermoves which have led them down a road they never chose, at a pace they never set, to an end they can only dimly discern. They are restive under the relationship, weighing at every season and every budget the comfort of American aid against the burden and strain American strategy imposes; they are unsure whether in the long run the one may not outweigh the other.

This restiveness of Europe will be, perhaps, the greatest problem of American diplomacy in the coming year. The victories of the Atlantic Alliance in Europe have been won under American leadership; they have been won, however, not alone but in a partnership to which the Europeans have contributed mightily. The numb, still years in which Europeans docilely submitted to American leadership have passed. Now, with the revival of energy, they are irritated and irritable with all the unhappiness of the convalescent. And, like the convalescent, they find most irritating of all their own weakness and helplessness in the strange new world which has changed so much in their absence.

For five hundred years, until the end of the Second World War, the nation-states of Europe enjoyed the luxury of rivalry or partnership, war or alliance, at their convenience. In all this long period, Europe stood for two things in the minds of other men. She stood, first, for the act of creation—she made the music and the letters, generated the ideas and tools that armed the wars, equipped the science, laid down the factories and charged the revolutions that have touched every single man wherever he lives anywhere in the world. She stood, secondly, for power—brute force, the ability to kill efficiently, uncompromisingly, in well-disciplined, cohesive phalanxes of men at whatever point in the world this force might be needed.

Today, all this is over. The wars of this century have wasted and ruined Europe at a time when newer people all around the world were growing in power. Though Europe is still a prodigious body of energy—its 300,000,000 people produce almost as much coal as America, more ships, half as much steel, have twice as many spindles and looms—its primacy is over. Europe stands caught between two descendent civilizations whose ideas, though borrowed from Europe, have come to strange fruit in strange soil. It stands not only between these two strange civilizations, but lives as a ward of one of them, its power of decision purely negative in the clash between the two.

It is not that Europeans seek to recapture again this solitary greatness and power. After the storms and passions of the thirties and the war years, Europe is still panting, hollowed out from exertion and spent emotion. The sound of drums in European ears, the shrill of bugles, the great flaming words with which East and West challenge each other, rather than exciting the Europeans, disturb them. This feeling, indeed, is one of the common qualities that sets Europeans apart from Americans and Russians. The United States and Russia constantly want to act, to do, to make history—and Europe has had a bellyful of history. Europe wants rest, quiet and forgetfulness. But even this it cannot have in the world of today, for it is helpless to calm the world.

This sense of powerlessness is the incubator of all European restlessness—this sense of being swung about by the actions of strange men in distant places. Where, to Americans a generation ago, it seemed grotesque that Americans should die because

147

someone had flung a bomb at a prince in the Balkans, it seems grotesque to Europeans today that they might be summoned to die because an American lad swooped to blitz a power station on the Yalu.

The years since the war in which this sense of helplessness deepened and developed might well be called the Years of the Pause.

For two decades previously, one great man after another had made European history revolve about his comings and goings, his speeches, sins, ambitions. Since the war there has been nothing but the blurred image of faceless men, scurrying from conference to conference wherein nothing ever seemed to be settled. No dramatic encounters have marked this period. Instead of Munich and Godesberg, Teheran and Yalta, the Europeans read each morning of some new conference in an interminable session of negotiations in which nothing ever changed within the drone. The dog races, the price of butter, the new tractor, the problem of where to go on vacation have all been more interesting and urgent to Europeans than what came out of the councils of state.

The Years of the Pause are now ending. It is obvious that new leadership in both America and Russia is now wrenching the whole course of world affairs into new patterns and perspectives. What is less obvious is that in this wrenching process Europe, forgotten through the postwar years as a factor in power, must contribute as greatly as either of the two new titans. Having now recovered from their wounds of war, and having seen this recovery reach a plateau and stagnate, the Europeans, however much they wish to drowse and be quiet, are being forced once more, against their will, to consider great decisions.

Two events within Europe in these coming years rival events in America and Russia in their dimensions. Both these events, paradoxically, are events that were conceived, launched and nursed to their present pregnant power by American diplomacy.

148

In the days when America's whim was Europe's imperative these twin movements seemed no more than the idle fancy of America's proconsuls in Europe. But now, rooted deep in European life, they have passed beyond the control of American diplomacy and challenge each other to see which shall shape the future of the old Continent.

These two events are the Birth of Europe and the Renaissance of Germany. Intertwined and locked together since their first stirring in conception, they move today in naked rivalry, each racing the other to realization; for whichever triumphs first will make of the other its servant.

The desire of Europe to be Europe, to become a union, is a vision that has haunted generals and priests, merchants and wanderers for all the hundreds of years since Rome ruled Europe and made it one. It is a vision of such grandeur and scope, and we have come so close and so swiftly to realizing it in the past few years, that it is impossible in our generation to tell what it may eventually mean for mankind. The vision has always been there; what has fleshed it out in the past few years has been the coming together of two great forces in the torn and tattered states of Western Europe. The first of these forces has been fear—sheer, brute, quivering fear of the Russian state which might at any moment strike and with its juggernaut weight crush any of the old West European states standing alone. This fear alone would not have been enough, even as the age-old idealism of the visionaries had never been enough, had it not been for the second force: American pressure. American diplomacy has insisted, year-in and year-out, in every capital of Europe from Oslo to Rome that the dream of union must clothe itself with flesh and institutions *now;* American diplomacy supplied the plastic of wealth and promise of arms to bind the European states together. It has been argued that American pressure on Europeans to unite has been too primitive, too impatient, too mechanical, too unfeeling in the single-minded insistence with which it has tried to force age-old enemies to forget their feuds and become brothers. It may well be that historians will read

149

THEODORE H. WHITE

American pressure as too unrelenting and too swift, and will make it responsible if the dream of European Union fails. But there is no doubt that without American diplomatic pressure and insistence this dream would still be a paper nothing or the stuff of student debating contests. Instead, it is already a half-reality. It is a power which can already tax, dispose, order, create and regulate the greatest industries of Western Europe over and above any national frontier of law. Six nations have already signed a compact which may, tomorrow, clothe the men of half a dozen different states in one uniform, under one flag, and send them out to die under one command. And the elected political delegates of these six states have already drafted the constitution of a new community, called simply "Europe," in which supreme powers will be taken from the old national parliaments and lodged in one great new suprasovereign, subordinate to an assembly elected by all the people of Europe.

The Renaissance of Germany is something as profound and powerful in its movement of the coming years as the Birth of Europe. Here, too, as in the Birth of Europe, the United States was the moving force. It was the United States that summoned Germany back to greatness, that fed and clothed her, equipped her with government and leadership, struck the chains from her will.

Were it not for the Germans, Western Europe would already be united—the fear of Russia, the pressure of America, the questing idealism of both religion and common sense would almost certainly, by now, have brought the scattered states of Europe together in an effort to regain their standing in the world. But the West Europeans looking east toward the Communist world see not only Russia, but Germany too. Germany is an unknown quantity. For fifty years this continent has revolved around the desperate urge of the Germans to make their neighbors conform to Germany's nightmare vision of what was right and just. More bitter than ever, half-healed from wounds they brought on themselves, the Germans are today being summoned to enter a new community in which, by the logic of power, they

150

must be the prime movers. Which way will they move? What will they do with their new and ever-growing power? How deep is the tissue of decency in the new German Republic? How much vitality is left to the terrifying German ideas which have brought the Continent to its present broken and enfeebled state? Caught between the power giants of East and West, seeking to regain some grip over their own destiny, the European statesmen know that the new Europe, in order to become a power giant of rival size, must include the resources and energy of a freely consenting Germany. Germany, they know, cannot be left out of either the Atlantic Community or European Union, for to leave Germany entirely independent and free to her own devices is to invite her again to play East against West to inevitable disaster. Yet they know that if the Germans are swept again by one of those sea-tides of emotion which so violently seize them, then the new Union of Europe is useless; better it were that it had never been born.

Perhaps the single most important question of the new Europe is thus what the Germans have learned from their own history as they are invited to a new loyalty, and the future of Europe depends on whether the Germans choose to accept the new world struggling to be born or whether they choose to wreck it.

The approach of these new movements cuts the years that have passed from the years that come as sharply as if a page were turned and a new chapter opened. It is not that these movements and growths have been swelling in a vacuum. Through all these years the morning newspapers of the Europeans have dutifully recorded each dry morsel of negotiation and event in studious detail. But the Europeans, preoccupied with the daily tasks of feeding their families, sheltering themselves, putting together the roads, factories and bridges destroyed by war, have not been listening. The coming years are the years in which they must decide where they stand and what they are to do about the new world in which they live.

151

The decisions of the Europeans about these movements and the fate of these new movements affect not only their own lives but the lives of everyone else in the world, Americans most of all. Even in its present weakness, Europe speaks for enormous power, the power that hangs as a balance between the strength of America and Russia. With Europe's 300,000,000 people and their industries added in friendship, the American perspective is one of expansion. With Europe subtracted or hostile, the American perspective is one of contraction in a spiral of gloomy isolation.

Upon Europe's decision in the next few years rests the relationship of the Western world to the Russians. It is, after all, the Europeans, not the Americans, who live next to that huge Byzantine state which combines the most modern techniques with the oldest form of despotism. As if by instinct, without deep thought, Europe has rejected in every state of the West the gospel of communism without finding any other gospel to match it in vitality. Until now, Europe has given a brave "No" to the Russians, yet it is unsatisfied with the answer, for America has failed to draw from it an equally steadfast "Yes."

THE END OF THE ALLIANCE

THE real story of postwar Europe begins at the Conference of Potsdam where, for the first time, the chiefs of state approached the root problem of Europe. What to do about Germany?

Germany lay stretched all about them in a state of chaos that it had not known since the end of the Thirty Years' War three centuries before. Nothing had been settled before Potsdam—no decision had been taken on how to dismember or how to centralize Germany in order best to control it; no frontiers had been set for it; no form of government considered; no measures of punishment settled.

The chiefs of state approached the great prize gingerly for none knew exactly what he wanted. They approved a control mechanism of four senior generals, one from each conqueror, to administer Germany while they made up their minds. And they marked out more clearly the zones already roughly agreed on at Yalta. The heads of state were in a great hurry to get home—Stalin to deal with the reconstruction and convalescence of his sorely wounded country, Mr. Attlee to launch the cautious social revolution for which a generation of British Socialists had waited, Mr. Truman to the termination of the war against Japan. So, after fifteen days of almost fruitless talk, the conferees accepted the ingenious suggestion of the American Secretary of State that a Council of Foreign Ministers be set up to deal regularly with the recurring problems of a new world at other times and other places and home they all went.

It is difficult now, before all the pertinent documents and memoirs are publicly available, to judge the importance of the blunders of each of the powers from Potsdam on. The contemporary American citizen, who can be compelled to accept the huge obligations of power only by being kept in a constant state of nerves, sees the events of the postwar world as a long chain of blunders in American diplomacy. The future historian will

153

probably record that the first, the outstanding, the overwhelmingly important blunders were made by the Russians. And that American diplomacy in Europe, despite some initial confusion and several minor fluffs, capitalized on these blunders, outwitted the Russians and won.

The initial Russian blunder began at Potsdam. There, without committing the Western Powers to any binding agreement on Germany, the Russians set out on a course of action which if it were emulated by the Western Powers, as it was certain to be, would give Russia the shabby end of the bargain. The real weight of Germany—the energy, drive, industrial skills and overwhelming portion of its peoples and resources—was as securely in the grip of Western military power as were the puppet lands of Eastern Europe in the grip of the Red Army. To seal the Western Powers out of Eastern Europe and Eastern Germany could only, inevitably, provoke the Western Powers to seal the Russians out of Western Germany, which was the real prize. In effect, the Russians thrust into the hands of the West that which they sought most to gain.

This blunder of real decision was multiplied by a blunder of manners. Slowly and aggravatingly, in conference after conference, at every fringe of contact with the West, the Russians rubbed the West raw, exhausting its patience and willingness to concede on each minor point of dispute, before ever approaching the main settlement on Germany where the West held every card in the deck except the trump of Berlin.

Though Russian strategy has remained transparently simple throughout the postwar years—to wit, to split the Western Alliance—their tactics seemed fashioned for directly contrary ends. Their initial preoccupation with the exclusion of France from any say in the settlement of Europe failed, and failing, thrust the French into almost total diplomatic dependence on the United States. Their initial attempt to divide Britain and the United States failed by the grossest miscalculation. Imputing to the new Labour government all the mythological imperial sins of the Tory diplomacy of Mr. Churchill, they thrust it, too, into

154

union with America in the first formative months, when its diplomacy might have entertained compromise. Having bullied the French and the British into closest partnership with America, they then frightened all other nations of the West into the association that later became the North Atlantic Treaty Organization. Instead of dividing the West, they unified it, creating by their own actions that which they feared most.

The unhappy alliance of Potsdam, its members still bound in solemn oaths and contracts to each other, stumbled through the first year and a half of peace in a series of four great meetings of the Council of Foreign Ministers. These conferences had, as their rough outline, a general agreement that the lesser spoils and conquests of their common victory must be settled and organized before they could approach the central problem of Germany. They confirmed a settlement that might have been predicted by a neophyte and might have been closed in a week. Wherever the Red Armies stood, the Russians were permitted to organize and manipulate governments to their own taste; wherever the West had stationed its forces, it was allowed to organize and manipulate governments to its taste. The vast tier of East European states thus fell to Russia as spoils of war. American and Western influence was excluded from them as completely as Russian influence was excluded from Japan. By the end of 1946, the pattern of Europe as it exists today was sealed in an interlocking set of treaties—except for Germany and its appendage, Austria.

The victorious alliance had been late in coming to grips with the German problem, the intractable, irreducible centerpiece of Euopean politics. Not until the summer of 1946, a year after Germany's defeat, did it become clear how violently divergent were their attitudes to the beaten enemy. The scene was Paris, the setting the Third Conference of Foreign Ministers, convened to discuss the peace treaties with the lesser enemies.

Mr. Molotov opened the debate with a carefully publicized statement in Paris on July 11, directed primarily at German public opinion but obliquely designed to bring the West to serious bargaining. Adopting an unusually conciliatory tone, Mr. Molotov declared that the Soviet Union did not want to destroy Germany but to make it work. Mr. Molotov called on everyone to admit that the levels of German industry (which the Soviets had previously insisted on restraining at impossibly low levels) were too restrictive and must be raised. He attacked those who wished to raze the Ruhr and insisted it be fostered and encouraged to work in peace. Then he got down to business. What he wanted was a thoroughly centralized Germany, rigidly controlled by the Four Power Commission set up at Potsdam, in which the Russians would sit with the right of veto. For the Ruhr, Germany's mighty industrial center, Mr. Molotov wanted an even stricter system of supervision to pump out reparations goods. Eventually, a German government would grow under this Four Power tutelage, and if it proved trustworthy, a peace treaty would be made in a number of years.

It took eight weeks for an official American reaction to develop to Molotov's position. When it came, it was delivered not in Paris, but in Germany, directly to the German people, and was one of the turning points of postwar history. This was the famous Stuttgart speech of Mr. Byrnes.

Mr. Byrnes' speech was, in tone, more minatory and less conciliatory to the Germans than Mr. Molotov's; it contained a more vivid evocation of the war just past, the sins of the Germans, the determination of the Americans never to let such crimes happen again, and their willingness to persist in sacrifice to preserve peace and victory. But, proceeded Mr. Byrnes, America too wanted the swiftest centralization of German economic life and government; she too was against any further reduction in the German standard of living. Moreover, America was adamantly set against any German reparations to be paid out of Germany's production so long as German production could not support Germans; and finally, America did not accept the Oder-Neisse line in the East as the final frontier amputating Silesia from the body of German politics.

The whole inner meaning of the Stuttgart speech was, however, summed up in one of its opening phrases: "It is not in the interest of the German people," said Mr. Byrnes, "or in the interest of world peace that Germany should become a pawn or partner in a military struggle for power between the East and the West." In that uncertain way history has of opening every great chapter with a negative, Mr. Byrnes had introduced the next chapter. Every intelligent German in the audience understood Mr. Byrnes instinctively. The speech was an invitation to every German to take precisely the attitude deplored, to become either pawn or partner in the struggle between East and West.

The divergence of American and Russian positions on Germany was now clear. The Russians still thought of Germany as booty; having chopped away East Germany from West Germany, they now wanted to press for a further share in the riches of Western Germany which the Atlantic Powers held. The Americans thought of Germany as a burden; they wanted now to lessen the burden by making Germany operate; they wanted to increase German health, not in order to get more out of Germany, but to end the downward spiral and sickening disorganization of her economy, which was retarding all European recovery. On this note of divergence, having only just approached the German problem, Mr. Byrnes ended his stewardship of American diplomacy in December, 1946. Fifteen months before he had begun his report to the American people after the First Conference of Foreign Ministers with the melancholy words, "The First Conference of Foreign Ministers closed in a stalemate." He did not bother to make a report on the last of the meetings he attended in December. Instead, in his memoirs, he wryly recorded the quip of Georges Bidault, the witty history professor who had become France's Foreign Minister. By this time the Council had degenerated into a debate that dragged each argument around and around, inflexibly, caught in a groove from which there was no escape. M. Bidault observed that the Council was now a merry-go-round and asked his colleagues' indulgence since he "was now going to ride his own horse around and say something about coal."

THEODORE H. WHITE

It was General George Catlett Marshall who decided to get off the merry-go-round. Until Marshall succeeded Byrnes in the leadership of American diplomacy, all decisions had been made in the frame of the fictitious yet legal alliance that still bound the West to the Russians. From January of 1947 on, American decisions were made not only apart from the alliance, but in recognition of the open and increasing enmity between the two halves of the old alliance. Indeed, the entire strategy which has propelled the Western world ever since was conceived and drafted in the first fifteen months of Marshall's two-year incumbency of office.

Marshall, a man in whom the powers of logic are coupled with dignity and force to an extraordinary degree, found himself caught in a situation in which effective diplomacy was impossible. Effective diplomacy rests on power, and by the beginning of 1947, the United States and her Allies were powerless. In May of 1945, the Army of the United States had stood in Central Europe with a force of 3,500,000 men, organized into 68 veteran divisions, supported by 149 air groups of planes, supplied by one of the most elaborate logistical systems ever flung over the globe. Some 47 divisions of Allied power braced this force on the Western Front. By March of 1946, ten months later, the American forces had dwindled to 400,000 men. The Air Force had disappeared.

George Marshall, a soldier by training, was never for an instant unaware of the relationship between power and purpose. He entered on his term of diplomacy conscious, as were few other men in the Western world, that the Russians massed 40 divisions of combat troops in combat position in Central Europe with over 100 divisions behind them in reserve, while America's forces stood at two divisions and its homeland reserve counted no more than six ready battalions. The instinct of survival made the first order of the day the recapture of a balance.

Marshall had been in office no more than six weeks, however, when another fact was pressed home to him: that the balance to be recaptured was not only military but, even more urgently, social and political. On the morning of February 24, 1947, without warning, the British Ambassador in Washington, Lord Inverchapel, called on Under-Secretary of State Dean Acheson at the State Department to inform him that Great Britain was pulling out of Greece and Turkey. Great Britain at this moment was not only garrisoning Germany and feeding starving Germans with British money, but also holding down garrisons in North Africa, in always-restive Egypt, in turbulent Palestine, in Burma, Malaya and Hongkong. She was also caught in an economic crisis of crushing weight. The cost of British support of Greece and Turkey, said the British, would in the coming year be $250,-000,000, which the British could not possibly afford.

More was involved in this British announcement than imminent danger in a distant flank zone. The basic assumption of American diplomacy had hitherto been that the United States, though the undisputed leader, was nevertheless a partner in a coalition of likeminded and powerful allies. This assumption was now about to be shown false. The British decision to abandon Greece was only the first in a series of sharp dramatic jolts that were to demonstrate that the strength of Western Europe had been ebbing over a period of decades. The spasm of war had temporarily hidden this erosion by those same exertions which speeded and deepened it. But in early 1947, a year and a half after the war had ended, the erosion could no longer be concealed. The United States found itself not in a combination of power but in an association of decay that made no social or political balance with the Russians possible until it was corrected.

Nineteen forty-seven was the year that Europe almost disappeared from world affairs. One violent blizzard had gummed up the delicate mechanism of the overstrained British economy, paralyzed her business, made her people shiver in unheated homes, set in motion the events that led to the end of her imperial pretensions. The drought of the following spring and summer months ushered in the dismal era on the Continent. There, blazing, rainless weeks produced the finest wines in a generation of memory and the worst food crops in a longer period. By the

159

fall of 1947 Europe was as close to destitution as a modern civilization can get; she could not grow enough food and she could not find the money or goods to buy food elsewhere.

Twice during his first year in office General Marshall sat down with the Russians to negotiate the problem of Germany, once at Moscow in the spring and once in London in December. Neither of these wordy bouts brought any conclusion or meeting of minds. By then, Marshall had set in motion those events and policies that were to separate the West from the East, perhaps forever.

The first of these policies, the Truman Doctrine, was an instinctive, almost reflex action. Three days after the delivery of the Inverchapel message to the State Department, the State Department and the White House had called in and persuaded the leaders of Congress (except for Mr. Taft) that the burden Britain was dropping must be caught by the United States. Demanding and eventually receiving $400,000,000 for the military and economic support of Greece and Turkey, the American government announced that its power was now, with a single bound, committed around the globe.

The Truman Doctrine was not, however, enough. Returning from his spring conference in Moscow, Marshall doggedly informed Washington of his conviction that Russia would not negotiate as long as we in negotiation could not win their respect for our force. It was impossible to discuss Europe with the Russians so long as Europe was quicksand. Europe had to be made firm before one could build on our side a bridge across to the Russians on the other. Europe had to be organized. In the busy spring weeks of 1947 while the technicians in Washington were translating the Truman Doctrine into the specifics of advisory groups, technical assistance, ships of supply, distribution mechanisms, the Marshall Plan was being slowly shaped in theory. On June 5, the idea, the policy, the techniques had matured enough in Marshall's mind to permit him to go to Harvard University and there at a commencement address to invite Europe, as a community of nations, to submit to the United States a pro-

160

gram of community needs that might make them healthy again, which program the United States would then consider as a basis for vast and continued aid. Within this program of European revival, as certain as seed in the womb, the revival of German health and strength was implicit.

The United States Army had begun to organize Western Germany long before the United States government had any clear idea of what should be done with it. The Army's mission was to keep Germany pacified, hold it in submission, feed it, make it work, and do all these things at the least possible cost to the American taxpayer. While the civilian statesmen, for whom the uniformed proconsuls developed an easy contempt, talked theory and policy, the Army had to act, every single day.

It was not until the middle of 1947, when the Marshall Plan was conceived and General George Marshall had rehabilitated the State Department enough in Army eyes to merit attention, that broad diplomatic policy in Germany and Army policy in Germany began to mesh. The Army wanted to make Germany a going concern as quickly as possible in order to cut the burden of subsidy out of Army appropriations; the Marshall Plan wanted to revive all European industrial life to new historic highs, and this was impossible without Germany. Ugly, distorted, its streets full of homeless refugees, its currency a paper nonsense, Germany, once the anchor of Europe's economic life, had become its crazy, unbalanced vortex. A sweeping reorganization of Western Germany was necessary to cleanse and purify the madness.

Two things were clearly in order: first, to create some native German instrument of government to pull order out of anarchy; second, to purge its business life of inflation so that men could toil productively. In the spring of 1948, after the final breakdown of the Council of Foreign Ministers in London in December, the Western Powers proceeded to both tasks at once. A conference of the six Western Powers in London invited the Germans to elect delegates to a constitutional convention which would create a new popularly elected government for all West

Germany. Simultaneously, they proceeded with the purging of German finances by a brutal repudiation of all paper money in circulation in Western Germany and the substitution of a new, hard, soundly controlled money.

These were the measures that provoked the famous Berlin blockade. The Russians, despite their own total exclusion of Western influence from every square yard of their dominance, could not bring themselves to believe that they were to be as totally excluded themselves from a share in the power and control of West Germany. To reopen discussion and provoke talk, the Russians knew only one method: force. This they invoked in the Berlin blockade, and when it failed, they had shot their bolt in Europe. By then, Europe and America were embarked on a new adventure of such magnitude that men scarcely noticed that the war had come to an end with no peace made.

DRAMATIS PERSONAE

IN WESTERN EUROPE live approximately 300,000,000 people governed and separated by twenty-five different nation-states that range from the Vatican City (population: 940) to the United Kingdom (population: 50,368,455).

A tourist guide to the life of these people records with equal enthusiasm a wild array of interesting facts about them: the fact that French policemen have a mania for hustling and speeding the driver to whirl through traffic faster and faster; that the best herring and cream in Europe is served in the legislative dining halls of the Saar; that one can buy a custom-tailored suit cheaper in Spain than anywhere else on the Continent.

What the tourist guide does not record is that although all these facts are distinctly related to the political process, there is one brutal and simple standard for deciding what facts in Europe count in current history and what do not. This standard is based solely on the name of the country involved, for in European politics there are only two kinds of country.

There are the Big Three—France, England and Germany. And there are the others.

The others cannot be ignored. As industrial producers, as geographical buffers, as zones of dispute, as contributory influences, they bring enormous impact to bear on specific situations. But what brackets all of the lesser states together as chanters of the chorus is the prime political fact that they cannot of themselves offer a solution to any great problem, nor can they obstruct a solution once the great powers of the world have agreed.

Only France, England and Germany have, in themselves, the internal potential of decision which may alter the march of great events. The leaders of France, England and Germany are no more brilliant or able than the leaders of Holland, Belgium, Italy or Sweden. Indeed, when the chiefs of the lesser states sit in council with chiefs of the great states, they frequently by sheer personality overshadow the Frenchmen, Englishmen and Ger-

163

mans with whom they gather. But the leaders of these other states can only comment, whereas the leaders of the Big Three speak out of traditions that goad them to act, whether they will or not, as historymakers.

England, France and Germany are personalities of power. They cannot be controlled, choked or bribed without an upheaval that shakes world power. They are the states that can vote themselves out of the Atlantic Alliance and, by this single act, destroy it. If they quarrel with each other, all strategy crumbles. If they are healthy, then all their lesser neighbors will throb with good health too, and if they are caught with inflation or depression, the contagion likewise ultimately infects all their neighbors. If they can be brought together in common purpose they might make a force almost equal to the United States or the Soviet Union. Since the war it has been the cardinal aim of American foreign policy to bring and keep these three great states together and in harmony with our purposes against the Russians.

If we can see what perplexes these people and what they seek, we can see how the struggle in Europe is shaped. And if Willi Schlieker in the Ruhr, Pierre Bertaux in Paris, Joe Curry in Yorkshire, claim more attention in this book than de Gasperi, Spaak, van Zeeland, Tito or Franco, it is because they speak for Germany, for France and for England—they are membranes through which the forces of history filter and show themselves.

THE MYSTERY OF FRANCE

EVERY country is a mystery composed of the lives of many men. Yet none is more sealed to the understanding than the mystery of France.

For a full generation the spectacle of French politics—fretful, whining, querulous—has become so commonplace, the hysterics with which French politics twist from turning point to turning point of decision without deciding anything has become, indeed, so normal that they have long since lost interest for anyone but a student of *psychopathia politica*. Frenchmen, like strangers, regard the politics of their country with the cynical detachment of total contempt.

The mystery of France is simple to describe. Here lies the richest and most beautiful land of Europe. Here live some of its most illuminating minds. Here are men of courage and great tradition, toilers of dogged diligence and consummate craftsmanship. Yet nothing comes of this human material, France wastes and abuses all the talents she possesses.

France, larger than England and Western Germany put together, is a jeweled country. Its fields roll in fragrant beauty from the English Channel to the Mediterranean, six hundred miles from north to south, six hundred miles from east to west. The great wheat plains of the Beauce that sprawl over the heart of the country about Paris, tender green in spring and golden dry in midsummer, are among the lushest in the world; many a wheat farm on the Aisne is more fruitful than the richest of America's midcontinent. The meadows of Normandy and the uplands of Gascony are speckled with fat cattle. Down the cleft in France's central mountain bulge runs the swift-flowing Rhône opening on a triangle of sun-washed, subtropical fruitland, vegetable land and wineland. Beneath French soil lie some of the most formidable deposits of iron ore in the entire world, substantial coal—though not enough—enormous reserves of bauxite for aluminum, potential pools of oil and natural gas as yet un-

165

tapped. Off the Alps, the Pyrenees, and the Massif Central plunge rivers with stupendous force to give France more natural hydropower potential than any other country in Europe. And what France lacks at home, she can find abroad, for her overseas empire, since the dwindling of the British, has come to be the largest colonial domain in the world. France is the envy of every nation in Europe, and the Germans, with that nostalgia of Germans for things which are not theirs, recite as a definition of happiness: "Fröhlich wie der liebe Gott in Frankreich"—"Happy as Dear God in France."

In this country, moreover, live forty-two million people of extraordinary skill, application and tradition. Second only to the British, they have provided the ideas and thinking of the modern world. The energy of the nucleus was first explored in France, the power of rushing water was first converted to electric energy in the French Alps, the medicine of the twentieth century descends from its beginning in French science. The genius of French art cramps the brush of every painter in the world today in imitation. French taste in clothes robes the women of all the world. Lastly, the individual courage of Frenchmen is unquestioned. Even now after the slaughters of the Second World War one cannot stand on the wild, torn slopes of Verdun before the great mausoleum of dead men's bones without imagination boggling at French bravery.

Yet all this adds up to nothing. Courage, brilliance, skill compounded with riches, land and sun come to fruit today in France, as for a generation, in bitterness, poverty and a paralysis of withering indecision.

This is the big mystery. But the mystery is a mosaic of lesser mysteries. Why, in a France that produces all its own foods, does butter cost twice as much as it does in a Britain that lives in a siege economy hauling butter from thousands of miles overseas? Why could the France of 1939 furnish 115 divisions to do battle whereas France today had such difficulty in furnishing an undermanned twelve? How have the Germans been able to erect out of defeat a solid, enduring government that has lasted four

full years, while the victorious French have had so many changes
of leadership in that period that not one Frenchman in a hundred can count the number of his Cabinets? Why should the
resources of a nation so great provide an average working wage
for her citizens of fifteen to twenty dollars a week, while a pound
of meat costs 80 cents, a pair of baby's shoes four dollars, a
black market apartment rental $150 a month? And why, finally,
should the French, conscious of all these mysteries, after eight
years of the most determined wrestling with them, have only
succeeded in tangling things more than ever before?

The first quick impression at the surface of French politics
is confusion.

But this confusion is only a many-faceted reflection of one
central fact, the great and dominant fact of French life: that
Frenchmen are divided against each other. All political alliances
in France are formed against something, not for something.
French life does not divide; it splinters. Frenchmen splinter on
whether to revile the Church or to cherish it, on whether to
socialize the country further or desocialize it. The rich hate the
poor, the poor hate the rich; the rich are divided between Catholic and non-Catholic; the poor are divided between Communist
and non-Communist; the city workers are divided against the
country peasants; and in every village and neighborhood, fresh
memory of wartime resistance and collaboration divides and
subdivides these groups all over again.

These divisions breed paralysis and paradox. The only way
so many disparate people can live together at all is to grant to
each group an almost total liberty and thus liberty is more complete, the air freer, the individual human more unfettered in
thought and expression—even if more perplexed—in France
than anywhere else in the Atlantic Basin. This liberty has its
counterface: a total social indifference to the hurts and aches
of anyone outside one's own individual circle. The suspicion,
mistrust and indifference of Frenchman to Frenchman breeds
a brilliant and dangerous courage in the individual man which,

167

when compounded in a community, breeds weakness and cowardice. It breeds lastly a crowning paradox: all Frenchmen passionately love France and hate all other Frenchmen for bemeaning her.

All these divisions come to their natural political negation in Paris, in that great Roman temple called the Palais Bourbon which holds the French National Assembly.

Within the National Assembly, 627 men make the laws of France, impose its taxes, conscript its soldiers and decide its role in the great world. The easiest way of understanding how the differences that bud in the villages harden into bitter fruit in this sovereign body is to sit in the gallery of its windowless chamber and look down at the deputies on their red plush benches spread in a half-moon about the speaker's rostrum. Only a long and dreary catalogue could list all the factions, splinters and purposes proclaimed in this hall. But if one disregards several dozen free-wheelers in factional coteries, along with the Arab deputies in their tarbooshes and flowing robes, and the Negro deputies sent by the dark peoples of Africa, then one finds that the people of France have succeeded in packaging their differences in six different party-packages of deputies of nearly equal size, each holding a few more or a few less than one hundred seats.

The six parties should be read from right to left. Farthest right are the Peasant-Independents, the repository of all French reaction, swayed chiefly by two men: the stubborn, parsimonious ex-village mayor, Antoine Pinay, and the bobbing acid little ex-Premier Paul Reynaud. Next, comes the Rally of the French People, the party created by General de Gaulle and now abandoned by him, a collection at once of some of the finest and most despicable men in French life. Following them come the Radical-Socialists, a party supported by businessmen and peasant smallholders. The Radical-Socialist is the great republican party of France's yesterday; it is studded with able names, yet is unable to decide whether to go forward or backward. The

MRP (Movement of Popular Republicans) which comes next, was born out of the wartime Resistance, is frankly Catholic in origin and inspiration, and is committed to a program of social reform at home and European Union abroad. Its two great leaders, Robert Schuman and Georges Bidault, have dominated French diplomacy and hence that of Europe since the war. The Socialist party to the left of it has become in France a middle class and white-collar worker party which, like its onetime rival, the Radicals, coasts on the memories of past greatness without a doctrine for the twentieth century; since the death of Léon Blum it has produced no great leader. Finally, there is the Communist party, a seamless phalanx of party hacks, rigid, inflexible, destructive, under a discipline that traces directly back to Moscow.

To produce any Cabinet at all in France, a majority can be formed in only one of two ways: either a national catastrophe must force divergent parties together, or their leaders must bargain out their various individual interests and claims to patronage until a weak compromise is reached, setting up a temporary partnership. Each new twist of events—a gust of inflation, the threat of war, the annual budget—wrecks the temporary compromise, destroys the voting partnership in the Assembly, and the Cabinet comes tumbling down. Since the Liberation of France in 1944, the National Assembly has chosen no less than twenty-two Cabinets from among its members.

It is unfortunate that Frenchmen and strangers alike are accustomed to judge France by what happens in the narrow arena of politics. It is unfortunate because if one's gaze is fixed on the forum of ants where French politicians debate their country's fate without ever coming to decision, the vitality and grandeur of all the unquenchable nonpolitical processes of France are ignored.

In their individual, everyday, working lives, the will of Frenchmen to live and flourish not only persists but pushes the nation forward, completely apart from politics. The politics of French

169

agricultural subsidy and protection may be ugly and squalid, but six times as many tractors now plough the fields of France as before the war. Politics ruined the French aviation industry for a year and a half after the war as the Communists colonized it with their agents, but individual French plane designers, who had been cut off from the development of world plane design for five years previous, survived both their isolation and the Communists to take off their drawing boards and put in cold production a new jet pursuit, the *Mystère,* which matches the best British and American engineering. French dressmakers who had thought that with the war the fashion center of the world had passed from Paris to Hollywood and New York found within three years after peace that they could again impose a New Look, an Old Look, a Wandering Waistline all around the world from Dallas to Delhi and Melbourne to Milwaukee.

Even in that most maligned of all areas of enterprise, the nationalized industries, the French, outside of politics, have achieved much that borders on the spectacular. To hear the politicians in the National Assembly shriek with indignation as they discover that the budget of the nationalized railways provides for the purchase of meat for the cats of lonesome night watchmen at level grade crossings, one might think that the French transport system was covered with cobwebs and directed by fools. Yet by 1952 the French railways system which had been shredded to bits by Allied bombing was the finest in Europe. It had repaired and rebuilt 2,250 blasted bridges, installed the finest roadbeds of the Continent, was running on meticulous time schedules, offered the cheapest transport in Europe per ton-mile or passenger-mile.

The talent, the devotion, the individual aspiration and courage of Frenchmen persist in the same measure as at any time in her history of greatness. And it is this that so tantalizes all men who deal with France or French affairs. If only the talent and the resources could be harnessed and directed to one end, then France would be in the Atlantic Alliance, as it was from 1914 to 1918, the cornerstone of all effective policy. If only the materials of greatness could be kindled, France might flame and warm all her citizens again with security and comfort.

So studying France, contrasting her frantic and ineffectual leadership with the promise of her people and resources, many foreigners have declared that France is suffering from nothing more serious than a case of nerves.

It is true that France is suffering from a case of nerves, but the truth ignores the fact that the nervous instability arises from certain cold, material situations which no magic wand or easy formula can erase.

The burdens of France are enormous. Someone has quipped that most of France's troubles rise from her effort to pay for three kinds of war at once—yesterday's, today's, and tomorrow's. She is paying for two wars of yesterday in pensions and annuities to veterans, widows, cripples, orphans, in the annual tax demands to rebuild the 1,500,000 homes either partially or completely destroyed by the Germans, in the physical effort to restore the public works blasted to bits as the liberating armies swept over French soil chasing Germans.

France is also paying for today's war in Indo-China. Indo-China has taken from France twice as much as the Marshall Plan gave her, more than has been spent to repair the last war's devastation. Indo-China costs not only money but men; it absorbs one out of two regular noncommissioned officers of her army, and two out of five of her commissioned officers. The war has continued for seven years. It has cost 35,000 men killed and missing, and 43,000 wounded; the number of officers killed or permanently disabled equals the number of graduates for the past four years from St. Cyr, the French West Point.

Finally, France is paying for tomorrow's war in her effort to brace the front in Europe. Alone among all the partners in the Atlantic Coalition, France has been singled out as the country spending more on arms—12.3 per cent of her national income —than NATO's economists thought wise.

These three burdens alone are enough to give France a task

of titanic proportions. But there are two others equally as heavy. One of these is the effort to master the Dollar Gap by modernizing or replacing the archaic, unproductive, generations-old factories and obsolescent processes of her industry. This has required a tremendous disgorging of national funds for investment in dams, railways, coal mines, assembly production. Since French private capital has stopped investing, these funds must be raised by taxation or inflation. The last of the five great burdens is to wring out of industry or the budget the great sums of money necessary to keep solvent the new social security system.

Over and over such lucid men as Pierre Mendes-France rise in the French Assembly to tell their colleagues that France must make a choice; they tell her she must choose where and how she will be strong, for she cannot be strong at once in Asia, in Africa and in Europe. Over and over again Frenchmen tell each other that they must strip one or another of the many burdens of their country, or else must decide who will bear the weight of the burdens or who will be stripped of his privileges in the community. But Frenchmen in their division, in village as in Parliament, cannot decide which of the many claims to the greatness they have inherited around the world must be abandoned, or how to finance these claims except by inflation which corrupts the nation.

All the seeming instability of France rises, finally, from her inability to reconcile herself with reality. The French are as capable in the simpler arts of government today as they have been in the past. In twenty thousand villages and towns across the country village councils order their local affairs judiciously and wisely, putting in new water systems or new swimming pools or new roads. In any major branch of French national government in Paris, brilliant civil servants direct affairs, analyze events, draw blueprints with exquisite intelligence. Even in their restless, rustling Cabinet reshuffles, a certain common sense prevails so that year after year the same men—René Pleven, Georges Bidault, Robert Schuman, René Mayer and

172

half a dozen others—shift their seats but preserve a common shared experience and knowledge of affairs.

Where France breaks down is at one point only: at the point where France must make new decisions. Each breakdown of a government, each new crisis inviting the formation of a new Cabinet is studied by foreign statesmen and Frenchmen alike in the hope that this is the moment when the French will decide how to organize their brilliance and resources and how to approach their burdens. Sometime, ultimately, everyone tells himself, the French must recapture their glories and importance, whether in the frame of a newer, greater Europe or in the frame of a smaller, nationalist France.

It might happen tomorrow or at the next crisis or in a few years. For eight years the world has been waiting for the French to make up their minds. And it still is.

THE STORY OF PIERRE BERTAUX

EACH MAN tells some essential part of the story of his country with the story of his life. A few, the great leaders, recite with their lives the story of command and decision that has shaped their fellow citizens' lot. Others tell how these distant decisions have pressed them unwillingly to do what they did, or endowed them, unconsciously, with good fortune. In between are the men who have both acted and been acted upon, who are the links between high politics and the impulses of their fellow citizens.

Pierre Bertaux is such a man. In his life is refracted all the story of France, that tortured country so rich in promise and human brilliance which so abuses its promise and wastes its talent.

I FIRST met Pierre on a sunny morning while waiting for a riot that never happened.

The Communists were clotted on one side of the Church of Alesia, drifting and milling in the mob-herd, their mass color flecked with the flower patterns of women's dresses and the white of shirt-sleeved men. The Gaullists crowded on the other side of the church, more sedately dressed in dark business suits, their women more soberly tailored than the Communist women. Between them stood the troop columns—blue uniformed city police, brown uniformed army Gardes Mobiles, helmeted men of the black Security Companies. The occasion was the renaming of Paris' ancient Porte d'Orleans. It was now to be called Porte Leclerc in honor of General Leclerc, Paris' wartime liberator, and General Charles de Gaulle had been invited to preside at the rededication. The Communists had sworn they would not permit him to do so and called a counterdemonstration a mile away up the avenue. Between Communists and Gaullists the government had flung a barrier of armed men, proclaiming that both its enemies should enjoy the right to gather in

174

the streets but that they must not fight and blood must not flow. It was all France in miniature there, straining with hating groups, knotted about the Church of Alesia.

My journalist's pass let me slip through the police cordon, and as I approached the radio command car at the base of the church, I noticed the presence of the Minister of Interior, Jules Moch. Moch, recognizing me, said something to the guards and they passed me into the command post.

Pierre was in the cluster of men about the Minister and we fell to talking. I did not catch his name but liked him. Tall for a Frenchman, wiry but not thin, he seemed to be one of the Minister's aides or secretaries, a type more at home in the cafés of St. Germain-des-Pres than here, at a command post, waiting for a riot to break.

No, there would be no trouble or bloodshed today, he said. It's the women who usually make trouble in a riot and look, the Communist women have their children with them. No, the Gaullists aren't ready to fight either. Besides, we have more troops, more manpower than either of the two mobs, and we have guns, too. It was a show of force in such overpowering quantity and quality that no one would be tempted to test it. (It turned out, of course, that Pierre was right—not a blow was struck, no blood was shed that day and never again did Gaullists and Communists try to face each other for a show-down in Paris' streets.)

Someone called Pierre away on an errand and before he took leave I said I'd like to talk to him again. He gave me his card and suggested I call at his office. I looked at it: "Pierre Bertaux" it said, "Directeur Général, Sûreté Nationale."

Bertaux. This was Bertaux, the cruel and brilliant Bertaux. Everyone in France knew the name, and most trembled at it. Men of the Left shuddered, for Bertaux was the man who had broken, in blood and violence, France's worst strikes since the war. Men of the Right froze. Bertaux, said the Right, was not malleable, you could not trust him, you could not deal with him. The card said it all—Pierre Bertaux, chief of the Sûreté

Nationale, director of France's secret police and her internal security forces.

I called on Bertaux at Sûreté headquarters a few weeks later in the summer of 1949, but it was some years later before I was to know him well. By then the politicians had put the knife to him and he had been removed from command of the Sûreté and left functionless as a "prefet hors cadre"—a general without command. We used to talk then in his house in the Paris suburbs. In summer we sat in the rambling garden where he was trying to make Virginia dogwood flower in Northern France. In winter we would sit in his study, a large comfortable room with a huge fireplace, lined with bookcases. The works of Lenin flanked Diderot's encyclopedias, primary textbooks that French children used seventy years ago sat next to volumes of German poetry. The latest copies of the *Reader's Digest* were jumbled with the current effluvia of the French intellectual Left. In the garden and study Pierre told me the story of his life and France.

"I am peasant in origin," he said when he began his story.

"All of France is forever peasant at its base and the word you must start with is the Roman word for peasant: 'paganus.' 'Paganus' is the best word, for it means both pagan and peasant.

"In France there are only cavaliers and peasants. The cavalier rides across history on his horse and the peasant bows his head and is silent. He waits. The cavalier makes his ruins and rides away, but the peasant lives in the ruins and makes them grow again.

"We tell our children in school of the Gauls, men with blond hair and blue eyes, we teach them about the Romans and the Franks. But these were the conquerors and the conquerors were never more than a handful on top and the base of France never changed: the base is dark, anarchic, peasant, Iberian. Every Frenchman has a little wall around him. He says, 'Nobody bosses me around,' or he says, 'Ni dieu, ni maitre'—'no god, no master.' The French dislike great men, they have known too many cavaliers. You look at this government today and you

say 'chaos' which is true. But it is what the French want, this
anarchy.

"So. My people were peasants from Lorraine, on the border
of Germany and the Low Countries. Wars always happen there.
My grandfather was captured by the Germans in the war of
1870 and they condemned him to death, just as I was captured
in this war and condemned. It's always the Germans—for my
grandfather, Les Prussiens, for my father, Les Boches, for us,
Les Fritz.

"My father was the one who broke from the peasants. He
grew up after the Franco-Prussian War and you must remember
how the Church and the state were quarreling then over who
should control the schools. When the state took the schools away
from the Church and made public schools, they opened a new
world to thousands of peasant boys, for the government wanted
thousands of young men to train as teachers. This was the way
my father went, but even after he became a professor he never
forgot the fields—every summer in vacation he would go back
to Lorraine and plough.

"I was born in 1907 when he was teaching at Lyons, but I
begin to remember things only later when he was teaching in
Rouen and the war broke out. I was seven years old then so I
can't remember much about that war. But I remember little
things—do you know that Rouen was the first town ever bombed
from the air? I was sleeping in my mother's room that night and
suddenly I woke up because the house was shaking and my
mother was holding me in her arms. I don't remember how the
war ended except that there was not the slightest trace of joy
or celebration when it was over. Only everyone saying, 'Enfin,
c'est fini.' "

From as early as Pierre Bertaux can remember, his parents
had planned for him a life of scholarship. They did not know
or care how a man enters any other profession; for them the
key to all honor was admission to the École Normale Supérieure.
All over France even today, thousands and thousands of families

consecrate their children to the École Normale Supérieure in the same way, and each year in France two or three youngsters still die of overwork and overstrain as they prepare for the bitterly competitive examinations that give entrance into this school for greatness.

Pierre Bertaux was one of the lucky few. At the age of eighteen, in 1926, he was admitted to the École Normale as the youngest member of his class and decided to become a Germanist. The choice seemed normal to Pierre, for his father, a border country man, had been a Germanist, too. Jakob Wassermann, Thomas Mann, and all the great men of German letters had stayed at the Bertaux home in Paris when Pierre was a boy. And Germany fascinated Pierre.

In 1927, when Pierre Bertaux was just nineteen, the École Normale sent him off to Germany to work on his thesis, and when Pierre arrived to enroll at Berlin University, he found he was the first French student at the University since the war. Berlin in the twenties, thrilled young Pierre. It is difficult now, he says, to look back at Germany across the Hitler years and remember the seductiveness of Berlin life in the late twenties, how like an island it sat in the middle of Europe, detached from the earth in a fever of brilliance.

As a literary scholar, Pierre selected for his thesis the life of Hölderlin, the purest of Germany's lyric poets, and back and forth, in the years that followed, Pierre traveled between Paris and Berlin. It was 1934 when Pierre made his last visit to Berlin to finish his thesis on Hölderlin, sneaking into the German capital without a visa, hiding in the nursery room of some friends, writing on a kitchen chair at the children's table beside the window. In the street below he could see the storm troopers marching by singing the "Horst Wessel Lied."

When Pierre returned to Paris in 1934, having finished his thesis, there were many openings for him, as there are for any young man who has finished his apprenticeship in ideas at the École Normale. He was chief assistant to a friend running for election to the Assembly in the Ardennes, and thus experienced a grass-roots apprenticeship in politics. He was summoned to direct the news broadcast of the French Radio and served there for a year. Next the Under-Secretary of State for North Africa appointed him as his personal emissary in Tunisia, and Pierre learned about empire. When Jean Zay, later to be shot by the Germans, became Minister of Education, Pierre was chosen as his chief executive officer. These were interesting jobs, but always, as every sentient man in Europe, Pierre had the sense of things rotting, life withering, war gathering. Europe was about to explode and Pierre did not want to be in Paris when the cavaliers trampled France again. Thus, in 1938, he requested a university appointment in the provinces, and in the fall of that year he was named Professor of German at the University of Toulouse, the pleasant city which is the intellectual, industrial and political center of southwestern France.

"The war," says Pierre, "came as I always dreamed it would. I had the reserve commission of a lieutenant and since I was a professor of German they sent me to the intelligence section in Gamelin's great headquarters at La-Fertè-sous-Jouarre.

"That was some headquarters we had at La-Fertè-sous-Jouarre. You know they say victory sterilizes the imagination—well, the French Army had been completely sterilized by the victory of 1918. Some of our agents got hold of the table of organization of a German panzer division and it came to me for analysis. You couldn't read it without realizing that the German panzers were not planned for infantry support but for deep break-throughs and penetrations of thirty or forty miles a day. But senior staff officers laughed at me. I was a reserve officer, they said, and naturally without the education of the War College in Paris. But if I had had the good fortune to have studied at the War College I would have learned there that no break-through can penetrate a front deeper in one day than half the width of the breach. This was an iron rule established in the 1914–1918 War and my theoretical analysis, they said, was nonsense.

179

THEODORE H. WHITE

"In April of 1940 they shifted me to Paris to direct the German broadcasts beamed at the enemy. So I was in Paris when the end came in June. There were thousands of Parisians who hoped, as I did, that the Army would stop and fight in Paris, for Paris is a wonderful place to fight. What if the Sainte Chapelle or Notre Dame were destroyed—*tant pis* for the ruins, but Paris would have been proud. By the night of June 11, the government had already left and my broadcasting section too. That night the city was full of movement, cars racing away loaded with baggage, smoke from burning papers, people drifting in the streets waiting for the Germans. Our German broadcast usually went out at midnight and when I came to the station the mechanics told me the radio net over France was fading. Radio Strasbourg was dead, Radio Lyons was dead, we were ordered to take Radio Paris off the air at midnight sharp. I asked them to give me fifteen minutes more; what difference does it make if Paris goes silent at midnight or midnight-fifteen, I asked. They agreed and so I sat down with the microphone in my hand and for fifteen minutes I talked to the Germans in the night, in German, about France. I told them not to think that just because they were coming to Paris tomorrow they would win. We are leaving, that's true, I said, but we're coming back and you can't hold it because all you have is force and force isn't enough. Other people have taken Paris and lost France, and even if you get to the Pyrenees don't think you've taken France, because France will last and we'll be back.

"The next morning a friend and I got into our Citroën before the Germans came into the city and we left, driving, driving south and west to Bordeaux and Toulouse and home. In Toulouse they demobilized me, my post at the University was waiting for me, and in the fall I was teaching again."

By November of 1940 Pierre Bertaux had joined the Resistance. It was an entirely natural act. Pierre had been visiting in the town of Clermont-Ferrand and had joined an old friend for a drink on the terrace of a café. As they talked, Pierre asked his

180

friend whether anybody still had contact left "over there," "over there" meaning London. His friend said, why yes, he had himself, and when Pierre journeyed back to Toulouse that night he, too, was in the Resistance. Pierre cannot remember now what made him do it; he supposes it was because of his children. He had one little year-old boy and there was soon to be another. No one knew how long the Occupation would last, but if it lasted long no man, he felt, could hope to shape his child's mind one way when all the power of the state would be shaping it another. The children would grow up little Fascists unless he did something. Therefore, if he could make France free again—good.

The first net that Pierre organized in Toulouse was ridiculously amateurish. It included a local filling-station operator, an Italian refugee who kept a bookstore and several young boys. They wrote letters in invisible ink; they tried to map German coastal fortifications; when they finally secured a radio they ranged the directional antenna on London using a map from a schoolboy's geography book. Not until the spring of 1941 did they make any real link with General de Gaulle in London and not until September of 1941 could they arrange for their first parachute drop.

Pierre was the first man of the Resistance arrested in Toulouse and in those days the Resistance carried no honor. It was only later, when the war was won, that everyone claimed a Resistance record and insisted that the Republic had never died in their hearts.

A French military court tried Pierre as a British spy. Pierre's lawyer wanted to make a flaming defense, confessing all, invoking the glory and honor of France and the nobility of Resistance. But Pierre insisted that such a defense, though it would give the lawyer an attentive audience for his eloquence, could only result in Pierre's own death. For if he confessed to the act, the Germans would force the French military court to execute him, but if he lied and denied all, then the court might make believe it believed the denial and let him off with a lighter sentence. The Military Advocate-General demanded that Pierre be shot forthwith as an example to all other traitors, but the court decided that a three-year jail sentence would do.

Pierre was transferred from prison to prison and life proved more enjoyable than he might have imagined, for, when he could keep from worrying about his wife and babies, he found that here was life with no decisions to make, no responsibility, nothing but quiet and time to think. The most pleasant of the camps was the last, a huge jail in Dordogne. Here Pierre learned about the world of the common criminal from the great jewel thief, Pierre-Paul Leca, never dreaming that this prison friendship would in later years cost him so dearly. Leca was a great patriot and had his own theory about France's defeat in 1940. "France was rotten," he used to say, "she never had a chance. The Army was rotten, the bourgeoisie was rotten, the people were rotten. It's only in the underworld that men know what true honor is; you in the legal world can sign papers and hold people to contracts. But we in the underworld can sign no papers. A man's word is his honor and I tell you even the underworld was rotten before the defeat. You couldn't even trust the word of a crook you trusted."

They sprung Pierre from jail at the end of 1943. By then the victory of the Allies was written clearly enough for all to see and the Resistance had become honorable. It was not too difficult, thus, for his wife Denise to arrange with the officials of Vichy a commutation of sentence which let Pierre slip out of jail in December and be spirited away quickly to the southwest, back to the old Toulouse region, where all through the winter and spring months he hid in the foothills of the Pyrenees.

By early 1944 the life of the Resistance had changed too. Pierre's own net had grown and expanded. It was now no longer a band of amateurs; it had arms; its codes were developed; its call signal from London was "the leopard's claws are varnished." All through the Toulouse region were other Resistance nets, both larger and smaller, of every shade of patriotism, ambition and political aspiration. The Germans, it was obvious, soon must lose. But who would replace them? And even as the groups prepared for the final insurrection, they stalked warily one about the other, maneuvering for position of leadership on the final day of freedom. Communist nets, Gaullist nets, independent nets all cooperated, but cooperated with a sense of mistrust and rivalry that grew each day as Liberation drew near.

All the Resistance nets of France were, by this time, loosely coordinated from Paris where the National Council of Resistance sat in clandestine session. It was Paris that decided that the insurrectionary Commissioner of the Republic for Toulouse would be Louis Finistere, as the Communists demanded, but that the Deputy Commissioner should be Pierre Bertaux, a nonpolitical Resistant.

Even down to the middle of August, when the battle was about to be joined, when the Allies had already taken the beaches and were plunging to Paris, the Resistance still lived to total secrecy. On the night of the twenty-first, a courier brought word to Pierre in the mountains that all chiefs of the regional Resistance nets were to meet that night in town. Even then Pierre could recognize only two or three names and faces among the fifteen men whom he met at the rendezvous. Each had a secret assignment and only Finistere, the Commissioner-designate, knew them all; only he had been informed that Bertaux was to be second in command. The meeting dissolved without setting a date for the insurrection, although each man knew that it could now be only a matter of days.

The Germans triggered the action. By late afternoon of the twenty-second, the movement of the Wehrmacht out of Southern France had begun to pour troops through Toulouse on foot, by truck, by train. By evening one could hear the occasional crack of a pistol shot, then later the whine of a sniper's rifle and during the night machine guns began to splatter in the city. Pierre rose before dawn, pocketed his pistol and made his way on foot to the insurrectionary headquarters. No sooner had he arrived than a courier rushed in saying, "Finistere is dead . . . they shot him . . . they shot him." The report, as it turned out later,

183

was untrue, for Finistere, though he had been shot by a German patrol in the night, was still alive. He had been gravely wounded, however, and on that morning of insurrection he lay in a coma in a Toulouse hospital. But for Pierre it was the same as if Finistere had been killed. No one but Finistere knew all the plans; no one but Finistere knew that Bertaux was Deputy Commissioner of the Republic. Yet now Finistere was in coma and speechless, Bertaux was the man upon whom the authority of the French Republic had been settled by order of Paris, and the sole instrument of his authority was the pistol heavy in his pocket.

For several hours Pierre wrestled with his problem, and then, finally, when it became clear that it was he alone who had to act, he set out to find two young men of his own net and do whatever had to be done.

"We set out on foot, all three of us," says Pierre, "to walk to the main square where the prefecture is. The prefecture is the seat of government; I was the authority of government. Across the street from the prefecture is the police headquarters, and there men crowded in the police courtyard, men in shirt sleeves, men without neckties, men unshaven, all in confusion. I walked into the courtyard very slowly. I was afraid. A man rushed over to me and I recognized him; he was one of the men I had met that other night at the meeting of insurrectionary leaders. He recognized me, too, and said his group was waiting for orders. What should they do?

" 'Finistere is shot. He's in the hospital. Unconscious,' I said. 'I am his deputy appointed by Paris. I am the Commissioner now.'

"He took it as simply as I said it.

" 'At your orders,' he replied, 'the police are with you. What do we do next?'

"I looked across the square at the prefecture and it seemed very logical so I said, 'Next, we take the prefecture.'

"The four of us walked across the square. Myself, with pistol

in pocket, my two boys and Sirinelli—that was his name, I
learned—the chief of the Resistance group in the police. I had
never been in a prefecture before, but I walked in and went
directly up the stairs. A pale little man was sitting behind the
desk in a big chair, the Vichy prefect. 'Who are you?' he asked
as I walked in.

" 'I am the Commissioner of the Republic,' I said. 'Who are
you?'

"He told me he was the prefect of Toulouse, that he was glad
to see someone with authority, and rushed around his desk to
shake my hand. I refused it; I walked around him behind his
desk and sat down in his chair. That chair was important, because from the moment I sat down behind that desk, I was
government. I questioned him: Waterworks operating? Electricity plant operating? How much food on hand in the city?
How much gasoline? When I finished, I told him that he was a
prisoner of the Republic, that he was to go home to his apartment and stay indoors until summoned. When he left it was
11:30 on Sunday morning, August 23, 1944, my two boys were
standing guard outside my office, and I was the Commissioner
of France in Toulouse.

"That morning! Outside my office, in my office, on the downstairs floors were the committees, the groups, the organizations,
the leaders who came and went, everybody asking everybody
else all day, 'Who are you?'

"The first person was a boy of twenty-three, his shirt open at
the collar, handsome, excited, wearing the bars of a colonel on
his shoulder. 'Who are you?' he said when he found me behind
the desk. I told him and he stood back in surprise. 'Who are
you?' I asked. He was Ravanel, I learned, the commander of
the Force Française de l'Intérieur for the region; he had just
made himself a colonel that morning and for him all the world
was romance; he was young, excited, happy and here was insurrection. Another self-made colonel came, a third colonel,
deputations came. Everyone was giving orders; German troops
were still in the city, the Vichy Security Corps was still armed

in their barracks, the FFI were racing around shooting, and the FTP, who had the most arms of all, were completely out of control. The FTP belonged to the Communists.

"From the countryside other Resistance groups were coming in. From north of us in the district of Lot, the Communist Resistance groups, supposed to be the toughest of all France, were coming down. From the east of us, in the Tarn, the tough Gaullists were moving in. Everybody had guns to shoot each other, and the Germans had guns too.

"We settled down that first night in Toulouse in chaos. I slept inside the prefect's office on the floor with my two boys. Eighty hostile Communist FTP's slept in the anteroom and corridors outside my office, bedded down on their mattresses and cots, supplied with their own food parcels for a long stay. I kept my pistol with me and before I locked the door I informed the people outside that if anybody tried to open the door that night, I would shoot.

"The next morning all the Resistance groups, big and little, FFI and FTP, Communist and non-Communist, gathered for a meeting in my office to decide what we should do. The Germans had left in the night, and the only enemy strength left was the Vichy Security Companies. It was a tense meeting. I had the title and authority from General de Gaulle, chief of the Provisional Government of France. But the FTP had most of the guns. They had expected Finistere, the Communists' choice, to be the Commissioner; now it was me.

"We argued; they insisted that the Vichy Companies be disarmed, I insisted I did not want to provoke bloodshed by fighting in the streets. There were many people in the room, knots of people waving hands at each other, yelling. One man in a corner caught my eye. I said to him quietly, 'Who are you?' He told me he was Colonel Georges of the Lot department. I knew Colonel Georges by name for he commanded the Communist FTP's up there, mostly coal miners, and tough. But I felt I could trust him. 'Will you bring your men down to the city to keep order at my command?' I asked. He said he would if Ravanel's armed

FFI would agree peacefully that Georges' FTP should come in with their guns. Then, and only then, I felt I could compromise. I agreed to use my authority as the Commissioner of the Republic to disarm and disband the Vichy Companies, if the Communists would place Colonel Georges and his Communist FTP's under my direct orders. To this they agreed.

"Neither Georges nor I gained any credit for this. Later when Paris was again the capital, the government criticized me for disarming Vichy's Security Troops without their permission. And the Communists threw Georges out of the party because he had cooperated with me in taking over. But we did it peacefully. Paris was far away and Toulouse was ripe for bloodletting; we had to make our own decisions. All over France that summer, men were making decisions by themselves, without Paris. There were eighteen regions of Liberation and everywhere, except in Marseille where the Communists got control, Frenchmen who knew nothing about politics took the government in their own hands and held it—a labor union leader here, a doctor there, a professional man somewhere else. The insurrection in Toulouse happened on August 20, 1944; it was weeks and months after that day before law came back."

The law crept back gradually because people needed it. But Paris control returned more slowly. It was December, 1945, before Toulouse felt the first tug of Paris restraint. A sugar riot had taken place in Toulouse that month and a great warehouse of sugar had been stormed. Pierre, as Commissioner, had sent first one company of police and then a second to stop the riot, but none had come back to report. At four in the morning, therefore, Pierre drove to the warehouse to see what had happened and found all quiet. In the entry of the warehouse, however, he found a large basket full of parcels of sugar. There were fifty-four parcels and on each was marked the name of one of the policemen sent to keep order; the rioters had shared the sugar with the police and each policeman had marked a package with his name before going back to the barracks to sleep. That

187

morning Pierre dismissed each of the fifty-four who had accepted sugar. And only two days later came the order from Paris: reinstate each of the fifty-four pending a full judicial investigation! Paris had begun to govern again; only on authority from Paris could a policeman five hundred miles away be fired.

Between the Liberation and the end of 1945, for a period of almost a year and a half, France had had no real national government—and France was governed better than for many a decade. For centuries before, Paris had drawn to itself all the brains, all the scholars, all the leadership of France until the beautiful capital city suffered from cerebral congestion, and the rest of France was a political desert.

Toulouse, where Pierre Bertaux governed as Commissioner of southwest France, now a regional capital in its own right, and it was with unbelievable excitement and enthusiasm that the people whom Pierre led proceeded to rule themselves. Before the war local criticism of affairs had to wait for a national election to voice itself in a new selection of deputies to be sent to Paris. Now, Pierre found, a critic could be silenced by putting him on a regional committee and telling him to cure what was bothering him.

Such a system could not last long, for by the end of 1945 the men of political talent and ambition were gathering again in Paris. It was clear they could not govern France from Paris as before, if regional governments divided authority with central government everywhere beyond Paris' suburban borders. The ministers of government disliked the regional governments, the civil services disliked them, and the Communists disliked them most of all because it was the regional governments like that of Toulouse which had frustrated their bid for power in the hot days of insurrection and revolt. The Communists, in France as elsewhere, wanted a strong central government. In those days the Communists sat in the French Cabinet and their bitterness was unrelenting.

In the spring of 1946, therefore, on March 31, the national government in Paris announced the dissolution of all regional governments, and with that the war, for Pierre, had come to an end. He no longer had an apartment to live in; he was in debt; he was tired. With Denise and his children, Pierre rented a cottage in the Pyrennes and went off for a long summer of rest in the mountains until fall should come and he might return to Toulouse to teach German.

It was only a few weeks before the school session resumed when Pierre found that, after all, he was not to become a school-teacher again. During the early days of the Resistance a stranger fleeing from the Germans had come south to the Toulouse region and fallen in with Pierre's net, where he worked on a plan for the sabotage of the electric power net in the Toulouse area. That man was Jules Moch, and now, in after-war politics, Moch was suddenly a Socialist chief of great importance. In September of 1946 Moch had just been named Minister of Public Works and Reconstruction and, casting about for an executive officer, he recalled Bertaux.

The Ministry of Public Works was an exciting ministry in those days, for its job was the repair of all war devastation in France. So successfully did the Ministry go about its tasks that Jules Moch rose to be a power in national politics, and Pierre Bertaux, too, came to general attention. But 1947 was the year that the Communists were expelled from the French government and by late summer it was clear that there would be trouble in the streets of France. Recalling Pierre's clash with the Communists in Toulouse, it was suggested therefore that he be sent south to be the prefect, or chief authority, of the great hub city of Lyons.

"Lyons in 1947," says Pierre, "was wider open, better pene-trated, more skilfully organized by the Communists than was Prague in the coup of 1948. The Communists controlled the city council, occupied the strategic buildings, dominated the streets and terrorized the police. When they wanted, they could throw 10,000 rioters in the city's streets. A few months before I came, in May of 1947, a housewives' demonstration had broken out,

189

spontaneously, over bread rationing and the Communists had capped it. This was their standard technique. The Communists shepherded the housewives to the prefecture, broke in, seized the prefect bodily and carried him to the radio station. Then, over the government radio, he was forced to declare that all outstanding bread tickets were cancelled and bread was free of the ration.

"I replaced that prefect in September and the Communists gave me my first riot two weeks after I arrived with Denise and the children. This one started at the Labor Exchange and they marched to storm the prefecture. We deployed the guards with machine guns and when the rioters charged us, gave them tear gas. When they had fled, I called in their leaders. They came to me with their eyes streaming tears and I told them how things would be run in Lyons:

" 'Here on my desk is a telephone,' I said. 'On your desk at the Labor Exchange there is a telephone too. You can see me any time you want just by lifting the telephone and asking. But you did not ask to see me, you came by force. I live in this house with my wife and children and you have no right to storm in. If I came with police troops to storm the Labor Exchange you would have the right to resist. So I resist when you try to force me. Next time, remember the telephone.'

"It took several months to reorganize the police, but by the time the Communists pulled the general strike in December of 1947 we were in control of the streets again. Lyons is the bottleneck for the rail and road traffic between North and South France; if the Communists could block it, they could cut France in two, which is what they tried to do. They pulled the switches on the railroads; they covered the highways with four-pronged spikes to puncture tires; they tried to seize the telephone exchange. But we survived. The trains were a bit slow, but they ran; the expresses never stopped; the roads were kept clear; they damaged the telephone exchange, but we repaired it very quickly; we held the radio station and twice a day I could broadcast to the people that all was well. We outlasted them.

"The last big strike was the coal strike in 1948—a bloody one. In our district the Communists tried to flood the mines by stopping the pumps, so our troops went down, 2,500 feet underground, to pull the Communists one by one away from the pumps and save the mines from flooding. We managed it without killing, and when the mines were cleared and the pumps going again, the strike was over.

"By this time, the situation had changed in Paris, too. Moch had become Minister of the Interior and responsible for all the internal security of France—he wanted me back in Paris, to be chief of the Sûreté Nationale.

"So there I was in 1949, police chief of all France. It amuses me even now to think of it—me, a professor, a man of the Left —police chief! My friends would say to me, 'You, you Pierre, a Normalien. . . . You Pierre, on the side of the cops!'

"Yes, yes, it was a paradox. But I said, good, let's take it that way. If this is where history has brought me, so be it—Bertaux and the cops, me and the *flics*. For it's time to peel away the old legends and look at society as it really is. There's nothing more important for the world than that democracy should work. To work, it must understand its problems and learn how to dispose of the toxins in the system. Police keep democracy healthy by cleaning out crooks and traffic violators, by catching thugs and arsonists, but also they must deal with totalitarians and terrorists. We talk so much about democracy being made of liberty and equality. But liberty and equality rest on two things we ignore— the police and the judges. The police must be efficient to preserve liberty; the judges must be incorruptible and honest."

When Pierre arrived in Paris to take command of the French Sûreté Nationale at the beginning of 1949, the great strikes of 1947 and 1948 were fading into history, but the organized power of the Communists and their threat to the state remained almost as great as ever. The party's peak postwar membership of 1,000,000 had shrunk to 800,000, but it still controlled the greatest labor unions of the nation, its largest chain of daily newspapers, important arms caches and a band of zealots ready to kill and die for it. To oppose the party as chief of France's internal security, Pierre had the secret services of the Sûreté Nationale, a corps of 55,000 to 60,000 police and security guards, scattered over the country.

Bertaux's basic principle was a simple one: that if a government is prepared to act, to use the terrible force of state intelligently and skilfully, there is no reason why any democracy should be destroyed by such a coup as destroyed the Czech Republic in Prague in 1948. In Lyons, fighting the riots of 1947, Bertaux had learned certain tactics of civil strife and order which he now proceeded to generalize over France. Of these the most important was the rule never to permit police power to be dispersed.

French security, today, is organized roughly on these Bertaux principles. The first line of defense is, of course, the civil police in any city; the ultimate reserve of defense is the Army. But between these two lines is the emergency reserve of the Companies of Republican Security, some 12,000 men organized in 60 companies of 200 each. These companies were organized by Bertaux to live, as they live now, in a state of constant mobilization. Linked all across France by their own short-wave radio net, equipped with helicopters and ground-to-air communication for observation, they are so organized that if any local situation threatens to get beyond local police control, the Companies of Republican Security can be concentrated anywhere in overwhelming numbers within twenty-four hours—long before the Army could get out of bed. They are used only as a last resort, never committed until the last minute when the Communists have shown their hand. When they are used, with their radios, tear gas, helmets, riot guns and superior communications, they act with lightning speed and crushing force.

Force, however, is not enough in dealing with Communists, and here Pierre disagrees with the American approach to the problem. "You Americans are wrong," he says, "in trying to force your methods on our country. You believe in theology, in sorcery, in witchcraft. For you, communism is a sin, and the Communists are witches to be burned. The fact is they are very simple, ordinary people. For fifteen years the Communists have pulled to their ranks the finest young people of France. France is such an old country, so much is rotten in it, and the Communist argument is so simple—to make an omelet, they say, you must smash eggs." To cope with Communists, says Bertaux, you need not only force but understanding. Communists can be stopped by force, but they can be wiped out only by understanding.

For two busy years Pierre Bertaux sat in contemplation of the Communists from the chambers of the French secret service. During those years, as normal life returned, as the Marshall Plan began to revive French economy and industry, as the French police tightened their security measures, the Communist party began that long steady decline in organized power which continued until the end of 1952, when the French economy became stagnant and Communist influence revived. Year by year the circulation of their newspapers fell, their union membership dropped off, their party dues-payers declined until now they are estimated to be less than 400,000. It was not the Communists who ultimately trapped Bertaux, but France's internal politics. In France, the Ministry of the Interior is the police ministry, and in France, as in America, police are the easiest means of paying cheap political favors in government. In his first year as chief of French security, Bertaux could and did fire between 2,000 and 3,000 officers, high and low, for graft, incompetence and unreliability. But by 1950 the peril had abated and Jules Moch, Bertaux's political sponsor, had moved from the Ministry of the Interior to the Ministry of Defense.

Bertaux's enemies within and without the police bureaucracy were by this time numerous. In one of his earliest investigations, Bertaux had muckraked to light a scandal which revealed some of France's most eminent generals as the source of leakage of information to the Communist rebels in Indo-China. The scandal had been hushed but it had left an area of bitterness. Many men waited for a tool to present itself with which to strike at him.

They had not long to wait. Suddenly, on June 30, 1950, after Moch had left the Ministry of the Interior, an embittered ex-police official whom Bertaux had dismissed for incompetence and expense-account padding presented to the government a bizarre and fantastic set of documents. In them he charged that Pierre Bertaux, chief of the Sûreté Nationale, rather than being a paragon of virtue, not only was an intimate friend of gangsters, but had used his Resistance net in Toulouse to cover a vast enterprise of racketeering. Moreover, said the official, Bertaux had personally masterminded the fabulous theft of the jewels of the Aga Khan's wife, the Begum, on the Riviera in 1949. Only one shred of information supported all these charges: the great jewel robbery had been organized by none other than Pierre-Paul Leca, Bertaux's wartime prison mate in Dordogne, and in chasing Leca, the police had discovered in Leca's personal notebook the name and telephone number of Pierre Bertaux.

The new Minister of Interior pooh-poohed the charges. The highest court of France set up a judiciary investigation of the accusations. It was no surprise to anyone when a year and a half later the court returned its findings clearing Bertaux of all charges and allegations. Bertaux, in his term of office, had broken up more gangster bands of France's highly organized underworld than any previous Director of the Sûreté. But before then, in the spring of 1951, it had been suggested to Pierre that while the charges were being investigated it were best that he leave the Sûreté to other direction.

For two years, thereafter, Pierre lived in honored semiretirement as a "prefet hors cadre," the equivalent status of general without command, until the final explosion. Then, in the summer of 1953, when the jewel robbers were at last brought to trial in the sunny, peaceful little town of Aix-en-Provence, the blow was struck. The disgruntled police official whom Pierre had fired three years before was brought to the stand and startled the court with the old charges, amplified and embroidered with new detail. By the rules of French law, such court testimony is immune from libel action so long as the witness can claim that he sincerely believes his charges to be true.

Taking the stand in rebuttal, Bertaux swept the court with the eloquence and precision of his refutation. Then, closing his testimony, he described Leca in terms of a Corsican Robin Hood, explaining that Leca, though not an honest man, was, by the underworld code of the prison where he and Bertaux had been friends, a "man of honor." Never, since their days in jail, said Bertaux, had Leca sought a special favor or asked aught of Pierre as Chief of the Sûreté.

It was the phrase "man of honor" that brought Bertaux low. For, in the eyes of the current Minister of the Interior, the phrase "man of honor" implied inferential tolerance of underworld activities. No man of such high rank as Bertaux, said the Minister, could permit himself such words in public. Specifically repudiating the accusations made against Bertaux, the Minister suspended him in rank for use of the phrase and L'Affaire Bertaux became, as it is today, unfinished business in the politics of the French Republic.

For Pierre, the future is obscure as he considers whether the coming years should be spent in government, politics, journalism, or scholarship.

"I think mostly about politics these days," said Pierre recently, "for politics is where medicine was three hundred years ago—a science of guesswork and hope. Yet somehow there must be a way of making politics exact, of linking thought and action, of finding an analysis so that freedom remains healthy and works. For France cannot go on this way, it must change or it will perish. It would be silly to sit by idle, not ever trying to save freedom, nor even thinking about saving it."

GERMANY: SPRING IN THE RUINS

I HAD been driving down from the north all morning, and as I returned through the traffic toward the Rhine bridge, I noticed a tall, frail figure posed in the melancholy appeal of the hitchhiker. I slowed for him and when he scarmbled in beside me I noticed that he was not frail but gaunt, a husky man fallen on evil days, and thin. He carried a knapsack on his back and clung to a battered brown suitcase over which he had folded an old oilskin raincoat.

"Where are you going?" I asked him in German.

He replied that he was going to Bad Godesberg and then, shifting easily to English, he said, "What is your language? English or French, I speak both."

I said I was an American and asked him how he came to speak two foreign languages. He replied that he was a schoolteacher who taught English, French and history. That is, he went on, I used to be a schoolteacher before the war and now, next week, I will be a schoolteacher again.

"Oh?" I asked, inviting him to go on.

"Yes," he said, "in Bad Godesberg there is a job waiting for me and next week I begin." He was looking forward to it, he said, because all during the war he had been an officer at the front and then, after the war, they had classed him as a Nazi. Because he was a Nazi he had been barred from teaching for three and a half years, but now, finally, he had been denazified and cleared for teaching again. The school he was going to in Bad Godesberg was a school for teen-age boys, where he would teach history.

By the time he had told all this we were across the bridge. Weaving through the traffic of Cologne to the autobahn that would take us south to Bonn and Bad Godesberg, I tried to draw him out of his quiet. "What will you teach your boys in history class about the last thirty years?" I asked. "You'll never

196

see me again and I don't even know your name. Tell me how you'll teach your boys about Hitler."

He began his story haltingly, and then gradually as he forgot me he began not to talk but to recite, staring straight ahead through the windshield down the ribboning autobahn.

It had all begun after the First World War when the German people did not know they were defeated. The leaders of the German people did not understand their own nation, they did not know how much the people loved their country. Best of the leaders was Stresemann, but the Allies would not listen to him; Stresemann tried to explain that the German people needed dignity, but the Allies would not recognize Germany as a great nation and they gave him nothing. Stresemann had no force so the Allies would not listen to him.

Then came Hitler. He made Germans proud again. He ended unemployment, everyone had jobs. He built the great autobahns which will last forever. He had force and the Allies of the First World War gave him what he wanted because he was not, like Stresemann, a beggar. Hitler's greatest success came at Munich, when everything Germany wanted Hitler got for her peacefully.

The German people thought Hitler wanted peace down to the last week before the war, and when the war came they were a little bit frightened because they did not want it. But when Hitler broke through the Maginot line, then every German knew he was a genius.

After that came the mistakes.

"I would not hide these mistakes from the boys," said the teacher peering out the window into space. "I would make them learn carefully the three great mistakes of Hitler.

"First, Hitler should have been content with the great peaceful agreement of Munich.

"Second, Hitler made the mistake of fighting a two-front war. This every German schoolboy must learn, Germany must never, never fight a war on two fronts.

"But the third mistake is the one for which Germans can never forgive Hitler. This was to keep fighting the war for months after he knew he had lost. Thus, he let the armies of the enemy enter on the soil of Germany and they destroyed it; many thousands of Germans died in those last few months just because Hitler wished to preserve his power for only a few more months.

"From the peace, also, we have learned much," he continued to his class of imaginary disciples. "We see that in one thing Hitler was right, that the world respects force. We find now the Russians are just as savage as Hitler, and the Americans and English are savage too, only they are savage in a gentlemanly way. They did not fight us to make democracy, but because they wanted to crush Germany forever. Germany must find a new way, only we do not yet know what the way is."

He had timed his story well, for we had come now to Bonn and there a turning separated my road from his. He got out, hitching his knapsack on his back, lifting the brown suitcase from the back seat. I stopped him as he got out, for I prickled with a desire to hear more.

"Tell me," I said, "won't you teach your boys about the concentration camps and what happened in them?"

He turned back to me. "Yes, I will teach them that too. I will teach them that the concentration camps were a shame to Germany. But you must remember that what is told about them is a great exaggeration. You Americans saw the camps at the end of the war and then, for several weeks, the food supply in Germany had broken down. The men in charge of the camps did not know where to find food for the prisoners, so naturally when you found them they said they were starving and the pictures you took of them made them look very thin.

"Auf Wiedersehen," he said, extending his hand to me in thanks for the ride, and then was gone.

It was February of 1949 when I bade good-by to my schoolteacher, and neither he nor I then knew that while we were talking Germany was passing the unnoticed midway mark between her total defeat and that volcanic Renaissance which is the hinge on which the story of after-war Europe turns.

The day I met the schoolteacher was just three and one-half years from that week in 1945 when, having ravaged the continent of Europe from end to end, having murdered some ten million people in the helplessness of captivity, having by combat cost the lives of another ten million people in the summertime of their manhood, having sacked the thrift, enterprise and creation of generations, the German state disappeared from existence. Disappearing, it had left a people shorn not only of strength but of pride and will.

For three and a half years, until the season in which I met my schoolteacher, winter hung over the land. It was a tiny land, as it remains today, for mighty Germany has been shrunk by disaster to a morsel smaller than half of France. In those Winter Years one-third of what was left was wrenched away by the Russians and riveted into another civilization. What remained of Germany was not even a land; it was a conglomerate of three separate zones stuffed with 48,000,000 people wedged together in a sliver of territory so narrow that a five-hour ride across its waist could take you from border to border.

The forlorn people who lived in the ruins in those Winter Years could feel little beyond hunger. Germans put thinking out of their minds and concentrated on simple things: how to find a job, and how to work. For only by working could one find food, find clothes, find a roof. Even work was difficult. Men accepted work no matter what the wages or hours, for if they did not there were millions more hungry, empty men waiting for the chance.

In this Germany of the Winter Years there were no politics. There was no time to think of politics, and all Germans had been numbered by politics anyway. Millions of them had filled out all the questions in the Allied "Fragebogen" and had been measured for the stain of Nazism, classified into Category I, II, III, or IV of participation in crime. They were through with politics of any kind. There was only work and individual survival.

The Winter Years continued, leaden month dragging after leaden month, until the events of 1948 and 1949, when slowly, almost unnoticeably, things began to change. It was as if the silent addition of the effort of millions of hard-working, desperate toilers had come to fruit just in that moment when international politics split open to give Germany the opportunity which only a few months before seemed inconceivable. The Russians and the West tore their alliance irreparably apart and the Berlin blockade burst; simultaneously the Western Allies decided to return their Germany to German management. Spring broke through the frost in hundreds of thousands of little lives; ex-Nazi schoolteachers, like my hitchhiker, found themselves denazified and free to teach again; in the Ruhr workers struck and refused to dismantle the installations that were their promise of livelihood; Germans gathered in groups, protested Allied acts. Politics were about to begin.

Four years later, by the summer of 1953, Germany could look out into a world in which she was not only the strongest and healthiest of European states, but in which she was courted by her conquerors who competed for her favors. Four years later the greatest German problem was whether or not to accept the invitation of the Western world to sit in its councils in dignity and equality.

THE STORY OF WILLI SCHLIEKER

GERMANY is energy.

Sitting on the flat plains between the great powers of the West and the Slav powers of the East, the Germans have learned always to respond to pressure on them with counter-thrust. To preserve their lives, they know they must work harder and think quicker than most of their neighbors. The energy that the pressures of history generate in Germany, the talent and ability that guide these energies, have been Europe's greatest problems for a century—now fructifying Europe, now blasting her to bits.

Fundamentally, this unquenchable energy is human beings. One of these is Willi Schlieker, who, in his brief life, can tell almost as much of Germany as a history book. Nobody knows which way Willi is going, not even Willi. But wherever he is going, he is moving fast.

WE crossed a half-ruined, tumble-down courtyard, and tramped heavily up a flight of creaking, wooden stairs. My companion, a young and leanly-intelligent British political officer, muttered something in German to a man at the door and off he went down the passageway. He came back and told us to follow him—down the shabby, musty little corridor until we came to a door which opened on a room, even darker and mustier than the corridor. A man stood waiting for us there.

"Hello, Schlieker," said my companion, "here's someone who wants to talk to you." He made the introductions briefly and Willi Schlieker asked us to sit down. They chatted for several minutes together and while they talked I looked at Schlieker.

He was a man of medium height and stout dimensions. Once, it was obvious, this man must have been as solidly muscled as a tank, but now the chunkiness had softened to a pudding of flesh that bulged and rumpled his suit with odd stretchings and creases.

201

The British officer finished quickly with Schlieker. In that crisp, sure voice of a Briton in command, he said, "Well, Willi, I've got to go now. Mr. White has a lot of questions to ask. See if you can help him out."

It was not quite a command; in January of 1949 the days of commanding Germans in defeat were over. Yet it was the voice of Occupation. This was Düsseldorf, capital of British Occupation of the Ruhr; I was American; and Willi Schlieker was German. He was permitted to resent the voice of Occupation, but his resentment must be hushed.

The resentment was easy to understand. For three and a half years, ever since the collapse of Hitler's Germany, people had been questioning Schlieker. The Russians had arrested him, questioned him, then used him. The Americans had hunted him down and questioned him to exhaustion. The British had arrested him, questioned him, used him and cast him out. The French had arrested him, questioned him, released him. He was tired of questioners.

I wanted to ask Schlieker questions too, and for the same reasons. Willi Schlieker had been the boy-genius of Hitler's war machine, the young man who, at the age of twenty-eight, had been the boss of all the Ruhr's iron and steel production, the coordinator and master of the Third Reich's war arsenal. Willi knew more about the Ruhr than anyone else, and since the Ruhr was the very essence of German power, people came to him for answers. I, too, wanted to know about the Ruhr.

Schlieker loved to talk about the Ruhr, as he still does, and as he began to talk, my questions stopped, for he knew more answers than I had questions to ask. He is one of those men enchanted by the making of things, by the organization of affairs, and the enchantment is drenched in a deeper, peculiarly German intoxication with the romance of steel-making.

For two hours he talked to me about the Ruhr. He told its history. He explained how the kinked and twisting pipe mains and the interlacing wires bind it together in a single indivisible unit, coke oven feeding gas to mill, which feeds low caloric gas back to coke ovens, which feed other gases to drop forges; he described how the gases of the blast furnaces feed power stations which fork electricity back into steels mills which pour their own surplus current back into the one great power grid that binds the Ruhr together. He described the men who run the Ruhr, the managerial dominance of a tribe of slashed-cheek engineers and businessmen whose closed and primitive aristocracy and pride no upheaval yet had been able to erase. And Schlieker declared that the Ruhr was indestructible because heavy industry once founded can never be dismantled.

That meeting was almost five years ago. I asked Willi Schlieker many questions that day and have been asking him questions on every visit to Germany, year after year since then. Now, however, I no longer visit Willi in Breitestrasse. Today when I come to the Ruhr I must telephone through a chain of secretaries to reach him, and Willi has many other places to meet me. He may send his car—a shiny, compact Mercedes-Benz convertible —to find me, and occasionally, in the evening, we roar across the Rhine bridge up to Meererbusch. Meererbusch is the swank suburb of the Ruhr, where Germany's captains of industry nest at night much as Detroit's captains of industry do at Grosse Pointe. In Meererbusch, Willi's new home, Am Willer, shines like a jewel.

Willi once more is a man of mark in Germany, and he is sought out by many men as a fountain of wisdom, which he is. It was not always so, for when I first met him Willi was a man of mystery, reported by British Political Intelligence in charge of Occupation as "possibly the most dangerous man in the Ruhr." In those days, if you were well-connected, one or two high American officials might let you glance fleetingly at the five-page, single-spaced report on Willi which the British had made available to them among other secret biographies of dangerous men in the Ruhr. The intelligence report is a dull account of Willi's birth, family and employment record; it compresses his dazzling rise to eminence in Hitler's Third Reich into twenty lines, reports his turbulent postwar career, gives his Nazi party number and gives the pro and con of whether Willi was a true Nazi or a nominal Nazi.

Willi, however, is far from dull. His story, as I have heard him tell it and watched it happen, is Germany's story—of energy, ability and will, as irrepressible as the force of life.

Willi's father had been a Socialist. But disillusionment with socialism had made him bitter. When the Kaiser's Empire perished and the milky-thin social-democracy of the Weimar Republic replaced it, Willi's father withdrew totally into himself.

Willi's mother, a Catholic, died when he was six years old, just when his father was growing bitter. On her deathbed she pleaded with his father that he let Willi be baptized in the Catholic faith and his father agreed that when the boy was twenty-one he might choose his own faith. Thus Willi was left to grow up almost by himself in the grim, dreary blocks of waterfront tenements of Hamburg in the topsy-turvy twenties. Only one man lifted Willi's imagination from the Hamburg slums—his schoolteacher, a man named Albrecht, a rare person who loved students. Willi, who was to be Hitler's chief armorer, was a teen-age pacifist; he wrote one long essay on the sinking of the *Squalus* in America, furious that men should die in preparation for war. He wrote another longer schoolboy essay on the Kellog Peace Pact, using everything he could find to prove why war must be outlawed. Willi might have gone on to be a paunchy, beer-drinking, very gemütlich Herr Doktor Professor at some German university had it not been for the depression.

But in 1930, when Willi was only sixteen, his father lost his job and, because he had to live on unemployment relief, shipped Willi off to work as a farmer's helper.

When Willi came back to Hamburg in 1931, he found a job as apprentice to an export-import house at five dollars a week. He was nineteen when that job ended, crumbling in the depression, and he, too, was on unemployment relief. It was then that Willi made contact with the Nazis. "I was hungry, I was nothing but hungry," he now explains. So it was quite natural, says Willi, that when a friend found him a job as a typist working for the Nazi S.S. in Hamburg, he took it.

Though Willi's life flowed imperceptibly but inevitably into the stream of Nazi change, it was, like most German lives, accompanied by the tiny halts and hesitations provoked by conscience and discretion. Willi lost his job with the S.S. within a year for voicing too freely his opinion about the Röhm purge. He found another as a clerk in the Nazi supreme court in Munich and lost that one too, under circumstances that were later to help him greatly. Willi purloined some papers in a case under consideration by the Nazi court because the principals involved were old Hamburg friends of his, and the major charge was that one of the members of the family had married a Jewess. For this Willi was fired, but the Hamburg merchant family was grateful and helped Willi find another job. This job carried him to Haiti as a salesman. Willi lived in the West Indies for three years, first selling German cement and machinery there, then working for a British firm and learning American and British business practice.

When Willi came back to Germany in 1938, he gaped at how much it had changed. Germany had been hungry when he left. The Hamburg he remembered was one where every open place, every square was cluttered with shuffling, rotting unemployed. By 1938, when Willi came home, Germany had a new face. No one loitered in streets or parks; Germany worked. Across the countryside the new autobahns stretched in long ribbons of concrete; in the cities at night the factories gleamed working the night shift. Hamburg was thriving and Willi's friends, even the ones he remembered as most democratic and anti-Nazi, all said it was good, it was going well.

Willi had left Germany a boy, but came back a man, full of vigor and self-confidence. Without any difficulty he succeeded in snatching for himself the Eastern European Agency of a large Ruhr steel exporting house. Within less than a year he had capped this coup with another: he sold the Rumanian government an entire new bridge across the Danube. But Willi had little time to savor his triumph for by then, back home, war had been declared and by 1940 the amount of steel that Germany could spare for commercial export had dwindled to nothing. So once again Willi came home.

By now even the big men of the Ruhr knew that Willi Schlieker was a hustler and he was hired by the biggest of all the Ruhr trusts, the Vereinigte Stahlwerke. His job in their raw materials department was to cut through the mad chaos of paper regulation and allocation quotas of the Hitler war effort and get them the raw ingredients they needed for steel-making.

Of all the major warring powers, the Germans, for the first three years of their war, were perhaps the most bizarrely inefficient in production control. During those years Hitler could afford to filter his dilettante commands down through echelon after echelon of ignorant Nazi zealots to the technicians of the Ruhr arsenal. By the end of 1941, however, as the cold terror of the Eastern Front suddenly made the war a mortal venture, the Nazi war machine began convulsively to tighten and men of talent began to move up. Among them was Willi Schlieker; by mid-1942 Willi had lone-wolfed raw materials for Vereinigte Stahlwerke so efficiently that the government drafted him as deputy coordinator of the tank production program. In Berlin, to which Willi now moved, he came to the attention of Albert Speer whom Hitler in the same year named boss of every phase of German industry and production. Speer, who now sits in the prison of Spandau serving a life sentence as a certified war criminal, was a genius untrammeled by conscience. He recognized Willi, then only twenty-eight, as a fellow genius, and by the beginning of 1943 he had chosen him to be chief of all iron and steel production, direction, allocation and control, not only for Germany, but for all occupied Europe. By then, too, Willi had decided to take out a Nazi party card—No. 8,759,242.

Willi was excited by the job. It was not money or comfort that made him happy, for his salary was only 20,000 marks a year ($7,500) and his home a one-room flat in Berlin. But Willi had power; every forge, every blast furnace, every rolling mill in continental Europe lay at his feet; under his offices on Friedrichstrasse, where he worked seven days a week, was a concrete bunker impenetrable by the heaviest bombs; in his bunker were teletype machines and long-distance lines that linked him to every headquarters of Nazi power and command; his eighty-odd staff members lived in barracks nearby to be close to him; the countries of Europe were provinces of his empire—Willi would fly to Italy once every fortnight just to currycomb the Italian steel industry and keep it on its toes.

The machine that Willi built, Allied investigators say, probably kept Germany in the war a full year after the date when she might otherwise have collapsed. The Speer Ministerium took over German production in early 1942 just as the bombings of the Ruhr began to hit hard. The measure of its success was that as the bombings grew, so did German production, until on the very eve of defeat when the rest of Germany had collapsed within, the Ruhr was producing more than ever before in the seven years of war.

Willi, looking backward, has told American bombing experts over and over again that they never succeeded in putting more than a minor dent in Germany's heavy steel production. What hurt was the bombing of the railways. The Ruhr, says Willi, ultimately collapsed not because of the bombing of plants, mills and mines but because the railway exits were so clogged with blowouts, breaks and burned-out locomotives that they could not carry away the 30,000 tons of finished goods the Ruhr produced every day. The Ruhr strangled finally, in January and February, 1945, on its own production.

Willi knew early, as early as the fall of 1943, that the war was lost, he says. Yet Willi stayed. He stayed to the end. In the twitching last days of his life, Hitler decided that he would fight to the end from the Redoubt of Bavaria and the Tyrol, and ordered Speer to draw up economic plans for resistance from the Redoubt. On April 21, Speer ordered Willi to fly south to organize arms production there. But Willi would not leave. He

207

telephoned Hitler's Führer-Bunker to say that he, Schlieker, chose to remain in Berlin to the end.

That night Willi was very nervous, for the end was near, and he decided to drive out to the estate of some friends in the country. He drove through the darkness that night, April 21, without lights, for the British were bombing Berlin as he left. Thus, in the dark, Willi smashed directly into an army truck and was hurled to the side of the road with half his ribs broken. All that night and the next day Willi lay by the side of the road, half-senseless, thinking, he now recalls, how curious it was to die by the side of the road at the age of thirty-one, being the biggest boss of labor in Europe and the largest steel producer in German history—a success story, ending in a gutter in defeat.

Some wayfarers found him the next day and delivered him to an army hospital. He was semiconscious when they carried him in and remembers through the haze that people examined his identity papers and an old doctor said, "This is Schlieker of the Speer Ministerium. Best let him die. Let's not make ourselves more guilty when the Russians come by having him here." But Willi is very tough and he would not die. Besides, one of the younger doctors did not agree with the older doctor and helped him to live. In eight days he was well enough so that his friends could come and carry him away to their country estate.

Willi's friends installed him in a large room on their first floor, on a clean white bed near a window that looked far out over the clear countryside. The next day at noon he saw a huge black puff of smoke rise quietly from the village, then another, then another. He lay helplessly in bed and watched the Russians shell the village, and knew that for him the war was over.

Out of the disaster Willi emerged with his skin and a new wife. For the friend at whose house Willi was staying took fright as the Russians came and fled like a rabbit before their advance. But his wife, Marga, would not leave Willi there helpless, and she refused to go. She stayed with Willi through the next two weeks of madness, and now she is his wife.

It took hours for the Russians to cross the field from the village to the house, and Willi was dragged down to the cellar where all the peasants of the village crowded for shelter. It was 4:30 in the morning when the Russian troops came into the cellar. They were combat troops and even Willi admits they were good; they looked at the huddled people and one of them said, "We are not like Goebbels and Hitler; you are safe." Then they went away. But after the combat troops came the clean-up troops, and by mid-morning Russians, drunk and sober, European and Asian, were pouring through. They did not hurt Willi, or Marga, who sat on the bed beside him, because, says Willi, Russians are madmen, but to the sick and the children they are respectful. It was not safe to stay, however, so the next day Willi, hobbling on two sticks and helped by Marga, made his way into the forest. They lived in the forest, sleeping on the ground for seven days. When they came back from the forest to the big house they had left, they found it empty, stripped of its furniture, silver, beds, clothes, everything. On foot and homeless, therefore, Willi and Marga set out for Berlin.

The Berlin they came to in May of 1945 was as quiet as death. People were hungry, says Willi, that was all, and they were dying of starvation. There was no cooking oil, no fat, no butter, no meat, only bread and the bread was always wet and soggy. Berlin lived a jungle life which reached its climax in the final days of June as the Russians stripped the city clean before the other Allied troops should enter and help occupy it. It was during these same days that the Russians arrested Willi and threw him into confinement along with several hundred other people, in a moist, stinking cellar where he would stay until they made up their minds what to do with him.

The Russians, it turned out, were like everyone else. Each of the conquering powers wanted to put its hands on Willi, to question him, to wring some punishment out of his body because he had made Hitler's machine tick and turn so efficiently. But as soon as people began to talk to Willi they found how useful he was, and instead of exacting vengeance they used him.

209

The Russians made him, very shortly, director of what was left of the industrial empire of the Flick concerns in their Eastern Zone, and Willi had an office again.

The Americans found Willi working for the Russians in Berlin, and sought him for cross-questioning. Experts writing the U. S. Strategic Bombing Survey wanted to talk to Willi more than anyone else except Speer. They were fascinated by him, but the United States could not use Willi's services because the American Zone of Occupation had much scenery but little industry. So they introduced him to the British, who governed the Ruhr and did need him. In February, 1946, therefore, Willi was flown out of Berlin to advise the British Occupation Authorities on the operation of the Ruhr which he had directed so well against them during the war.

Willi's job, said the cold employment description, was to "advise on production planning and office organization on the basis of his ministerial experience." Actually, as the British honestly declare, it was he who pulled the Ruhr together in 1946 as he had before in 1942 and 1943. The Ruhr in those days was leaderless, for all its top men had been arrested as Nazi collaborators. Soon, however, when the zeal of conquest slackened, they would all trickle back from denazification camps to look for plants to command once more, as they always had.

Willi had been a well-hated man in the Ruhr from the days of his first eminence when, as a young upstart, endowed with all the power of the Third Reich, he had pushed the proud barons of the German steel industry into the frame of priorities and controls that the Wehrmacht needed for production. He was even more hated by the Ruhr barons after he worked for the British, for he imposed on them a new set of statistical controls, directing their orders and allocations at British behest for reconstruction and repair. As the tight thongs of Occupation loosened, as the Ruhr slipped rapidly back to German leadership and German direction, Willi's days as boss were numbered.

By the beginning of 1947 Willi's many enemies had closed on him. A local German court which, Willi claims, was inspired by some of the oldest Nazis in the Ruhr, convicted him of being a Category III Nazi, a minor criminal offender. Therefore, by the rules of British Occupation, Willi had to be dropped from the employ of the occupying armies. For months he was a cause célèbre in the Ruhr as Germans and Britons discussed the precise shade of his guilt.

It took almost two years for Willi to clear himself of the Nazi charge—lean months in which he and Marga lived on 250 marks ($80) a month, while he tried to earn his way as an industrial advisor and small-time trader. It was not until the spring of 1948 (he had been arrested and released by the French, too, during this period of wandering) that Willi was unblocked as a Nazi, oddly enough on the appeal and intervention of some German Socialist chiefs who recognized his talent for pushing the tycoons of the Ruhr about. In July of 1948, in the very week that he was cleared, Willi began a new career. With 2,000 marks as capital (which his wife Marga had raised) he bought an old trading name, Otto R. Krause & Co., the Düsseldorf outlet of a famous East German firm of the same name, and set up his business. On July 29, 1948, he opened the doors on the shabby office at 1 Breitestrasse, a stone's throw from the gloomy mansion which housed the old German Steel Trust.

That was when I first met Willi, in Breitestrasse, smarting, aching, itching to show the world. The businessmen laughed at him for, said they, "You're smart when you're working for Speer with the whole state behind you, and you're smart when you're working for the British with the Occupation behind you. But can you be smart by yourself, Schlieker, can you make money?" Willi wanted to show them; he wanted to show the men he had bossed that he could do as well as they, boss or no boss. "I'm thirty-eight years old now," Willi told me several years after I first met him. "I am going to stay at this until I am forty, then I will see whether it's worth doing something else."

By then, though Willi's office was still in Breitestrasse, he was well on his way to being a rich man. His postwar career was securely launched.

211

Willi brought to the art of the businessman the perspectives he had first seen from the height of German war production. Willi knew better than any man not only how the Ruhr fitted into the broader life of all German industry, but how it was linked and meshed with the huge, outer patterns of world trade. He understood what moves governments as they prod and push industry to compliance with the graphs of office economists and the concepts of political necessity. Willi could sniff a turning wind in business or in politics and swing with it quickly, before any of the older, stodgy businessmen of the Ruhr knew the turn was approaching. His career since the war has been a series of successes in catching these turns, riding with the spin, dropping off just in time to catch the next one, always increasing his wealth, power and importance.

Willi's decision to settle for a meager livelihood as industrial advisor and small-time trader of iron and steel goods after his expulsion from the Occupation was underlain with a shrewd gamble: that the worthless paper marks which were then the currency of Occupied Germany someday must be wiped out, and that the thing to clutch was not money but hard goods. So Willi tried to accumulate not marks but stocks of steel and iron. When the currency was wiped out and the early speculators of postwar Germany were ruined, Willi sat secure on his little pile of undevaluable steel and iron bars and was already a junior capitalist when he opened his new venture. There was nothing illegal in what he had done; it was simply shrewd. Later the Bonn government tried to raid Willi's house when he was off on a trip, to find ways of clipping him for an extra income tax or to turn up some special skulduggery. They found nothing; Willi had cheated no one, he had simply outfoxed everyone.

Willi's enterprises now cover all Germany and are beginning to reach out around the world. From his handsome new office building he directs, in addition to his vast steel-trading firm, a recently launched housing development, a nationwide net of scrap iron collection, a new pipe and sheet steel mill he has built, plus another cold-rolled strip steel mill he has acquired. His new shipping line has interested him in Hamburg again, where he is, at this writing, preparing to open a shipbuilding concern.

Willi works hard, very hard these days, for work is his delight and the source of his enthusiasm. Also he has to work hard, for all his many firms, by now doing very big business, depend on his one-man direction. In 1951 the iron and steel trading corporation alone did a business of $70,000,000. Willi is not yet forty, the age he set as quitting age. He has come a long way from the broken boy-genius of 1945.

In the evening Willi muses a great deal. What he wanted five years ago, he told me once, was "a base where I can stand and they can't hurt me"; he has the base now. What he does next he does not know; in business, of course, there is a new vista opening up now that Germany may soon be permitted to make arms again, for Willi knows how to make arms better than any man in Germany. But beyond business Willi is unsure of what comes next. Politics, of course, is interesting. But Willi has not found any political party in new Germany he can join yet. "Everyone is waiting for a party," says Willi.

ENGLAND: NO FLAGS FOR THE REVOLUTION

ANY American who goes to England carries with him a baggage of memories that he has inherited from the centuries. Most of these memories are suffused with the soft green haze of country England from whence the ancestors of Americans came.

The city of London broods over this England, and beyond London are the stately country homes, the cottages of hewn stone, the villages of cobbled streets surrounded by fields of heavy wheat and pastures of fat sheep. This storybook impression of solid, nourishing roots in the earth is, however, entirely false and hides one of the most stubborn facts of Atlantic politics. England is a miracle of man's imagination, a daily denial of realities. No other country in the world is posed more delicately or perilously on the edge of perpetual disaster and collapse; no other country so completely unable to support its own weight supports so great a part of world politics and causes so many men to listen when she speaks.

The England that lives always ten paces from chaos and accepts this condition as normal is not the country England of our memory, but the city England of world politics. City England is not so much London, as the faceless towns that jostle one another across the central belt of the island. Of Great Britain's 50,-000,000 people, eighty per cent live in cities and towns, and these cities and towns are crowded one on another so densely that within their country, smaller than Oregon, live more people than live in all of the United States west of the Mississippi. A century of industrial history has clotted these cities together in patterns: the steel cities—Sheffield, Rotherham, Birmingham and their suburbs—black, smoking, gray, sulfurous, sprawled about the Trent; the wool cities about Leeds, wet, dismal, chilly in the Yorkshire winds; so cramped, say the local chroniclers, that a squirrel can run for twenty miles out of Leeds without de-

214

scending once from the rooftops; the cotton cities, on the western lip of the low hills of the Pennines—the red cities, of red brick, of red factories, of red cottages, that follow one another monotonously into the cotton capital of Manchester which dominates a larger urban agglomeration even than London.

All these cities were created by the world of yesterday, and today their citizens live in pawn to a world which tomorrow may leave them starving. Their island—the green fields and meadows to the contrary notwithstanding—cannot feed, clothe, fuel or make comfortable even half their number. All English politics start from this one fact. All Britain's movements in the world —diplomatic, military, economic, political—are magnetized by this fact.

The real England, city England, begins at the wharves. To feed the British, half of all Britain's food—12 million tons— must be unloaded at the wharves each year; to fuel her industry and move her trucks and automobiles, 28 million tons of oil must be piped out of the tankers; to clothe her people, 750,000 tons of wool and cotton must arrive. To pay for this food, oil and clothing, the British must export what the skill of their fingers can produce. No nation in the world is balanced more precariously on the shifting tides of trade. In war the best of Britain's blood and courage, and in peace all her skills of diplomacy and persuasion are devoted to keeping the trade lanes open.

The genius of the British is a difficult thing to transcribe in the cold accounting of power politics. Yet to ignore how greatly it multiplies the British is as impossible as to ignore how the perverse genius of the French divides and reduces them. For genius in England is not only the individual flowering of the human mind, but also the coming together of these minds and personalities in a kinship of community which no other free state can approach. This kinship is the source of Britain's fundamental political strength—the ability to hang together and respond to leadership in such a way that the whole effort of the nation may be devoted to one end, without terror, without police.

The political genius of the English starts mysteriously far down in the roots of everyday life. British differences with each other may be generations old, frozen on cleavages of class and status. But they know, almost instinctively, how to gather for common effort. They have somehow acquired a trust in each other that rises tier by tier to their trust in government and willingness to let it lead.

The ultimate expression of this attitude to politics is the House of Commons. Grave differences separate Government and Opposition by far more than the width of the green carpeting between their respective benches. But these are differences without hatred, differences that permit the men on one set of benches to laugh in a deep, rolling, healthy laughter at the quip of a speaker on the opposite benches that touches them to the quick; that permit a man to nod quiet assent to some particularly clever thrust of the opposition without being regarded as a traitor by his fellows.

Though men dispute in the British Parliament, they do not hate; they are gathered in a common cause, which is not to destroy but to provide leadership.

Leadership in England carries with it a special reverence, even when it is unimaginably dull or open to the most human criticism.

In no other country could a failing giant present himself day after day before the eyes of an alert opposition and come out so unscathed in personal dignity. No one comments on how different is the Churchill who leads the Tories of today from the Churchill of 1940. Sir Winston of today is an old man, his great brilliance is more and more obscured by the darkness of age and the forgetfulness of senility. Only rarely does a newspaper, public speech or gossip column in Britain fasten on these human frailties. Political debate still limits itself to the quality and purpose of leadership offered, attacking Churchill's deeds or applauding the rare greatness of his utterances.

It is these people, then, with these problems in an unstable world, under this kind of leadership, who have accomplished in the seven years since the war one of the most amazing and deep-flowing revolutions in the history of man.

The place where this revolution has come to focus is called Whitehall.

Whitehall is the name of a broad thoroughfare which runs flanking the Thames for little more than half a mile, from Trafalgar Square to Westminster Abbey. Whitehall, in history, means the government of England.

You will see very little of the revolution as you walk, for the revolution has been almost invisible to the naked eye—it has borne no flags down its pavings, shed no blood, scorched no buildings. The blackened five-story buildings that follow one another down the northern side of the avenue are black not with flame but with the peaceful soot of old age. Admiralty, Treasury, Board of Trade, Colonial Office, Home Office, Foreign Office and War Office follow one another in the same order they did half a century ago, halting before the same smooth and verdant lawn of grass that separates them from those abiding twin witnesses of change, the Houses of Parliament and the Abbey where the sovereigns of Britain are crowned.

It is as difficult to detect the change inside the buildings of Whitehall as from outside; Gladstone and Disraeli would feel quite at home in the offices and easy chairs within. Little, indeed, has changed at Whitehall except its meaning and function. In the past fifteen years Whitehall has gathered in its thousands of dingy cubicles, in tighter space, more power over the lives of ordinary human beings than has the government of any other free country. Whitehall controls not only the safety, the politics, the education of the nation as all governments do, but nearly the sum totality of the citizen's life—almost everything, indeed, but his thoughts. Whitehall decides how much meat, how much butter, how much sugar, how much cheese every English family shall eat each week. Whitehall insures against unemployment and sickness, provides orange juice for babies, wigs for bald pates. Whitehall can dictate to any owner of real estate in Eng-

land how he shall use his land or deprive him of his land; Whitehall sits in judgment on every farmer as he farms his acres, fixes
the price of his produce and, if it chooses, can turn the farmer
off his acres for farming them badly. Whitehall controls and
channels all investment in England and says where and how it
shall be made. Whitehall owns and controls all the mines, all the
railways, the total power system of the island nation; it buys
most of its foods and much of its metals abroad; it sets its credit,
determines or allots its scarce materials, effectively decides how
many new homes shall be built each year. Whitehall determines
whether or not Englishmen may go abroad for vacation, and
how much they may spend when they go.

No other capital in the tradition of democracy has ever held
so much power over the lives of so many individuals; no other
nation has ever voted into one single dot on the map of one
city such immense control and stayed free. Yet the English have.

The measure of any revolution's power is how quickly and
deeply it is accepted by the people whom it has disturbed. By
this measure the revolution in Britain has passed its tests, for
in the past two years it has been reluctantly confirmed and accepted by the party that fought it, tooth and nail, for the fifty
years of this half-century. Two years of Tory government, after
six years of Labour adventure, have proven that no power now
exists in the island nation which can undo or reverse what has
been accomplished by the quiet revolutionaries of the postwar
years.

THE STORY OF JOE CURRY

THE BRITISH are quiet people.

The roads of history are strewn with the wreckage of great states and empires which have underestimated the British by trying to read Britain's strength and purpose from the surface pomp, the mumbled eloquence, the archaic glitter. Underneath are millions of sturdy, determined, undemonstrative men and women like Joe Curry, solid as rock and just as enduring.

Joe Curry does not look like a revolutionary. Certainly, he does not think of himself as such. But he and millions of men like him in mill, mine and factory have pushed England along through these living decades to the transformation that has made her a land more changed from her past, yet more true to that past, than any other in Europe.

WHEN Joe Curry came back to Doncaster in the fall of 1952, a large sunlit office awaited him in the gray, ivy-covered mansion of the National Coal Board. As he walked down its corridors people said, "Good morning, sir," and drew back shyly, in deference and respect.

This Doncaster had quite a different feel from the Doncaster that Joe Curry had first seen twenty-five years ago when he stepped out of the dark station, tired, hungry, threadbare and with but two coins jingling in his pocket. The car, the office, the waiting secretaries were only part of it; the deputies and administrative assistants attendant on Joe's instructions were only a detail in the change. The change, if it could be traced, was somewhere in the hearts and lives of 140,000 coal miners in the pits and villages of England's largest coal field, who were watching, waiting, to see what Joe Curry, the new chief of labor relations, was going to do. Some there were, but only a few, who could remember Joe in the pits with them, stripped to the waist. But the others, the young men who knew Joe Curry only by reputation—as the new man sent up from London to take over labor relations in England's richest and most turbulent coal field. "Poacher turned gamekeeper" they called him, thinking back to Joe's old days as a labor leader, summing up the suspicions and dreams that mingle in the gathering places where British workers talk about the revolution they have won.

Joe Curry knows both the suspicion and the dream, for he grew up with the suspicion and he bled and fought for the dream.

It had all seemed much simpler that cold December day twenty-five years ago when Joe and his brother, drifting, blacklisted miners, climbed off the coach from the North Country with three shillings and sixpence each in their pockets to look for work in the Yorkshire coal field. Behind him Joe had left father, mother, two brothers, three sisters and a girl eager to marry him. Behind, also, Joe had left the memory of the General Strike, with its blood and hunger, and all the bitterness of the ancient exhausted mines of Durham. In those days the hate and the dream went hand in hand. The hate was generations old in every miner's heart and included all the masters and all their ways; the masters were the men who let you work only when they wanted to, who paid you as little as they could when you did work, and then dumped you when they didn't need you longer. The dream was fresher and simpler: to take the mines away from the masters, nationalize them, socialize them.

The dream has been won now, for the mines are nationalized. But the suspicion remains. And the dream can only work when the suspicion goes. It is Joe Curry's job to see what he can do about the suspicion. He knows it well.

The suspicion was already old in the home of every miner when Joe Curry was a boy, growing up in the village of High Spen fifty years ago. High Spen is too small to appear on any map, but lies just fifteen miles off from Durham City. Men like to say that when Joe Curry was a boy, just after the turn of the century, such villages were flush and prosperous, as English miners dug 250,000,000 tons of coal each year and shipped nearly 100,000,000 tons out of that to a world that had not yet learned how to use oil.

Joe remembers High Spen differently. One gaunt, black skeleton of a colliery rose in the heart of the village, another rose on the village fringe, and everyone worked at coal. One muddy street ran down the center of High Spen, flanked by rows of two-roomed, hewn-stone cottages where the miners lived. When Joe was born into a family of four children, two rooms housed them all; not until much later, when the family had grown to fifteen, including nine children, a brother-in-law, a cousin and two orphan boarders, did it expand into the luxury of four rooms.

Englishmen had been digging at the coals of Durham almost two hundred years when, in 1903, Joe Curry was born. Joe's father worked in the mines, as *his* father had before him, and his father's father before that. Joe's father, like all the miners, was a man's man, which meant that he met the standards of High Spen—he worked hard, drank hard, gambled hard.

Joe's mother was a miner's woman with a miner's family of nine children to wash, cook and care for. "She wasn't an educated woman," Joe says of his mother, "but she was the finest woman in the world. A beautiful woman she was, dark, strong, attractive and well made. She never went beyond being a worker in any cause, but she was always reading, she was the first woman in High Spen to join the Woman Labour Party's Cooperative Society. 'Twas her sounded the tune of socialism in our family."

In High Spen, the union was religion. From the first time a lad went down as a pit boy, he was expected to pay his sixpence a week to the union, and he did. Weeks when there wasn't any food in a miner's house, a miner paid his dues. The years when Joe was growing from boy to man were the years after World War I when the unions of England were first feeling their strength. The men were coming home from France, spent with four years of trench war, full of new questions, wanting new things—more pay, better working conditions, more respect. And what they wanted of the coal industry, the coal industry could

221

not give. The coal mines of England were aging, as were all of England's old industries. They were unable to meet the harsher competition of the continental mines, unable to find an outlet for the millions of tons of coal once shipped overseas to a world that now dug its own coal or used oil.

The Curry brothers, like hundreds and thousands of miners all over England, felt change whispering in them. Even when they were youngsters kicking tin boxes around in the street, Joe and his older brothers would walk miles in the evening to hear Socialist speakers at miners' meetings. Long before they could vote Joe and his brothers were in politics, tramping from village to village, canvassing votes for Labour candidates for local or national office.

Joe's first strike came soon after the war. The pit Joe worked in belonged to the Priestman family and had never had a strike before. The Priestmans were fairly decent among the hard masters of the North Country; they took a good profit but gave their men consideration. Joe and the men went out in the summer of 1921, not in anger, but because striking was in the air. Joe cannot even remember now what the strike was about.

The strike lasted thirteen weeks and a "bloody, glorious time" it was, with nothing to do but look at the sun and the open sky.

By the time the strike was settled, Joe had another interest. He had met a girl named Ruby on a merry-go-round at a village fair. Ruby was the only daughter of a miner's family and she knew what a miner's life offered, but she loved Joe and was willing to wait until he could afford a home. "Don't get married, Joe," said some of the older union men. "It'll be a trap and you should get on with the union work." But Joe thought differently, and for the next five years he was quiet. He paid his dues and loyally attended the meetings, but his extra time went into courting Ruby, until the year of the General Strike.

No whistle blew the workers of High Spen awake on that May morning in 1926 when the General Strike began. No whistle blew in any coal town of the North, for there was no one at work even to blow the whistle. Everyone had known for weeks the strike was coming and that it was to be big, the biggest thing a generation of English workers had ever tried to do.

The long slump of English effort had finally, in 1926, brought England's mining industry face to face with ruin. The seams that had powered the world's first industry were old and hollowed out with generations of digging; their costs were high; overseas, men dug coal more efficiently. According to the masters there was only one way out: to cut the wages of the men and make them work longer hours. For months masters and unions had talked about the matter with no agreement and both sides hardened. Backing the masters was the Tory government. Backing the miners were other workers, millions of them. As the miners' unions stiffened against the wage cuts, the other unions of England, in their massive Trades-Union Congress, lined up in support, promising that if the miners had to go out, every other union in the country would back them up. General strike it would be, the long-awaited master stroke of organized labor.

In High Spen, as in every other working village and working district of the land, Councils of Action were set up—"Soviets" the Tories called them. These Councils of Action were, in fact, shadow governments with their own police forces organized in flying picket squads that patrolled the country's life and movement. Only those trucks which received Council of Action permits because they carried food and emergency supplies could pass the patrol picket squads on the North Country highways.

No strike in England had ever been so well prepared before as the General Strike of 1926. But the leaders, unaware of what they were doing, did not prepare for a revolution, and so they were doomed to lose. Looking back on the General Strike a quarter of a century later, the men who led it, now sober, middle-aged officials or parliamentarians, still do not know whether it was naive or brilliant. For a general strike that closes an entire country down must be centrally organized and centrally directed. Whoever directs it successfully dominates the country and is, in effect, its government. If a general strike is victorious

223

it is, therefore, a revolution. The General Strike of 1926 was called out over a wage dispute and revolution was far from the minds of its leaders.

There were two parts to the General Strike, first the violence and then the hunger.

The violence came everywhere as it did to the Currys in High Spen—swiftly, with short-lived sharpness. For Joe it was no more than a brutal clubbing over the head in a moment caught off guard. It happened this way: two of Joe's brothers had been assigned by the Council of Action to patrol the highways; they clashed with a potato truck cruising the road without a Council of Action pass. Joe's two brothers, along with a number of others, including Will Lawther, now Sir William Lawther, the President of the Miners' union, were caught by police and swiftly brought to trial at the town of Gateshead. On the day of the trial miners from all the neighboring villages, Joe among them, gathered, marching with lodge banners flying, their bands playing, their women and youngsters tailing along in the procession of protest. They invaded Gateshead, flooded its streets and courthouse square, demonstrated, and having made their protest, started away. Joe was at the head of his column on the way home when down at the rear he heard the sound of women screaming. He had just turned to run back when suddenly in front of him there was a policeman and before Joe could dodge, a club was swinging down on his head, and then blackout.

Joe came to on the couch of some people he never saw before or since. They were friendly to the strikers, as were all the North Country people. They had dragged him unconscious from the road. They bathed his head, bandaged him, warned him that the police were out over all the roads looking for rioters, that he must stay with them until dark. When dark came, the young man of the family took him out the back way, over the back fields, around the police blocks on the road.

That was the end of strike violence in the High Spen area, as it was almost everywhere in England. Once the government called force into being, the unions were bound to lose, for they had only two choices—either to seize the country by force or to crumble when the government struck back.

The General Strike was over in ten days, as union after union all over England went back to work, the labor leaders nursing their wounds and pondering the lessons they had learned. They had lost on the picket lines. But they had learned that government is an instrument of power that can be used either way. This learning was to flower only much later, after the Second World War, when Labour won the government and made its own peaceful revolution.

For the miners the hunger began when the violence ended; other unions went back to work when the General Strike collapsed, but the miners stayed out. In High Spen they stayed out six full months and would have stayed out for twenty years, says Joe, if it had been only a question of spirits. But it was a question of hunger. Finally, when winter came and it was cold, there was no other way but to admit the strike was over and they were beaten.

The morning the strike was over the men of the Curry family trooped to the pit with the other miners. At the entrance the manager met them. "No work for you here—today or forever," he said to every man in the Curry family. Joe, his brothers and his father waited for weeks in High Spen, not knowing what to do, and then they realized, as did thousands of other black-listed miners all over England during those months, that now they were men without jobs, or homes, or futures.

It was then that the Currys gave up the North Country altogether and came down to Yorkshire. The coal beds of south Yorkshire about Doncaster were new beds and in the nineteen-twenties they alone would hire new men. From Wales, from Scotland, from the North Country, hard men, black-listed men, desperate last-ditch strikers drifted down to Yorkshire to seek work there.

Yorkshire was good to the Currys and, their passion spent in the General Strike, they settled down quietly. Doncaster was not a coal-patch town like High Spen, but a vigorous, healthy York-shire working town with quick, alert politics. It was years before Joe was able to become part of it. But by 1937 the Labour party had put Joe up for the Sprotborough Parish Council, and a year later he had become its chairman. By this time, too, Joe had gone ahead in the union. Labour elected him to various public authorities, and by 1941 he sat on the West Riding Magistrates Court.

Joe Curry was thus a man of solid local substance, if not of fame, when the war came to England. War did not come to Don-caster as it came to London, Coventry, Birmingham and the burning, bleeding towns of the Midlands. Only occasionally did a night-raiding plane, aiming for Hull or Sheffield, disturb the peace of Doncaster. War came to Doncaster through the change in the pits around it. There it found Joe and took him out, and changed his life forever.

For the miners of England the war was an escape. As the na-tion's factories expanded and all England called for manpower, the men bound to miners' wages and miners' sunless jobs began one by one, and then in scores and thousands, to desert to the clean above-ground jobs that were offered everywhere. By 1942 the drift from the mines had become so serious that Mr. Church-ill's government established a Ministry of Fuel to control all the mines of England and the men who worked in them. Men were forbidden to leave the pits without permission; young men were drafted into them; the industry across the country was divided into regions, and in each region a panel of three men—one for labor, one for the masters, one for the mining engineers—con-trolled the pits. In Yorkshire the labor director was the secre-tary of the Yorkshire Miners' Union, W. E. Jones, and Jones in turn insisted that his deputy be young Joe Curry. One day Joe was in the pit, his hands grained with coal dust and his finger muscles cramped about a pickshaft, and the next he was in an office, with a telephone, a typewriter and a secretary.

The mines looked different from above ground, and Joe had to learn about mining in a new way. The problem was not only to keep the men from moving out, but also how to move them around so as to get the most out of those who stayed. The coal faces screamed for more men, and Joe's job was to gather men scattered in old, poor pits and bring them to work in richer, more bountiful pits. But miners are stubborn people who do not like to be moved, and though a war was going on in Europe, they felt their old private war with the masters had never ended. Stronger than ever now, while England screamed for coal, they settled old grudges with lightning strikes and quick stoppages. The Ministry needed men like Joe Curry to talk to the miners, men who knew that now was not the time to strike and knew how to say it in the words of miners.

By 1944, when Jones left the Ministry of Fuel, Joe Curry was ready to take his place as regional labor advisor; two years later, in October of 1946, Joe was ready to leave Yorkshire and go to London when summoned. In London, Labour was now the government, socialism was being made and the King had proclaimed in the ancient words "Le Roy Le Veult" that on New Year's Day of 1947, the mines would no longer belong to the masters but to the nation.

Generations of dreams had gone into socializing the mines of England, but the new Labour government that proclaimed the dream to be reality had neither plan nor program. Seven hundred thousand miners, one thousand pits, more than one billion dollars of invested capital had accumulated over the years in England's greatest industry, but no one had explored how they should be put together under socialism.

In May of 1946 the Labour government had set up an organizing committee of nine men, later to become Britain's National Coal Board, to plan the reorganization of the resources on which all England's welfare rests. But the Labour government was busy with many things at the moment. "Here are the mines," it said in effect to the committee. "Do what you want, tell us what you need, we'll finance your schemes, off you go."

Off they went, nine men and two secretaries in frantic travel

227

by coach and plane around England to survey their domain, while in London, almost overnight, staff and experts and secretaries began to gather.

Joe Curry arrived in the midst of this hubbub in London, in the fall of 1946. His title had great ring—deputy to the chief of the Coal Board's labor relations, who was Ebby Edwards, the grizzled old union chief. But, in fact, it was different. In all the vast, rambling confusion of the Coal Board, few people noticed that only two men in the whole new Socialist apparatus had ever been working miners down in the pits themselves—Ebby Edwards and Joe Curry. The mines, everyone assumed, belonged to the nation and that was enough to satisfy the miners. There were other more important problems on the Coal Board's mind than labor relations.

These other problems were indeed imposing and difficult; they had been generations in reaching their ugly complexity. For thirty years coal owners had let their mines run downhill. The best and easiest coal had been taken out; the workings were ancient, obsolete, inefficient; mechanization was twenty years behind time. It would be a fifteen- or twenty-year task, estimated the engineers, to reorganize and modernize the mines of England, but meanwhile coal had to be taken out at any cost and so, on with the work. First nationalization, then reorganization. Thus, on January 1, 1947, the miners who had gone down in private pits on the night shift at ten o'clock came up at six in the morning to check out of nationalized mines.

Within three weeks of Vesting Day the Coal Board learned where its real problem lay. Nature provided the occasion—a vast low-pressure area in the mid-Atlantic came swinging down over Scotland and England on January 23 of 1947, to lacerate England with her worst blizzard in living memory. As the snow piled up, life stilled. Trains stopped, factories stopped, electric power ran down. England had no reserves of coal for power; trains could not haul coal to the cities; miners could not even get through the snowdrifts from home to pit head. The thin margin on which English life had run for decades was worn through. There was no reserve coal, no energy. And there was no reserve coal because men did not want to dig it.

Mining depended on men, and surveying their enterprise, the directors of the Coal Board learned that there were less men mining coal in England than for over half a century.

From 1947 to this season and as far in the future as one can see, the problem of England's mines will be to find enough men, and once having found them, to do something to their spirit to make them want to stay and dig. Ten per cent more coal, say the economists of England, and England's basic trading problem would be solved, and that ten per cent could easily be taken out of the mines, without any new engineering, if only the miners wanted to take it. But something lingers in the miners' minds, bred out of generations of bitterness and cruelty that no edict of socialism can cure. Miners' pay packets are fat these days. Around Doncaster many of the white-collar workers are so envious of miners who earn twelve and fifteen pounds a week that they vote Tory out of jealousy. The pits offer clean showers, milk, good food, fresh opportunity. Houses are better; the rations of the miners have been the best in England for seven years. Yet the spark has not come. The miners work, to be sure, better than they did under the old system, but miners come to work when they want and are absent when they want. Lightning strikes still come and go.

For six years Joe Curry wrestled with the problem from his desk in London, a pit-head oracle for the white-collared engineers, technicians, administrators, economists and scientists of the Coal Board. "Joe," they would say, "what would the lads in the pit say to this?" Joe answered questions for six years before the Coal Board decided that he was needed more in Doncaster than anywhere else. Doncaster is the center of the Northeastern Division of England's Coal Board; here in this region more and better coal is dug than anywhere else in England; here in this region absenteeism is higher—one out of every five face-workers in the northeast region was absent every day in 1952. Here suspicion has lasted longest, for here in the Yorkshire beds thousands of men beaten and black-listed by the General Strike, drifted to find employment in the twenties. They still remember. Joe Curry knows, for he is one of the men that came that way.

As director of labor relations for the Northeastern Division of the Coal Board, Joe Curry is responsible for more big pits (114 in all) and more miners (140,000) than fall under the direction of any other division of the National Coal Board. He has come a long way from the days when he learned about socialism in his mother's kitchen at High Spen and since his head was cracked by the police of Gateshead. Dressed now in a neat, gray business suit, his sandy hair now less thick and bushy, his ridged eyebrows vigorously protruding over green-blue eyes, Joe is still cast in the miner's mold. He is short, chunky, possessed of the enormously powerful shoulders of a pit worker, walks with their sturdy, heavyfooted gait. Only Joe's ideas have changed; he has seen socialism made; now he wants to make it work. His problem now is not the masters, it is the men, his mates, and how to ignite them.

"You can't ignite them overnight," Joe says. "All you can do is plant the spark and fan it and let it smolder; it will smolder a long time before it burns up into a good, strong fire.

"It's true the men aren't working like they used to. God grant, they'll never have to do it again. Those days when you had to count every penny in the packet and when you lost a penny it was sorrow, those days are gone. Ah yes, in those days the miners were disciplined. They were disciplined by fear and hunger and economic compulsion.

"They call this work of mine personnel management. I hate the bloody term. That's one the efficiency experts brought in, it's not a human term. What's got to be done is not big things but a lot of little things. The average pit manager thinks of his problem as work attendance. But you've got to think of this thing as men. Nationalization is just a soulless machine to the men up to now.

"It's not the intentions that count with the men, it's their seeing that the Board thinks of them as human beings, their seeing that the industry listens to their ideas, that the Board offers redress for anything that goes wrong, and if there's a doubt, the benefit of the doubt goes to them. But you can't do it by appeals. For ten years England's been appealing to the miners—for Dunkirk, for the Middle East, for Italy, for the Invasion of France, for the Dollar Drive. They're tired of appeals and they say, 'Let t'buggers come down t'pit themselves and see how it is.'

"What they've got to do is feel that they're part of the mines, and they've got to be loyal to the mines. I speak, whether I like it or not, with a mind that's been broadened. I won't go back on anything I thought or said when I was twenty-four. There's been no change in my principles or intentions. I've just been forced to see things differently."

THE BASIN OF FREEDOM

I N POLITICS, those things we cannot see are always more important than those we can. This is because the most stubborn and important facts are ideas that exist in people's minds and not the way those ideas express themselves in guns and concrete, buildings and roads. This is why the biggest political fact in the Western world is the most difficult to describe.

The name of this idea is a dull alphabetical label, NATO, an addition of four initials which stand for the North Atlantic Treaty Organization.

Much of NATO is, to be sure, hard, tactile and visible, showing itself in a thousand faces. Just six miles outside of Paris the western speedway of St. Cloud throws off a dark ribbon of cobblestone that deposits you before a gray building called SHAPE, outside which snap the flags of fourteen nations in brilliant reds, golds, blues, whites, greens. This is a part of NATO. But NATO is also six noncoms in the early hours of the morning, monitoring spitting radios and clicking teletype machines in one room that centralizes a web of invisible lines that make the Atlantic Basin, from Washington to Istanbul, from the North Cape to Sicily, one net of instant communication. NATO is an airfield in northern France with the pilots of six nations scrambling into the air, flying French, British, American jets, listening to the command of an Englishman who takes orders from a Belgian who is under control of an American, and all getting up to combat height within two minutes to attack the imaginary enemy. It is also a white, hushed building on a hill above the Seine, carpeted with thick brown felt where permanent delegates of 14 nations, supported by an international staff of 150 economists, soldiers and diplomats sit in constant session, totting up the plans and powers of 365,000,000 people.

NATO is all this—but these are only its outer faces. At its heart NATO is an idea, an idea which has taken years to flesh out into the imposing fact of its present dominance in world politics. This idea is that somehow, in a way no one can quite describe, there grew up about the Atlantic Basin a civilization which is like no other in the world. In this civilization the individual man and liberty are the measure of political value. Together the people on both sides of this great ocean (less than a sixth of the population of the world) makes a community in the greatest sense, bred out of traditions, religions and technology that none of the other major civilizations of the world share. It has taken centuries of internecine bloodshed to make them realize that they are one. Not until now, when desperately challenged by other counterattacking civilizations, have the men who live around the Atlantic realized that they must band themselves together to defend, each people with its lives and substance, the lives and substance of every other member. It is an alliance like no other in history, for at its base lie no objectives of spoil or conquest. All the rest of the globe may be bargained over, but NATO itself was not erected for bargaining. It was erected for defense of the heartland of freedom and a heritage which only too late was realized to be common property. It is within NATO that America finally came of age in world affairs, pledging herself for the first time, by a revolutionary act of statesmanship, to sacrifice men and treasure not at her own will and timing but whenever any member of the Community of the Atlantic should be wantonly attacked.

Like all great ideas, the vision of NATO did not come full blown to a single prophet, contemplating the world in solitude from his mountain cave. It grew out of the minds of many men, burdened by responsibility in a period of trouble. But since its story must start with a time, a place and a name, the moment when the concept was first uttered can be fixed on the evening of December 16, 1947, in the flat of Ernest Bevin, England's Foreign Minister, at 22 Carlton Terrace, London.

The sixth meeting of the Council of Foreign Ministers had just ended. Mr. Molotov had that afternoon said NO in a hundred different ways to the ministers of the West, covered them with scorn and abuse for the last time, and left.

On that day, the great wartime alliance which destroyed fascism had finally come to its end. That evening, Ernest Bevin invited the Secretary of State of the United States, General George C. Marshall, to a quiet dinner at his home—just the two of them. Bevin had an idea. He had become convinced that at no time in the future could anybody look forward to a day when the Russians would deal in any other terms but force. He was convinced that there was only one way for the West to survive. The Western Powers had to work out some sort of union that would put Western Europe together and then back it with the military strength of the United States and Canada. Later, Bevin had the word-smiths of the Foreign Office work out the idea in a polished diplomatic phrase calling for such a "mobilization of energy and spiritual forces as would inspire confidence and energy within and respect elsewhere." But in the beginning it was a simple idea, the kind of idea that comes to a shrewd, hard man who has been organizing for thirty years of his life. Ernie was a union man; he had organized the biggest single labor union in the entire world in his lifetime. Now that he was Foreign Secretary, the way out of a problem still seemed to be in organization.

Marshall liked Bevin's idea. But, he warned Bevin, he was in no position to do anything about it right away. He had his hands full pushing the Marshall Plan through Congress; Congress was in no mood to offer blood and manpower at the same time as money. But go ahead with organizing Western Europe, Marshall said to Bevin, and we'll see what we can do to help in Washington. On the boat trip back to New York, Marshall tried the idea out on several of his aides as well as his Republican advisor, John Foster Dulles. By the time they got off the boat in New York, Dulles, too, thought the idea was a good one. By New Year's Day in Washington, at the seasonal rounds of eggnog and highballs, the idea had begun to circulate: the British had proposed a new kind of alliance, a complete break with American tradition, one whereby America pledged itself to a permanent military alliance guaranteeing the safety of the western half of the European peninsula. Most people at the State Department liked the idea—that is, if Congress could be persuaded to buy it.

Congress was in a particularly propitious mood early in 1948. The Republican oracle on foreign affairs, Senator Arthur Vandenberg, had just spent a year recasting the Monroe Doctrine to meet the needs of this century. At first glance there seemed little connection between the Monroe Doctrine and the proposed European Alliance. But, one hundred years before, the Monroe Doctrine had proclaimed America's intention of defending the entire Western Hemisphere against outside attack. The changing values of a postwar world had made it necessary to rephrase this lordly pronunciamento in more democratic form, and after several years of negotiation, by the end of 1947, Pan-American defense had been set up as a cooperative enterprise of equal partners. This was a substantial achievement, and Senator Vandenberg who, as the chairman of the Senate's Foreign Relations Committee, had largely captained it was rightly proud. Therefore, when Secretary of State Marshall explained Bevin's idea to Senator Vandenberg, Vandenberg replied immediately that it was a very good idea. It seemed a logical and complementary regional agreement to the one he had just masterminded with South America.

From the spring of 1948 down to the beginning of 1949, committees revolved about committees in Washington, as all the various layers of interest, American and global, were consulted. State met with Pentagon to elaborate a draft of the American point of view; Marshall and Lovett sat with Vandenberg and Connally; Vandenberg and Connally pushed an empowering resolution through the Senate; State Department negotiators met with the Ambassadors of Britain, Canada, France and the three Benelux countries to bridge the gap between European and American opinion. By January all the proper formulas had been correctly phrased, including the key formula which bound all powers to a declaration that:

235

". . . an armed attack against one or more of them . . . shall be considered an attack against them all, and consequently they agree that . . . each of them . . . will assist the Party or Parties so attacked by taking forthwith . . . such action as it deems necessary, including the use of armed force, to restore and maintain the security of the North Atlantic area."

With this, the definition of the Treaty was complete. There remained the final task of inviting in the flanking powers of the Atlantic Basin, those lesser states necessary to guard the long sea lanes between both halves of the Free World. Norway, Portugal, Iceland, Italy and Denmark all received invitations and accepted. Ireland and Sweden were invited but declined. Two years later, two more states were added, Greece and Turkey. But, on April 3, 1949, twelve nations signed the North Atlantic Treaty in Washington, and for the first time in history, the peoples of the Atlantic recognized their kinship and pledged themselves to its common defense.

The central problem of the Atlantic Alliance is a hard physical job that involves killing and fighting. It is to prevent, by force, the Russians from breaking through the political line drawn across Central Europe to occupy and annihilate the countries west of it. This is a problem of map and terrain, of men, of materials, and of spirit.

In 1948, while the Soviets were attempting to strangle Berlin by blockade and while the protocols of the North Atlantic Treaty were being worded in Washington, the shadow of Soviet force darkened all of Europe.

In those days, the Red Army in Central Europe might quite literally have marched out of its garrison dormitories in Germany and in a fortnight have taken all of Western Europe; it would have met no more than token resistance and very little of that. Russian fighting strength in Europe outweighed Western fighting strength by more than three to one. "All the Russians need to get to the Channel," observed one American military statesman at the time, "is shoes."

To counter this enemy strength, the West had but one weapon —the Strategic Air Force of the United States, laden with atomic bombs. During the years of crisis, the sole deterrent to Soviet impulse was the vast investment of free minds and free energy in the exploration of the deadliest of sciences. But already the Russians were at work creating their own Strategic Air Force and fashioning their own bombs.

This is now history. The politics of the entire world have changed because all this is like a remembered nightmare. Billions of dollars, hundreds of thousands of men, incalculable thought and effort have been invested by the Atlantic Community to create one new fact, among the half-dozen most important facts in the world today. This fact is as simple as it is important: in Central Europe today, the power balance has shifted from the Russians to the Atlantic forces.

The Atlantic armies are based and in position. No longer are the troops scattered in hopeless garrisons, helter-skelter through Germany. They are poised on a known line, with presited positions and deployment areas, with avenues of attack and withdrawal surveyed, engineered and zeroed in. The Atlantic armies are now, moreover, armed and equipped. Four million tons of American military supplies, plus 503 planes and 82 warships, had arrived in Europe between the beginning of NATO, in the spring of 1949, and January of 1953—enough to make of every army in Europe (except the English who equip their own soldiers) a fighting composite of American hardware and native flesh.

For five years, in Paris, the Communists have cast around for words to smear the effort of the Western world to organize itself. Each word has been chosen by the Communists in an effort to pack the phrase with contempt. Western Europe has been called *les pays colonisés*, or *les pays marshallisés*; the Communists' adversaries have been denounced as "the americanized press," or the "americanized governments"; the process has been deftly

237

ridiculed by calling it the "coca-colonization" of European civilization. Recently, at last, even the Communist press has been wrenched about to use a new word we have forced on it—the word "Atlantic." The policy of the West is now called "the Atlantic policy." This, in a fundamental sense, is a victory, for now communism recognizes a new field of force, a new, if primitive, source of political energy.

It would be pleasant if NATO could relax now with this force in being and its dearly purchased triumph of military equilibrium in Europe. Yet the Atlantic Community is only at the beginning of a new chapter, probably even more difficult than the old. For it is only by comparing NATO, the governing body of the Atlantic world, with its adversary, the government of the Communist world, that its weaknesses become apparent.

The Russian dictatorship possesses the matchless advantage of being able to deal with an entire family of problems at the same time. The same Politburo decision that ordains an army-in-being ordains the factories and resources to provision it; ordains swift turns between peace offensive and malevolence; balances arms, propaganda and resources, between Europe and the Orient, between politics and arms, with a silent shifting of gears. The Russians, globally and politically, are mechanically flexible.

What cramps the Atlantic Powers is lack of flexibility. When the Atlantic Community acts, fourteen different powers must agree at the same time to a common decision. When a startling peril confronts them as did the crises of 1948 and 1950, they can call into being the mighty array of military force that SHAPE now commands. But as each new problem arises in the long balancing contest between the Soviet and the Western world, a new travail must be endured as the fourteen nations attempt to strike a common attitude.

New problems tumble one upon the other in a cascade that no one is yet prepared to sort out. There are the geographical and political problems of Asia and Germany. The central position of power in the Atlantic is secure, but meanwhile in Asia, in Korea, in Indo-China, in Malaya, the Communists have mounted a vast flanking operation. There can be no strong and healthy France in Europe so long as she is mired and sickened by the infection of war in Indo-China.

Germany is as difficult a problem as Asia—great as have been its sins, as troublesome as its Occupation has been, its very health has contributed to the revival of Western power. Germany trembles half in, half out, of the Atlantic Community, unable to decide whether, ultimately, to throw its weight with the Community or stand aloof. The larger Atlantic Community cannot be healthy until its leaders have decided on a common attitude to Germany.

It is here, in political direction, that NATO is sadly wanting. Each nation cautiously shares in NATO a tiny portion of its secret intelligence on the Russians, and the ultimate product is a fuzzy blur in which the enemy's purposes are never seen clearly, and our own purpose frays as a result. British and Americans divide in NATO on the measure of the menace—is it over or is it increasing? Has it ceased to be military and become political, or is it an ever-growing military peril? Americans and French divide violently—do the Russians now plan to upset the economic world in which we live, precipitating us into cycles of depressions, while increasing their own welfare, comfort and economic capacity, as the French hold? Or is their purpose to build and build and build simply to erect a military machine that can crush freedom in one blow, as the Americans hold?

The Atlantic is an area in which people live who are set apart from all other peoples by one underlying concept—that of the free man, his body free from arbitrary arrest, free from arbitrary tax, free to speak, free to gather, free to think. It is this civilization, challenged from within and without, that its member states have joined to protect. Yet they have not even arrived at the definition of their common enemies. Are other peoples with different concepts of life enemies because they are different, or enemies because they are organized by Russian control for potential assault on our homes? Is China an enemy because she is Communist, or is she an enemy because she has become the instrument of Russian diplomacy? Is the civilization of the Middle East dangerous because it wishes to change its relation to the Atlantic Community, or because it flirts with Russian purpose? There are many communities in this coagulating world, only one of which is sworn to destroy Atlantic civilization, the Russian. There are the civilizations of the Moslems, of the Dark Africans, of the Chinese, of the Indians, of Southeast Asians. Toward each, in the new diplomacy of great communities of men, our civilization must have an attitude.

The Atlantic Community has, in short, won its first victory—it has created that field of power that finally inspires as Ernest Bevin once hoped "confidence . . . within and respect elsewhere." But this has been a negative victory—it has been a victory of defense, a triumph of resistance. Wars are not won by defense, nor are souls won by men who are simply "against." With the equilibrium of 1953, NATO has arrived only at the end of the beginning. It is what comes next that counts.

COMMUNISM—THE CHALLENGE

AMERICANS are so frightened by the evil in communism that they fail to see that the greatest danger is not the evil but the attraction in it.

The magic appeal in the Communist faith is simple. It is the belief that pure logic applied to human affairs is enough to change the world and cure it of all its human miseries. It is buttressed by the belief that the processes of history are governed by certain "scientific" laws, which automatically guarantee the triumph of communism when the situation is ripe, if only its protestants have the courage to strike and act.

This simple credo carries an almost irresistible attraction to two kinds of people everywhere in the world: first, to small coteries of able and ambitious young men hungry for the ecstasy of leadership, and, secondly, to larger masses of miserable ignorant people who have just begun to hope.

To both these schools of converts, the fatal flaw in the Communist faith is neither apparent nor important. This fatal flaw is embedded in the nature of human beings whenever they gather politically. Human beings tend to be illogical. The logic of which communism boasts is never certain, therefore, of success in any political operation unless simultaneously it imposes so rigid a discipline as to make ordinary people mere bodies in the sequence of their masters' planning. Any political organization which sets out to be totally logical thus calls for total discipline; total discipline inevitably requires police, and police bring terror.

But the weakness of communism lies less in the calculated immorality of terror than in the inevitable internal appetite of the discipline. The discipline feeds on itself; it shrinks the area of discussion and decision into ever narrower, ever tighter, ever more cramped circles. Fewer and fewer men have less and less access to the raw facts which are necessary for wise judgment.

To those who come to communism out of ambition or out of misguided intelligence, this flaw is not immediately apparent.

Each of this type of convert cherishes the illusion until too late that the ever-shrinking circle of discipline will leave him safe at its center of creative leadership, rather than crushed and tortured as discipline contracts about his own soft human body. To the second category of converts, those who come to it out of hunger and ignorance, this flaw in communism (even if it could be explained to them) seems unimportant. They have always been excluded from decision and control over their own lives. Communism promises thcm simply "more"; they are ready to believe.

Communist strength today is radiant with power at two levels. It possesses, in Russia, a base of physical force adorned with every instrument of compulsion and combat, still in flood tide of expansion. It possesses, also, the fire and power of a missionary faith, seducing men's minds everywhere with the simplicity of its logic.

Dimly, the Atlantic world has recognized the twofold nature of the challenge and has attempted to cope with both. It met the challenge of Russian power with magnificent audacity in time of danger and, by its great Alliance, threw up that shield of power which shelters it now in Europe.

It is here, now, in this chapter of history, that the new masters of Russia must be reviewing the Atlantic Alliance as it lies before them. It must be obvious to them, as it should be to us, that Russia has gone as far as force will carry her, and that where the pressure on us is still alive, it is carried primarily by the missionary faith, not by armies. If now the outer world can be lulled or soothed into stagnation, with all its social tumors and cancers still poisoning its health, the faith may succeed where the armies and intrigue failed. But it can do so only if the Atlantic world sits still—which is the problem all the free states of the great basin face, and America, its leader, most of all.

American purpose overseas is quite simple—to achieve peace and security. But in the chief area necessary for American security—Western Europe—the fiber of life has rotted and weakened so that it can resist the Communist message only with difficulty. Vaguely, and with some success, we have tried to help or compel the European governments to give their citizens those comforts and benefits of everyday life which Americans at home increasingly enjoy. But this has been done usually in terms of specifics—of financial advice, military equipment and training, engineering and techniques. Yet all these specifics and techniques are only the visible end-product of a generation of social upheaval and experiment in American life which, when it is not duplicated in Europe, causes our techniques to fall on barren ground.

Most Americans accept the faith of America wordlessly, for they live by it. America is, at its heart, the fluid society. It is the restless, unceasing desire of Americans that opportunity remain forever open, that society never lock in layers and classes of fixed privilege and fixed entry.

This has always been the faith of America. But this generation of Americans has kept its rendezvous with destiny by keeping opportunity open even through the growth, complexity and concentration of twentieth century science, industry and communications. Americans have done so in myriad interlocking experiments with their system—by the stabilization of the cycle that once made farming a gamble and not a way of life, by the powerful intrusion of labor unions on American production and society, by government fostering of research, science and education, by the spread of arts in every form all across their continental expanse; by the leveling brutality of their income tax, by the constant application of research and invention to the ever-expanding industrial capacity of a nation which has doubled its heft in thirty years, by new roads, new schools, new systems of social security. None of these changes were achieved easily; most were torn out of the country in fury and contention. But all have flowed from the inner spirit which holds that people must remain fluid, that society must remain open, that no group or groups must be able permanently to cling to yesterday's privileges in society because it profits by them and fears what comes

243

next. It is this faith in the opportunity of tomorrow, more than anything else, which has kept America from any infection of communism. And it is this faith, totally lacking in some countries of Europe or unable to express itself effectively in others, which we have been trying, without realizing, to spread in Europe by the injection of techniques and "expertise." A system that sometimes fails because the techniques are misunderstood.

The contrast between the Russian and American expansion in the modern world is one of direct opposites. The Russians sell an idea, above all their idea of the revolution and the logical state. Then, having penetrated with their idea, they follow to consolidate with their techniques, cold, brutal and bloody. But Americans bring their techniques first, the logistics and mechanics of their system, they leave its mothering, begetting idea to follow naturally behind.

Over and over for the past fifteen years I have watched strangers studying American ways, as if by dismantling an American combustion charger they could learn how to make themselves as warm as Americans. And over and over I have seen Americans trying to show them how the combustion charger works without explaining that the trick is not in how the metal parts of the combustion charger fit together but how the combustion charger is used socially, and to whose benefit. In every possible different context, I have watched puritan and conservative Americans thus transformed by their efforts abroad into radical symbols of disturbance.

The last chief of the Marshall Plan in France was a tall, blue-eyed Bostonian—Republican and rather conservative—named Henry Parkman, whose duties required him to deal with a French Cabinet including three different shades of Socialists. His final months in Paris were scarred by a continuing wrangle with the French government, and the substance of that wrangle was public housing. It was the conservative American who kept insisting that the French government must use some of the Marshall Plan financing to push decent housing for its slum-sheltered

Communist-voting citizens, while the French, all the while paying lip service to their progressive party names, wriggled and dodged to avoid the obligation.

Like all peoples, the Europeans hate being disturbed by outside forces except as they themselves invite these forces and transmute them into native political doctrine. The less able such countries have been to resist American pressure, as in France and Italy, the greater the number of those who hate us. The better able they were to resist, as in England and Belgium, the greater the number of those who still respect us.

What has baffled Europeans is that they see their need for America; they see the techniques of America; but the purpose and inner essence of American society finds no expression in American policy abroad. Europeans have, over the past five years, submitted to incessant prying, pushing and prodding by Americans. They try desperately to placate such Americans by agreeing to create a payments union that can link their currencies, to equip a division and place it as directed under American command, to stimulate the production of one commodity or embargo trade in another.

But every minute they do so they sense a smoldering, unexpressed indignity working within them, because America still keeps asking for more and remains forever unsatisfied. Europeans cannot recognize, for Americans never explain, that what America seeks is not simply technical innovation but something else. What America seeks are changes in spirit and society that will meet the challenge of the black revolutions of this century.

AMERICA ABROAD

IN THEORY, the burden of bringing America's influence to bear on the world should fall upon the Foreign Service of the State Department. These professional diplomats-by-career stand to the new recruits of the American community abroad as regular army officers stand to civilians recruited for war emergency. Out of approximately 15,000 Americans employed by the government in Europe, only 260 are men who have been trained professionally and chosen officially as permanent career Foreign Service officers to speak for the United States abroad. Theoretically, they should be in command, applying the policy of the elected Congress and directing the new machinery of experts and reserve recruits in its application.

Actually, nothing could be more remote from the truth, and few fragments of current affairs tell better of the built-in handicaps of United States foreign policy than what has happened to the once-proud Foreign Service of America in the years since the war.

The Foreign Service officers of the United States are recruited much as army officers. There are, at present, 1,496 such officers scattered around the globe. In taking their oath of office as young men, they accept a life and career that may send them scuttling from the jungles of Africa to the arid wastes of the Middle East. When they move, they move with wives and children, who grow up far from home in strange languages, subject to strange diseases and the neuroses of homelessness. All this they accepted with their oath of office; their job is to observe, to understand and to report accurately and coldly to the United States wherever they are ordered to go. There is no wealth to be gained in this career. At the end of his career, a Class I officer may earn $12,500 a year which is reduced to very little by the extra expenses of his position and constant travel. When he retires, if he has served well, he expects only two things—a pen-

246

sion, and a certain amount of dignity and honor because he has served the Republic well.

Today, it may be flatly stated that few men who serve the United States do so with less honor, less respect, or less reciprocal loyalty from their fellow citizens. In the decade in which the foreign affairs of America have become the most important problem in politics, the officers of the Foreign Service have become the favorite whipping boys of public debate.

The beating the Foreign Service has taken is not, of course, accidental. It flows from the nature of the turbulent world in which America must live. For thirty years two of the major problems of American foreign policy were states and societies in boiling change—Russia and China. The Foreign Service, back in the pre-Roosevelt days of a Republican State Department, therefore, began to train among its younger officers specialists in the particularly intricate problems of those countries. Since both these countries were moving at a furious pace to ends no man could see, the specialists so recruited were among the more brilliant and venturesome young men who entered the Foreign Service twenty years ago. Both in Russia and China, these men achieved such eminence as scholars and communicants of the strange cultures they lived in that they evoked the jealousy of the foreign offices of every other nation dealing with China and Russia. In China, as a matter of fact, the Russians were so impressed with the China Language Service program of the American State Department that in 1943, in mid-war, they began to imitate it.

In both Russia and China, events then proceeded to pose problems for Americans which are among the most tragic and difficult of our history. In the long debate on our attitude to these countries, the reports and attitudes of the Foreign Service officers have since been published, aired, investigated and disputed, not for what they were—clinical professional reports on the progress of a disease—but in order to determine how much the reports themselves were infected with the disease. It was as if Americans, tortured and frantic with the growth of a cancer they could not arrest, turned with savage blindness to wreak their vengeance on the doctors who had failed to cure it.

What has happened to the China Service officers of the Foreign Service has been an object lesson to every other career diplomat.

The basic burden of the reporting of the China Service in the critical years was that, in the inevitable clash between the Chinese Communists and Chiang Kai-shek, Chiang would be the loser. This correctness in judgment has resulted, however, not in honor either collectively or individually to the China Service. China has gone Communist. In some fashion the men of the China Service were held responsible. The China Service, therefore, no longer exists. Of the twenty-two officers who joined it before the beginning of World War II, there were in 1952 only two still used by the State Department in Washington—both had had the luck not to be in China during the war, or anywhere near the center of Chinese politics previously. Most of the rest were still serving the American government, but not in Formosa, Japan, Central Intelligence or anywhere else where their intimate knowledge of a China with whom we were desperately at war in Korea might be useful. At the moment of writing, all the postwar chiefs of the China desk of the State Department who have not been dismissed are stationed in London, in Paris, in Bonn, or in Rome—and are pleased with their obscurity.

During the course of the past seven years the candor and thus the value of the professional Foreign Service officer of the State Department has been reduced almost to the vanishing point. It has been reduced, moreover, at a time when the boldest and most revolutionary approaches are needed in Europe and the world to accomplish America's purpose of revitalized societies. But boldness is now the rarest of qualities in professional American diplomacy, for to be wrong is dangerous, and to be both wrong and out of step with Congress is disastrous.

The boldness which has, occasionally, broken through the timidity of the State Department since the war is almost never the kind of professional boldness which we expect of our generals in time of war. It is the boldness of the gifted amateur, of the man whose entire career is not at stake if a trenchant memorandum he writes now is published ten years later for hostile scrutiny. Thus, the boldest of American enterprises in Europe—its push toward European Union—owes nothing at all to the professionals in the State Department. Its two godfathers were General Dwight D. Eisenhower and David K. E. Bruce, American Ambassador to France. But Bruce was not a State Department professional; he was a Virginia gentleman, who had acquired considerable fortune in private business as well as much political judgment as a member of the legislatures first of Maryland and later of Virginia. Bruce entered upon his stewardship of the American Embassy in Paris with the simple belief that because America was the kind of country it was, and because he was America's Ambassador, American influence should be felt in creating the kind of world Americans sought. Of Bruce's two chief lieutenants in the diplomatic push that rammed through the Schuman Plan and brought the European Army and Constitution as far as they have come, one was a young Treasury official similarly invulnerable to the hazards of a diplomatic career. The other was a brilliant twenty-nine-year-old Foreign Service officer whose friends thought him too young and devoted to his mission to realize how far he was sticking his neck out.

At any mention of the European Army, one can arouse among the professionals of the Foreign Service the best informed and most intense discussion both pro and con of whether the Bruce captaincy of European Union was wise or not. But, it is quite safe to bet that only the rarest few have gone beyond the coldest reporting of fact. No Congressional committee ten years hence will be able to charge the great majority of them with strong opinion one way or another; their dispatches are neutral. They have found it best only to list the facts, not weigh them, which is what the American taxpayer paid to train them to do.

What has cramped the State Department's professional diplomats, baffled our allies and reduced the usefulness of our wandering experts and proconsuls is something peculiar to the new diplomacy of the twentieth century.

The new diplomacy which America practices is a multiplication of two things—of the orthodox instruments of power on the one hand, by the dynamic social ideas which beget them on the other hand. In this newer diplomacy, the older tools and servants of foreign policy are, whether they wish to be or not, bent to the service of an expanding, penetrating system of political ideas. The pressures that America exercises, fundamentally, on Europe are not pressures for specific gains or objects but the pressures of a home community continuously overflowing and spilling with radiant, change-making energy.

In America, therefore, the true source of foreign policy is neither the President, nor the Pentagon, nor, least of all, the State Department. It is the people themselves, expressing their voice through Congress. While the President, the Pentagon or even the State Department may be allowed to advise Congress or act in a critical emergency, in the last analysis it is Congress that decides how American influence overseas shall be cast.

It must not be thought that the Congress of the United States is a distant comptroller of events at long range. In these days of twelve-hour transatlantic flights and easy Congressional junkets, Congress is just around the corner from Europe. In the first seven weeks after the Congressional recess of 1951, no less than 150 Congressmen visited Paris either on committee, junket, vacation or sharpshooting.

Whether present in the flesh or not, Congress is master. No paper is prepared in any outpost, and no proposal is ever received from any intelligent foreign chancery without forethought of how it will sound to Congress. Long before Congress has reconvened in January, the overseas branches of American operation are already preparing "presentation" hearings.

Everyone who does business with America knows that Congress is the true source of American decision. Some foreign powers now bypass both State Department and President in order to make their appeal directly to Congress. Most of our major allies keep men in Washington whose job is chiefly to lobby and to entertain American Congressmen. The emotions of individual Congressmen can result in a hundred million dollars more or less for their strained budgets; they must be cultivated.

Given the freshness with which the American Congress has come to the scenes of world action, its record of statesmanship is imposing. The two most positive expressions of American dynamism—the Marshall Plan and the North Atlantic Pact—were both expressions of Congressional determination and understanding. Congress' instant support of the two swift emergency gestures of the Executive—the Truman Doctrine and the intervention in Korea—were, again, illuminated with wisdom.

Yet it is from Congress, too, that the greatest weaknesses of American policy abroad spring. For where Congress is strong is in the forthright act, the clear response to a clear issue clearly presented. Usually, it acts correctly. But where Congress creates weakness is, paradoxically, where it should be strongest—in the expression of American philosophy of which it is the embodiment. And in the multiplication factor of modern diplomacy—which multiplies the instruments of diplomacy by the social pressures behind them—Congress frequently comes close to crippling American purpose overseas.

Congress has been at war for some eight years with the executive leadership of the Presidency. For some fifteen years before that it was led, frequently over its bitter protest, through a program of social reform which many of its members, to this day, accept in practice but denounce in theory. In its surveillance and suspicion of the Executive overseas, it now insists that the Executive conduct itself in a way that will satisfy a range of Congressional opinion that can only be satisfied by the blandest generalities. The instruments of American diplomacy overseas are hobbled by their fear that an experiment may arouse Congressional vituperation, and that a blunder, honestly made, may become the subject of Congressional inquisition.

It is not only this split between Congress and Executive which weakens policy. American policy is weakened even more by the

behavior of Congress—or rather Congressmen, as individuals—
at home where Congressmen consider their action unlinked to
the broader struggle going on in the world. No censorship shelters American politics in their little follies. Yet these little follies,
however small, when amplified and rebroadcast abroad speak
louder than the Voice of America.

The death of Stalin, the first tactical tentatives of the new
Russian leadership have changed the rivalry of the West and
communism from the rigid contest at arms—in which we are so
close to overtaking them—to the more hopeful, yet more difficult, contest of political judgment and shrewdness. To maneuver,
American policy needs a complete flexibility, for it must be fast,
shrewd, cold and imaginative. It needs, first, an Executive un-
blinded by its own propaganda, endowed with wisdom, courage
and boldness. But it needs, beyond that, a Congress willing to
let its Executive lead where it cannot go itself and a Congress
self-disciplined enough not to destroy, by its domestic behavior,
the spirit that supports its actions overseas. It is not too much
to say that the future of the world lies less in the struggle within
the Kremlin than in the struggle within the American Congress.

DECISION AT WASHINGTON

O NE day in Paris the scholarly Ambassador of a very minor
power told me a story.

He had collected the White Papers, Blue Books, Yellow
Books, Orange Books and all the published notes and dispatches
of the diplomacy that had led to the First German War in the
summer of 1914. He had wanted to trace, day by day, the negotiations of the last six weeks before that great accident. For
the First World War, he insisted, was an accident that might
have been avoided, while all the horrors that have since followed have flowed inevitably from that accident as flame from
fire. The Ambassador had been, therefore, naturally disappointed in studying the clocked and dated cables that went Vi-
enna-Belgrade, Belgrade-St. Petersburg, Berlin-Vienna, Vienna-
Paris, Paris-London, London-Berlin to find that, even with a
generation of hindsight, he could not pick out the man or the
decision or any precise moment-of-no-return when the war
might have been stopped before it was triggered off.

But he found something equally exciting. It was an omission.
For, if his researches were correct, said he, in all the published
cables of foreign ministers, sovereigns, ambassadors and chan-
cellors not a single European diplomat had mentioned the
United States, speculated on its strength, or wondered about its
attitude. Not only that—none of the published records of those
last twilight weeks recorded the intervention, remonstrance, or
initiative of any American emissary in the six great capitals to
assert the will of America in the century which she was to domi-
nate.

The Ambassador told this story in a moment of exasperation,
adding, "But that was only thirty-five years ago! And now—now
we cannot plan, we cannot think, we cannot breathe without
asking first, before anything else, what will America do?"

The Ambassador was not unfriendly. He represented, indeed, one of those nations on whose automatic support America instinctively counts. What exasperated him was that he and his country were no longer fundamentally independent. They had been dragged by this century's events into an association that made them, willy-nilly, members of a community from which they dared not break and in which leadership was irrevocably American.

It is with similar exasperation that Americans sometimes look out on the world. They are annoyed like the Ambassador because they can no longer act independently and dare not break from the community they lead. They are upset because they cannot face, alone, a world of ever larger social-and-power agglomerations. Powerful as America is, she cannot ignore the fact that decisions are no longer made by single nations; decisions are made by a diplomacy of communities of nations, in action and in contest with other communities.

Let us look at these communities.

The two major blocs of power in the world are the Atlantic and Russian-satellite blocs. But beyond these are other sharply defined communities—the Moslem Community of nations with particular problems and aspirations of its own, the Latin-American Community, the Africans, only now emerging into an awareness of their own kinship, the community of peoples called India, called Southeast Asia, the Japanese, and the Chinese.

At this writing, America is no longer at war with the Chinese but is still greatly threatened by the Russians. It can count on the support only of the Atlantic Community and the Latin-American Community. All other civilizations and communities hang in the balance, in various degrees of disturbance and ferment, between ourselves and the adversary.

The simple listing of community names suggests the strategy imposed on the Atlantic world.

Defensively, it is to preserve and strengthen the unity of our community and defend it from Russia's effort of disruption.

Offensively, it is to swing the communities-in-between firmly to our side and then, ultimately, go on to divide the adversary's community from within and leave him isolated.

For Americans, in this strategy, Europe is the key.

It is the defense key because it gives us a line of resistance that starts 3,500 miles east of Staten Island and multiplies our military strength with powerful allies.

It is the offensive key because Europe is an association of powers who still wield far greater influence than ourselves in the changing civilizations of Africa, Southeast Asia and the Middle East, whom we hope to swing to our side.

The defense approach to strategy requires, above all, that Europe be kept content within the Atlantic Community, immune to the seduction and intrigue of Russian diplomacy. This brings us, therefore, to the two current problems of Europe which press like twin nightmares on the day-to-day operation of American diplomacy across the Atlantic.

The first of these is the recurrent economic stagnation of Western Europe; the second is the German problem.

The first complication—Europe's economic stagnation—is the most inviting area of vulnerability to Russian attack. Nothing is more eloquent of Russian thinking than the stability of their garrison strength in Central Europe since the war. It is questionable, looking back, that the Red Army's garrison divisions were ever deployed for attack at a preconceived date. It is more likely that they represented an insurance policy, a guarantee in the Russian mind that if an accident happened they would be able to strike swiftly and mop up easily, or, at any rate, jump off with an advantage while their home reserves rolled in for a second and finishing blow.

The NATO effort to purchase a counterinsurance policy was as necessary in our counterstrategy as was the Russian garrison in theirs. But this effort has been so costly and the emotion needed to force it on the taxpayer so intense that it has diverted the United States from the original interrupted purpose of Amer-

255

ican intervention in Europe in 1947, which was the Marshall Plan whose goal was the reorganization of European economic life.

Western Europe thus lies vulnerable today not so much to Russian military aggression as to Russian political-economic aggression. At this writing, the Organization of European Economic Cooperation reports that production in Western Europe, after rising ten per cent a year from 1948 through 1951, has been stationary since the beginning of 1952 and is sustained chiefly by the American boom and the domestic arms effort which is so unpopular politically.

Although the full political impact of a rising standard of living in Russia may be twenty years away—or even further—Russia's growth has given her powers of economic disruption which are immediate. Though Russia's masters may be unable to give their growing population for many years much more than their present meager pantry supplies, they may find it quite profitable politically to dump wheat on the world market, selling it cheaply to England, Germany or the other major European importers, at once, to cut them away from America. Though millions of ordinary Russians do not even dream of driving their own automobiles, Russia's masters may well buy up oil they do not need in order to break the Anglo-American petroleum control of the Middle East. Other raids in the world market are equally possible. They would be disturbing in any situation, but in a Europe that marks time, socially and economically, as it does today, these raids could be devastating.

The second problem within Europe—Germany—is diplomatically even more perplexing than economic stagnation.

Since 1947, all American diplomacy in Europe has been erected on the assumption that Germany was permanently split and that Western Germany could thus be brought to mesh its strength in a greater dynamic West European Union. The rigid counterdiplomacy of Joseph Stalin made this assumption valid and permitted us what success we have so far won. But it now lies in the power of Stalin's successors to undo our diplomacy

by undoing his. Should they offer to give up Eastern Germany
on condition that Western Germany repudiate association with
the West through European Union, they might be able to undo
all our work overnight.

This prospect of a Russian offer on Eastern Germany haunts
our statesmen. But what is usually ignored is how deeply intertwined this problem is with the problems of Europe's economic
health. The Germans, whether split or united, will probably
swing to the power bloc that offers them the greatest opportunity
to thrive and earn a living. Germany's amazing recovery has
taken place in the post-Korean boom, when both devastated
Germany and the entire world clamored for hard goods. But
the Germans have not yet been forced to face a buyer's market,
or meet the competition of the more efficient heavy industries
of England and the United States. The slight downturn of 1949
in world trade found the Ruhr eager and avid to sell and trade
its goods with the Russian world; a major depression might twist
all German commercial aspirations in that direction. The Germans are a people not yet naturally and traditionally convinced
of democratic values; while many Germans cherish freedom,
many would willingly sacrifice it for other benefits. Behind the
dignified façade of the Bonn government these contrary impulses
clash. The problem of the division of Germany is technically
manageable as long as the Western world is booming, for Germany reunited, no matter what compact is signed on paper, will
gravitate to the most inviting and most vigorous of the rival
blocs. In a depressed Europe and a depressed world, however,
Germany, even staked down by our half-million troops, will be
tugged politically and emotionally away from us.

If these twin problems—Germany and economic stagnation—
are intertwined, certain strategic measures are obviously necessary to meet them at once.

The first is so necessary even from a domestic point of view
that it needs no laboring. It is that our economy be so managed,
at whatever cost, that no nineteen-thirty-style depression recur.
A depression of this depth is the only thing absolutely certain

to rip apart the entire structure of resistance to a Communist-dominated world.

The next is the encouragement of a system of trade which lets Europeans both trade in our markets and share in the resources of the trading world which at the moment is dominated by America. It is impossible to keep Western European industries from exchanging what they produce with the Soviet world if they cannot squeeze through the tariff barriers of the United States to earn the dollars they need to buy our goods.

Yet, again, a third measure is the support of the movement toward European Union. This movement is important not so much because the German troops it promises may be useful militarily, but because it is the only authentic structural change yet proposed that may rock West Europe off dead center.

European Union, it should be stressed, is not an iron-clad guarantee of dynamic forward motion; it is only the opportunity. The use Europeans make of the opportunity depends mostly on them.

But the United States can help. It can help, technically, by underwriting on the American capital market the investment loans of the Schuman Plan already adequately underwritten by its High Authority, or it can help by tax concessions to American investors in such foreign bonds as are deemed in the national interest. It can help, even now, with money. Though the first enthusiasm for the Marshall Plan is over, the United States will be appropriating billions for foreign aid for years to come. At the moment, this aid is rigidly linked to military purpose. Yet if Congress would permit, once more, a flexible approach so that the sum might be used either for military or civilian aid, we might be able with far less money to do more good. For now, with the experience of the Marshall Plan behind us, we know where the bottlenecks are which must be smashed, where the Communist political strongholds are, what the argument is about, and we could earmark our grants, politically, not for relief, or for budget-balancing, but for specific social and structural reforms.

If these are the burdens on American policy, burdens equally grave lie upon Europe. For the Europeans are as responsible for the present peak of strain in the Atlantic Community as are the Americans.

Europeans have a tendency all too human to blame all their ills and failures on American leadership, as if the perils and problems which America crudely forces them to grapple with were of American confection, not the ugly face of reality. Sometimes their petulance has the same ring as that of a sensitive adolescent forced by a coarse parent to do his ugly, unpleasant, but necessary homework.

Much can be overlooked—even the European attitude toward the Korean War. Though nothing in postwar history, except the Marshall Plan, more swiftly raised American prestige in European eyes than our defense of Korea, no other American action was more swiftly transformed into a source of emotional criticism of America. Many Europeans look on the American effort in Korea as a twentieth-century reproduction of the Northwest Frontier between India and Afghanistan—a far-off frontier, held on a skirmish line between civilization and barbarism, which can be manned for decades with adventure-seeking regular officers and the sodden outcasts of industrial unemployment. For them, MIG Alley is the equivalent of the Khyber Pass. Although European soldiers fought on the front lines in Korea, no European appreciates the extent of American involvement, nor does he grasp the fact that thousands of Americans, drafted from the age of eighteen, fought daily in defense of a land which was not theirs, that the United States was strained emotionally and physically by a major war, and the dead returned with each ship from the Orient. Europeans focus generally, in their thinking, on the ugly phenomena the Korean War produced in American domestic politics, or on the exaggerated military burdens which American emotion demanded of them.

American diplomacy can—and must—overlook this attitude if the Community is to survive; it must overlook many other European failings and faults.

What American diplomacy cannot overlook, what it must hold Europeans primarily responsible for, is to provide the initiative and will to make of their own resources a new life. If the chief burden of America's diplomacy in Europe is to aid Europe toward the expanding, fluid society, the chief duty of the Europeans in this strategy is to make themselves healthy, to tear down what is ancient, or has become useless with age, and go forward to make opportunity for each of their individuals.

This is the essential drama of Europe, for there is fire in the ashes of the old civilization. America can fan it to flame or smother it, but the flame cannot be fed from America, it must blaze from its own sources.

Adventure
Happy

JULE MANNIX

ADVENTURE HAPPY

DAN and I were still honeymooning in our little New York apartment when the telephone rang frantically and a man's voice said, "This is the hotel across the street. Just keep calm, but a large eagle has come in through your window."

"I know it," I told him. "She's gone into our bathroom to take a bath."

There was a pause on the line. Then the man said, "You mean you know about this eagle?"

"Yes. She's a pet."

"Well, I didn't know that so I phoned the police, the game commission and the S.P.C.A."

I hung up the phone feeling very much annoyed. It was a fine state of affairs when you couldn't let your own eagle sit on the balcony outside your window without having some silly man call the police. Our eagle was part of the family and an important investment. Dan and I had spent weeks training the bird as a hunting falcon, and we were going to take her to the mountains of southern Mexico and use her to capture iguanas . . . the giant, six-foot lizards that live in the hills. We'd planned to write articles and prepare a lecture on the hunts. I didn't think there was any law against keeping an eagle in your apartment, but authorities are strange people, and it would be just like them to confiscate our wonderful bird.

Dan was out getting some meat for the eagle . . . she ate a pound and a half of the best rib roast every day . . . and when he got back he told me not to worry. I was afraid he might be cross with me for letting the bird sit on the balcony, but Dan said it wasn't my fault at all. Our eagle had to sit on the balcony to sun herself and the hotel man across the street was an officious idiot. But like me, Dan was afraid the police might not understand. We tried to think of some place to hide the bird when the police came, but we had only a one-room apartment and there's really no place in an apartment to hide an eagle. Before we could do much, the various authorities began to arrive.

The police came first. The patrolman looked our eagle over, said that there were laws about keeping dogs and cats in certain areas but as far as he knew the laws didn't say a thing about pet eagles. That hazard over, the game warden arrived. At that time, eagles weren't protected by law, so he said that the case didn't come under his jurisdiction. He asked us what we intended to do with the bird and, after we'd told him, he just shook his head sadly and left.

The only real trouble we had was with the man from the S.P.C.A. He said that he had to inspect the eagle to make sure that she was not being badly treated. The eagle was sitting on the back of a chair and when the man walked over to her, she screamed and began striking at him with her wings. Our eagle had a six-foot wingspread and the power of a windmill. Pictures fell off their hooks, books keeled over in the bookcases, and Dan and I jumped to get out of the way. When we looked around for the S.P.C.A. man, he was flattened against the wall, shaking with terror.

"As far as I can see, that eagle is in fine condition," he said hoarsely. "Now for heaven's sake, hold her until I can get out of here."

I am probably the only bride in history who was ever required to train an eagle during her first year of married life. Sometimes I'd wake up during the night and lie in bed thinking, "How on earth did I ever get myself into this fix?"

Ever since I was a little girl, I'd been determined to go on the stage, but our home was in the suburbs of Philadelphia and Philadelphia doesn't give a stage-struck girl much chance to express herself.

I did my best. I put myself through dramatic school by getting jobs as a model with various Philadelphia photographic studios.

One afternoon a friend of mine named Mary Ludington asked me if I'd go with her to a carnival that was playing near Philadelphia. Mary knew a curious young man named Dan Mannix who was working in the side show as a sword swallower. I told Mary that I'd be delighted to accompany her, although I couldn't imagine why she'd want to know such a grotesque individual.

The side show was very hot and jammed with people. A very tall man was standing on the platform, naked to the waist, and with tattooing on his forearm. He was brandishing a lighted neon tube. Suddenly I realized that he was going to swallow it. I quickly closed my eyes until I heard a burst of applause and then asked Mary, "Is it over?"

"Oh, yes," said Mary. "Now he's going to swallow a giant corkscrew so you can see his Adam's apple jump around as it goes down."

That did it. "I want to get out of here," I said firmly. We fought our way through the crowd and back to the car. My shoes were ruined from the mud of the midway, my new dress was a limp rag, and I was furious with Mary for taking me to see such a disgusting sight.

A week later, Mary gave a cocktail party and both Dan and I were invited. At first I was amused rather than interested in him. He had had such an unusual life. His father was an admiral and Dan and his mother had followed the fleet from one port to another. As a result, Dan had been in twelve different schools before he was ten years old. To make matters worse, by the time he was twelve years old he was nearly six feet tall and seemed like a clumsy giant to children his own age. His schoolmates either ignored him or made his life miserable. So Dan was thrown largely on his own resources. He developed a passion for books, almost as strong as my passion for the theater. He also loved animals. Dan understood animals and was remarkably good with them. I imagine they gave him a sense of companionship that his human contemporaries didn't.

Dan and I had several dates after that, and I got to know him better. At first, I'd thought of him as simply an unusually cheerful and amusing exhibitionist . . . rather like a college boy who goes in for swallowing goldfish. I soon learned that there was a good deal more to Dan than that. He had an insatiable curiosity. Whenever he heard about anything strange and different, he tried to find out more about it. While he was in college, he'd become intrigued by occultism. Dan had always loved circuses and carnivals, and he knew that many of the strange feats which the reference books said could only be performed by oriental fakirs, marabous, and various other wonder-workers were actually being done by performers in side shows.

But exactly how did they do them? Dan was sufficiently interested to join a carnival to learn how to perform the tricks himself. Now, he was writing a book on his carnival experiences and after it was finished, he hoped to take a trip to India to see some fakirs at first hand. We used to talk over our plans together, taking for granted that we'd soon separate and not in the least worried over the simple fact that if we were apart for forty-eight hours we were both wretched.

I put off going to New York as long as I could, not (at least consciously) because of Dan but because of my family. When I finally told them that I was leaving, I don't believe mother could have been more upset if I'd told her that I was going to Buenos Aires to enter the white-slave trade.

For the first few weeks, I had a wonderful time. Then I began to get lonesome and restless. Dan came over to see me several times. The first time I saw him, I almost publicly disgraced myself by falling into his arms. Dan and I had gotten very used to each other. I think each of us supplied some quality the other lacked. Dan had such a wonderful imagination and was so big, and gay and gentle and charming. Dan claimed to admire my determination to succeed on the stage. Fortunately, he also thought I was pretty. He liked to sit and look at me with an expression of pleasure on his face I'd never seen there except when he was looking at a particularly fine falcon.

266

Of course, by this time I had often considered marrying Dan, but I didn't see how I could be married and still go on the stage. Dan and the theater didn't seem to mix.

Then I didn't hear from him for a week. I was nearly frantic. Any doubts I had about wanting to marry him were completely resolved in that long week. Nobody knew where he'd gone. He might have joined another carnival or just wandered off on some other weird project. I bitterly regretted not having taken a firm stand and married him before this, but I comforted myself with the reflection that sooner or later he'd turn up, and I wouldn't make the same mistake twice.

One night at eleven-thirty, the doorbell of my apartment rang and there was Dan. He looked very woebegone, and, without wasting any time, he asked me to marry him. He seemed so unhappy about the whole thing that I did my best to comfort him. I told him marriage wouldn't be nearly as bad as he thought and anyhow almost anything was better than being as miserable as we'd both been for the past week. Dan had been miserable too. He'd moved in with a friend in West Philadelphia to devote himself to his carnival book, but he couldn't work on it and had finally decided to come to see me.

We sat down together on the sofa and talked about the future. We decided that we'd live in New York so I could go on with the stage. Dan didn't care where he lived as long as he could work on his book. Everything seemed to be solving itself nicely, and I wondered why I'd thought marriage and a career couldn't be comfortably combined.

WE ACQUIRE AN EAGLE

NEW YORK is a wonderful place for a young couple very much in love. Everything went along smoothly until Dan finished his book and sent it, proudly and confidently, to the publishers. We waited happily for their enthusiastic letter of acceptance. Instead, the manuscript was returned with a rejection slip. Dan sent it to five other publishers. His book was turned down by all of them.

Dan was terribly cast down, and I could do nothing but try to bring up casually in conversation the names of famous writers who'd had their first manuscripts turned down by stupid editors. Then, one evening Dan said suddenly, "Jule, how would you like to go to Mexico?"

I was willing to go anywhere that would get Dan's mind off his rejected manuscript, but this suggestion, out of a perfectly clear sky, was a little startling.

"Why Mexico?" I asked.

Dan began to talk with some of his old enthusiasm. It did my heart good to hear the excitement in his voice again.

"There're giant lizards called iguanas that live in the mountains of southern Mexico. They can run like deer and bite like bulldogs so they're very hard to catch. Now my idea is to get an eagle, train her for falconry, and go down to Mexico with her. We'll catch iguanas, bring them back to the zoos, and write articles about it. Also, we'll take motion pictures. I think we can make up a lecture on it."

"Dan, have you ever trained an eagle?" I asked.

"No."

"Has there ever been anyone in history who's ever trained an eagle?"

"Yes," said Dan triumphantly. "The Laplanders hunt wolves with eagles from the backs of reindeer."

I hastily changed the subject. The first thing I knew, I'd be riding a reindeer over the Mexican mountains in addition to training an eagle.

"Do you know where to get an eagle?"

"Yes, I do." Dan sounded very proud. "That's what gave me the idea for the trip. About a month before we were married, I met a man named Thompson who's a game warden from Salem, New Jersey. He has an eagle. The bird came down in a sleet storm with her wings covered with sleet. Thompson caught her and put her in his chicken house. She's been there ever since, and not feeling too happy about it. The warden tried to let her go a couple of times but she'd lost all fear of humans and just hung around the town, robbing chicken houses. He's been planning to give her to a zoo, but I don't think an eagle wants to spend the rest of her life in a cage. I think if she lived with us, she'd at least have some excitement."

For the first time since his book was rejected, Dan looked eager and alive again . . . like the Dan I'd married. Bang went the career of one of America's greatest potential actresses. "Dear, my girlhood ambition has always been to hunt lizards in Mexico with a trained eagle," I assured him. "When do we start?"

We invested a major part of our capital in a station wagon for the trip. At that time, you could get a station wagon for eight hundred dollars but our bank roll looked very depleted after the purchase. In our new car, we drove down to Salem to interview the eagle.

Mr. Thompson took us to the spare chicken house in his back yard. He had covered the front of the house with heavy gauge wire and the eagle was sitting behind the barrier looking unpleasant. I had no idea eagles were so big. This one looked to me the size of an ostrich. She had talons as long as my finger and a huge, yellow, hooked beak that she was obviously prepared to use on the slightest provocation. I looked at the eagle and she looked at me. Obviously, neither of us made a favorable impression on the other.

Dan and Mr. Thompson had a little trouble getting the eagle into a sack. It took them about an hour and a half. Wriggles, my little Cairn terrier, helped by leaping around and barking, thus distracting the eagle's attention when she tried to grab either Dan or Mr. Thompson. I couldn't believe that furious, screaming bird would ever be tame enough to handle, but I had great confidence in Dan's ability with animals. I only hoped that Wriggles and I could live through the taming period.

When we got back to our apartment house, we smuggled the bird in her sack up the stairs so no one would see us. I had the pretty illusion that the eagle would be kept in a cage, although where we'd put the cage I had no idea. Dan sprung the news on me that hawks intended for falconry are never kept in cages. They are either carried around on your gloved fist or sit on perches. Dan had been practicing falconry for years and claimed this eagle was just a big hawk. As the falcons used in falconry aren't much bigger than a large pigeon and this bird had a six-foot wingspread, it seemed to me that was like saying there wasn't much difference between a house cat and a Bengal tiger, but Dan said the basic training principles were the same.

Before letting our eagle out of the sack, Dan cut a hole in the burlap so he could get hold of the bird's legs. He tied leather straps called "jesses" around each leg so he'd have something to hold on to when he let the bird out.

When the jesses were in place, Dan put on the heavy falconer's glove that hawk trainers wear on their left hands and got a firm grip on the jesses. Then I slit open the sack with a razor blade. Instantly the room seemed full of screaming, thrashing eagle. Dan yelled, "Don't let her break her feathers!" I rushed around the room, shoving chairs and tables out of the way of the eagle's wildly beating wings. I smashed two vases and a lovely porcelain figurine, but I'm proud to say I kept the eagle from damaging her feathers. After all, you can always buy vases and figurines, but it takes a feather a year to grow back.

Finally Dan managed to swing the bird up on his gloved fist.

The eagle sat there panting for a minute, eyeing us maliciously. Then she suddenly struck out at Dan's face. Her hooked beak missed his eye but got him in the cheek. The tip of her beak hung in his flesh for a moment and then tore loose. There was a trickle of blood on Dan's cheek but when I rushed to the rescue he waved me back, shouting, "Keep away! You'll excite her!"

When Dan had told me that he was getting the eagle, it never for a moment occurred to me that I'd have to handle the bird myself. I took for granted Dan would do all the eagle training. But if you're locked up in a tiny apartment with a raging eagle, you can't very well ignore her. Just to be able to stay alive, I had to learn how to handle our new pet . . . if pet is the right word.

I wasn't afraid of our eagle in the ordinary sense of the word but I was petrified with fear that she'd either bite or claw me in my face. I do have a great dread of being scarred, and that horrible bird seemed to sense it for she always struck at my face. Except for that first time, she seldom bit Dan. In order to train her, "manning" falconers call it, he had to carry the bird for hours on his gloved fist. It was simply uncanny to me how quickly Dan and that bird seemed to develop an understanding. I don't mean they quickly became friends. The eagle would scream and hiss at Dan and he would curse the eagle, but after it was all over there were obviously no hard feelings on either side. But when I so much as walked past the eagle, she would put up her neck feathers like the ruff of a cock, bend over, and look at me with cold, calculated hatred that she never showed towards my husband.

I wasn't the only one to suffer from the eagle. The bird insisted on regarding poor, little Wriggles as something to eat. I felt if she ever touched Wriggles I would personally strangle her with my bare hands, Dan or no Dan, but strangely enough the bird soon got used to the little terrier and paid no attention to her.

Eventually, the bird did get so that she tolerated me as well.

She would follow me around the apartment while I was house-cleaning with a funny pigeon-toed gait, twisting her head around to watch what I was doing until I thought it would come off. I soon found that when I wanted to move her from one spot to another, I couldn't just shove her out of the way. The bird would instantly go into one of her terrifying fits of rage. I had to put on Dan's glove and induce the bird to step up on my fist. Then I'd move her over to her perch and go on with my house-work. Sometimes I wouldn't do it the right way and then the eagle would either get mad or go into a fit of sulks. When Dan got back, he could always tell if the eagle and I had gotten into an argument. Neither of us would be speaking to the other.

At the end of a month, Dan announced that the eagle was manned. I sat in respectful silence while Dan held out his gloved fist with a bit of meat on it, whistled, and the eagle un-folded her vast wings, gave a great bound, and landed on his arm. I remembered the many nights I'd lain in bed, listening while Dan had struggled to calm that screaming, biting, fighting bird and thought to myself, "Why, oh why doesn't he give up? Why doesn't he admit it's impossible?" Yet Dan had succeeded and I realized now he'd known all along that he would succeed. It made me feel very humble.

Of course, the eagle still wasn't trained for hunting. She would have to learn to circle over Dan's head while he put up game for her, and come to his whistle even though she were miles away. But this latter part of the training would have to be done in Mexico.

TAXCO

WE PLANNED to head for a little village in southern Mexico called Taxco. A friend of Dan's had been animal collecting near there and said there were plenty of iguanas in the hills. Taxco is now famous as a tourist resort but at that time few people had ever heard of it.

After four days of hard driving, we reached Laredo, Texas, a small town on the Rio Grande River which is the gateway of Mexico. We found a lovely tourist court just outside the town, and we settled down there for a two days' rest before going on to Mexico. The owner of the court was doubtful that the Mexican authorities would let us enter the country. "There'll sure be some head scratchin' and hand wavin' when that thing hits the border," he said gloomily, regarding our eagle.

Early one morning we drove to the International Bridge in fear and trembling. The United States officials on our side of the bridge told us that we'd have to register the bird if we wanted to bring her back; otherwise she'd be considered a wild animal and wild animals can't be imported into the United States without a lot of special permits. After registering our eagle, we drove anxiously across the bridge and stopped at the Mexican immigration station.

I can only say that we caused a sensation. The Mexican officials searched feverishly through their books to see if there was anything about American tourists arriving with pet eagles. Finally they decided that there was not, but they insisted that we also register the bird with them to make sure that we took her out of the country with us when we left.

We heard the word *águila* repeated so often that Dan finally asked what it meant. One of the officials explained that it was Spanish for "eagle." During the next few days, every place we stopped a crowd of little boys would come running out shouting, *"Un águila! Un águila!"* Finally we picked up the word ourselves and named our eagle, "Aguila." Aguila she has remained ever since.

Knowing Dan, I realized that we wouldn't be in Mexico too long before he started picking up pets. Turning Dan loose in a strange, new country teeming with unusual animals was like turning a clothes-conscious woman loose on the Rue de la Paix in Paris. But I did think that we'd at least reach Taxco before starting our collection. I was wrong. We made our first acquisition in a town called Victoria, about two hundred miles south of Monterrey. We had stopped for gas and while the station attendant was filling the tank, I noticed a woebegone ball of fur tied to the fuel pump. Looking more closely, I saw the ball was a baby animal mainly composed of a long nose and a pair of mournful eyes. I called Dan's attention to the poor little thing.

"What does that one call itself?" Dan asked the attendant in his best high school Spanish.

"It calls itself a *tajon, señor,*" the attendant replied. "This one's name is Poncho and he belongs to my little boy."

Dan examined the wretched little creature. "It's a coati mundi," he told me. "They're a little like a monkey and a little like a raccoon. Let's see if the man will sell him."

The man was perfectly willing to sell Poncho for a peso . . . then worth about twenty cents. Before we left, he told us that Poncho had a brother, named Pedro, that was being used as a doorstopper by a neighbor. We bought Pedro too.

The next day we went on towards the great mountain range that surrounds Mexico City. As we climbed, we could look down and see below us the green roof of the jungle through which we'd been driving a few hours before.

Mexico City is an enormous place, full of cars that pay no attention to traffic signals and go charging by you like maddened bulls. We hurried through it for Taxco is only a hundred miles from Mexico City, and we thought we could make it easily in two hours. But we hadn't counted on the twisty mountain roads. Night fell and we were still cautiously crawling along roads that seemed to be nothing but bends and turns with no guard rails to give you confidence and sudden drops of several hundred feet into the valleys below. By ten o'clock I was beginning to think Taxco was a myth and we'd drive on endlessly.

Suddenly we went around another of the interminable bends and there on the mountainside ahead of us was a cluster of little yellow lights. We had arrived in Taxco.

The next morning we told the proprietor of the minute hotel where we had found a room for the night, that we were house hunting and he suggested that we see Natalie Scott. Natalie Scott, he explained, had come to Taxco some ten years before, and had fallen in love with it. She had lived in Taxco ever since and was the recognized authority on houses for sale or rent.

Natalie was a handsome woman in her late fifties with almost snow-white hair. She didn't seem surprised when we told her why we'd come to Taxco. We later found that Taxco was famous as being a sort of refuge for all types of eccentrics from all over the world so the news that two people had arrived with a trained eagle didn't disconcert Natalie in the least.

We explained that fifty dollars a month was all we could afford to pay for a house, and Natalie pulled out her lists.

"I'll show you Casa Riding. That has a nice patio and only one servant. She's an old Indian woman named Maria. She flits around the house like a ghost and I don't think even an eagle will bother her." The servants went with the house, we learned, so finding the right servants was as important as finding the right house.

Natalie took us to Casa Riding. We passed under one of the archways of the church, down a steep street where burros laden with firewood were trudging to and fro, and at last stopped by a great hand-hewn wooden door with huge hinges. Natalie beat on the door and eventually it was opened by a very old

275

Indian woman with a black shawl over her thin gray hair. She seemed so thin and fragile that I felt she would break if she moved. She folded her hands in her apron, bowed, and said gently, *"Buenos días, señor y señora."*

This was Maria, who was to be our servant, mother, and comforter for many, many months. She led us into the house. Dan and I knew at first glance that this was the home for us.

We walked into a great room, almost as big as a medieval banquet hall. Along one side ran five big arches that looked onto the patio. Through the arches, we could see the bright green grass of the patio and two trees, one a mango that threw a circle of pleasant shade in one corner and the other a tall, thin banana tree. Along two sides of the patio ran a waist-high wall. On the other side of the wall was an almost sheer drop into the valley beneath. Across the valley we could see range on range of purple mountains, their green slopes covered with a cobweb tracery of fine white paths.

At the far end of the room was a huge "picture window" with another view of the mountains. Against another wall was a huge fireplace, big enough to roast a whole pig. Near the fireplace, a door opened into the "master bedroom." There was a tiny kitchen with a big, adobe stove. Crossing the patio, we entered the other wing of the house where there was a bathroom and a spare bedroom. There was a magnificent tiled bath, almost big enough to swim in. Not until after we rented the house did we discover that none of the plumbing was attached.

Dan put up Aguila's perch under the mango tree and we fitted out the coatis with homemade collars and staked them out on the patio. We were ready to settle down.

IGUANA HUNTING WITH AGUILA

A S SOON as Aguila became acclimated to the high altitude of Taxco, Dan began the last part of her training.

When first we took Aguila off her line and allowed her to fly free, she flew casually to Dan's fist over short distances and apparently didn't know that she was loose. Then the realization dawned on her. She leaped into the air with a single, great downstroke of her wings and went soaring away over the mountains. She flatly refused to pay any attention to Dan's whistle or the steak he was hopefully holding out on his gloved hand. Fortunately, Aguila soon grew tired and had to land on a rock to rest. We managed to retrieve her. But the next day and the next she did the same thing. She was constantly growing stronger and we knew that eventually we'd lose her.

I, not Dan, discovered a sure way to bring the bird back. Aguila still carried a grudge against me and no matter how far away she was, if I stood on a hilltop and shouted insults at her, the bird would come charging back at me. Then I'd run and hide behind Dan until he caught hold of the furious bird.

After a few days of this, Aguila began to steady down. She learned to come to Dan's fist for food and, as she got more and more exercise, she became increasingly eager for the bits of meat we always gave her as a reward. She even learned to tolerate me, and would take meat from my hand without trying to grab a finger as a bonus. Finally, Aguila actually consented to fly to me and land on my gloved fist.

These daily trips to the mountains taught Dan something about our bird that he hadn't taken into account. Aguila was heavy. The bird only weighed ten pounds which doesn't seem like much, but when you have to carry ten pounds on your bent arm up mountains for several hours, you begin to feel it. We knew that when we started looking for iguanas, we would be in the mountains all day long and finally even Dan had to admit he couldn't carry the bird continually during that time.

So far on this trip, I hadn't been of much help to Dan. Now I saw a chance to earn my board and keep. Dan didn't know much about horses, but I did. I was sure I could train a horse to allow Aguila to be flown from his back.

What I needed was a steady, docile animal and yet one with enough spirit to look well in the pictures. After days of search, I finally found Teresa.

Teresa belonged to a neighbor of ours who had gotten the horse from a suspicious-looking gentleman with drooping mustachios. This man claimed he had been a general until the police caught up with his army and hanged them. During the revolutions that plagued Mexico, Teresa had had three such generals shot off her back and nothing could surprise her any more . . . nothing, that is, until she met us and Aguila. The first time the mare saw Aguila headed her way she tried to solve the problem by jumping off the side of a cliff.

I practiced riding Teresa around with Aguila sitting hooded on my fist. As Aguila sat as still as a stuffed bird when she was hooded, Teresa gradually got used to the sight and smell of the eagle. Then I tried it with Aguila unhooded. Finally came the great day when I could call the eagle to me from horseback and Aguila would come swooping in, dropping almost as low as my stirrup, only to swing up at the last instant and settle on my gloved fist while Teresa stood as still as a bronze horse.

Ever since we first came to Taxco, we'd been trying to find someone who could guide us to the haunts of the iguanas. There were iguanas around Taxco. We occasionally saw their skins offered for sale in the market place, for, like snakeskin, iguana hide makes very nice belts and shoes. But nobody could tell us where the iguanas lived.

Then one day while wandering over the hills we met Chon. Chon was twelve years old and stood some four feet high on his bare, brown feet. He knew all about iguanas. He often saw them sunning themselves on big rocks. We offered him a job as combined iguana-guide and assistant eagle trainer for the handsome sum of fifty cents a week.

Chon turned out to be a wonderful investment. He soon lost all fear of the big bird and treated her with a cheerful familiarity that alarmed me. Aguila was perfectly gentle with the boy, but just the same I didn't like to see him chuck the bird under the chin and rub her head as though she were a chicken.

Our first iguana hunt came quite unexpectedly. We were returning from a ride in the hills with Aguila when Chon said casually, *"Hay un iguana, señor."*

For a second, the import of the boy's words didn't sink in. Then Dan said eagerly, *"Donde?"* Chon nodded towards a ridge of rocks that stuck out of the mountainside like the backbone of some prehistoric monster. Lying on top of the ridge was a black form. The creature was so motionless that he looked like part of the rock but as we watched, I could see his forked tongue flicker in and out.

Aguila crouched her head down between her wings and studied the countryside with her wonderful telescopic eyes. She could have seen a rabbit two miles away . . . a moving rabbit. But birds of prey, like all animals, don't seem able to distinguish a motionless object. Aguila stared at the iguana less than two hundred yards away but obviously couldn't tell it from the rock.

There was nothing to do but ride closer. I touched Teresa with my heel and the mare trotted forward, picking her way daintily over the loose rocks. For a second the lizard squatted down like a rabbit freezing. Then without any warning, he made a sudden bolt up the slope.

Aguila could see him now. Before I had a chance to throw her off, the eagle sprang into the air. Her great wings began to beat, slowly increasing in speed. Aguila always took an appreciable time to get underway and we waited in agony while she built up momentum. Then she overcame her initial inertia and shot away after the lizard.

Unfortunately, the iguana hadn't waited for the end of these maneuvers. He was racing up the hill so fast that his long body seemed to be only a black flicker. But fast as the lizard was going, he seemed almost to be standing still compared to the speed of our eagle. Aguila was overhauling the reptile with every wingbeat, but the iguana still had a long lead. It was anybody's race.

Aguila half-closed her wings and shot down for the capture. The lizard was now only a few feet away from the edge of a perpendicular cliff. I saw Aguila's long, yellow legs flash forward as she reached for the iguana. Her wings began to reverse their beat as she tried to slow herself up so she wouldn't crash into the reptile. The iguana had reached the edge of the precipice. I knew the bird had him now for there was nowhere for him to go.

The iguana never paused. He rushed straight on out into space, his speed actually carrying him a foot or so into the air before he began to fall. Aguila shot upwards, turning her head as she did so to watch the falling lizard. Then, keeping her wings rigid, she dropped sideways down the side of the cliff, cutting the air like a falling knife.

She was too late. The iguana hit the bottom of the cliff, his feet beginning to move while he was still in the air, and started running. Such a fall onto solid rock would have killed an ordinary animal, but the iguana didn't seem to mind it at all. He darted into the mouth of a cave with Aguila snatching for his long tail. When, after half an hour of climbing, we reached the spot, Aguila was peering into the black pocket but there was no sign of the iguana. Our first hunt had failed.

In the next few weeks, this fiasco was repeated with many variations. Aguila couldn't see the iguanas until they moved and our bird took so long getting underway that the lizards were able to reach holes before she could catch up with them. Even Dan had no idea how to overcome this handicap. We finally solved it by pure luck.

Wriggles always hated to be left behind if we were going

anywhere. Every time I mounted Teresa, Wriggles would come prancing out, sitting up to beg hopefully and wave her forepaws, certain that we'd take her along. Finally, I broke down.

"This time I'm going to take Wriggles," I told Dan. "She can play around the rocks while we hunt with the eagle."

Wriggles triumphantly rode on the pommel of my saddle while Dan protestingly carried Aguila. When we reached the hunting ground, I put the little terrier down so she could run around. Aguila and Wriggles were good friends by this time but the first few times we flew the eagle, I kept an eye on her to make sure that the bird didn't mistake Wriggles for an iguana. But I needn't have worried. Aguila paid no more attention to Wriggles than she did to Chon or us.

While Wriggles was investigating some brand-new smells, Chon pointed out an iguana to us. The animal was crawling among some tiny flowers, apparently eating the buds. We prepared to go into action.

We had adopted a new style of hunting. While I held Aguila on my fist, Dan would circle around behind an iguana and try to scare the lizard towards me. Aguila flew better from horseback than she did from Dan's fist. The added height of the horse gave her more altitude from which to start her flight. If the iguana bolted towards us, Aguila was pretty sure to get him. Unfortunately, very few of them did.

Dan took a long time to crawl up the slippery rocks behind the iguana. Meanwhile, Wriggles got tired of playing about and started over to me. On the way, she caught sight of Dan and went cavorting towards him.

The iguana saw her, but the dog was actually smaller than the lizard and the big reptile simply half rose and hissed at her. Wriggles was charmed. She approached closer to sniff. The iguana snapped and swung around, keeping his open jaws facing the dog. I was terrified that the lizard would grab Wriggles. Hurriedly, I threw off the eagle.

All the iguana's attention was taken up with Wriggles. He never even saw Aguila coming. The eagle dropped down on him like a thundercloud, and before the lizard knew what was happening, Aguila had him pinned down. Wriggles bounced around like an excited mechanical toy while Dan rushed in and after tying up the iguana's mouth to keep it from biting him, added it to our bag.

After that, Wriggles became a regular member of our hunting parties.

After we had gotten a few iguanas, we decided to concentrate on taking pictures. Dan, Chon, Aguila, and Wriggles hunted the iguanas while I tried desperately to follow them with the motion-picture camera. We ran off hundreds of feet of film trying to get a few good shots. To make matters worse, I knew nothing about photography and although Dan, in his calmer moments, did try to show me how to handle cameras and light meters, I never seemed to learn. Dan and I alternated as cameramen, he taking pictures of me flying the eagle from horseback and then I'd take pictures of him rescuing the captured iguanas. In some sequences, we both had to be in the picture so we trained Chon to run the camera. Later, when all three of us appeared in a sequence, we even pressed Maria into service.

The captured iguanas we kept in our patio, each lizard fastened to a small stake by a cord tied around his middle. We tried keeping them in boxes, but then they wouldn't eat and also got into fights. We fed them banana, or rather Chon did. If you simply left a banana near a lizard, he'd refuse to eat it but if you poked it at him, he'd bite at the strange object. Once he got a mouthful of banana, he'd swallow it.

Of course, flying Aguila day after day as we were doing, something was bound to go wrong eventually. Disaster came late one afternoon while we were preparing to return to Taxco after a long day in the mountains.

Dan, Chon, and Wriggles were looking for iguanas along the side of a hill while I stayed at the top, sitting comfortably on Teresa with Aguila on my fist and waiting to see if they'd put up anything. They finally gave up and started down the slope. I rode around to meet them at the bottom. As the hill was now between us, I lost sight of them. Then I heard Wriggles barking. I turned Teresa towards the sound. There on a pile of rocks was the biggest iguana I'd ever seen.

To my astonished eyes, the reptile looked as big as a crocodile. It was actually well over six feet, counting the long, whiplike tail.

I kicked Teresa into a slow canter. Wriggles saw that reinforcements were arriving and began to dance in closer to the iguana.

Then Aguila took off with one great sweep of her wings. She glided towards the lizard with open wings like a skimmed piece of slate.

Instantly the iguana reared up, his blood-red mouth wide open, his long tail lashing behind him. He had a moment to get ready. Then the eagle reached him.

The iguana led with his tail. Aguila countered with a terrific left wing to the lizard's jaw. The iguana grabbed a mouthful of feathers and hung on. Aguila broke away, pulling out the feathers. The lizard thought he still had the eagle and stood holding the feathers and looking a little surprised. This gave Aguila a chance to fasten a headlock on the reptile with both feet, a difficult task. The iguana promptly rolled with her, like an experienced wrestler. I saw the white under-coverts beneath Aguila's tail flash as the bird lost her balance.

Then Wriggles came charging in from the side lines. Keeping a wary eye on the lizard's tail, he nipped at his flank. The iguana spun around, snapping angrily. This gave Aguila a chance to get on her feet, but the lizard charged in again.

He got in two nasty blows with his tail and rushed Aguila up against a rock. The eagle leaped up in the air, turned, and came in again. She landed on the reptile's head. Holding him down with one foot, she grabbed his tail with the other.

The iguana, hissing like a steam whistle, tried to roll with the big bird. Aguila stopped him with her outstretched wings. The iguana countered by pushing forward, trying to throw the eagle over on her back. Aguila spread out her tail like a fan and braced herself against it. That did it. The lizard lay helpless, making a sound like the Twentieth Century Limited warming up at the station. While the two animals struggled there together, Dan tore his shirt into strips and tied up the big dragon.

When I came up, I found Aguila standing in a rapidly widening pool of blood. Dan, having secured the lizard, picked up Aguila and began to wipe the gore off her yellow feet. "I don't know where this blood came from," he said in surprise. "The lizard doesn't seem to be hurt."

We had flown Aguila at so many iguanas that we'd begun to think that the eagle was invulnerable. Suddenly Dan said very quietly, "He's bitten off one of her toes."

I felt sick. But Aguila didn't seem to be in any pain. When we examined the foot more closely, we found that the toe was hanging by what seemed to be nothing but a bit of skin. Dan simply stuck the toe in place, holding it there with adhesive tape. Incredible as it sounds, the toe grew together again. But we didn't fly Aguila at any more iguanas.

HOME TO LECTURE

WHILE Aguila was recuperating, Dan and I worked away at the lecture. Unfortunately, we wouldn't be able to see any of the film that we'd shot until we got back to the United States. Mexico didn't have facilities for processing color film. Not knowing whether your pictures are any good is a horrible feeling. There's always the unpleasant doubt that perhaps there's something wrong with your camera or your exposures have been a little off. But we had to take that chance. In the meanwhile, we went on taking pictures that didn't involve Aguila or the iguana hunts.

But after a while we got restless. We wanted to see the film that we'd worked over so long and so hard and we wanted to see how lecture audiences would respond to our efforts. So when Aguila's foot was completely healed, we were ready to leave. Once again we loaded our station wagon. Packing the car was far more difficult than it had been in New York. We had some fifty iguanas, including the big fellow who was our pride and joy. He had gotten very tame and had even learned to eat bananas from my hand. We had a large cage made for the coatis which took up a terrific amount of room and also a few of the usual Mexican souvenirs. Altogether, there was hardly enough room in the car for us.

We said good-bye to all our friends in Taxco. Maria and I wept on each other's shoulders. I thought at the time that we'd never meet again and felt as though I were losing one of my dearest friends. During the six months we had lived in Taxco, Maria had taken care of Dan and me like an affectionate mother looking after wayward children. She advised us in time of trouble and comforted us when things went wrong. Yet Maria "went with the house" and was as much a fixture there as the walls or the roof. The owners of the house paid her a few pesos

285

a month to stay there and take care of any American tourists who were idiots enough to pay what to them was the fantastic rental of fifty dollars a month. Maria never questioned her fate. The next renters might be dipsomaniacs. Maria would have made sure that they were put to bed at night and that there was always a plentiful supply of liquor. She was always wise, kind, and efficient. Yet she had no security, no future, and no private life. Today, I have a home with all the latest modern appliances . . . electric stove, electric dishwasher, electric drier, and electric washing machine. I would still cheerfully turn them all in for Maria.

Even Dan and I, optimistic as we were, realized that we couldn't keep an eagle and two coatis in our one-room apartment in New York. Fortunately, there was a simple solution to this problem . . . the top floor of my parents' garage. It was large, airy, and had a nice view from the windows. So, instead of going direct to New York, we stopped off at my parents' home.

Mother was a little taken aback when we told her about the eagle. Mother doesn't like birds particularly. We assured her that Aguila was no trouble and John, our Japanese houseman, offered to look after the bird.

We disposed of our cargo of iguanas, most of them going to the Philadelphia Zoo, and Dan and I left for New York with the coatis, Pancho and Pedro. They hadn't been in our apartment ten minutes before they learned how to turn on the faucets in the bathroom when they wanted a drink. Unfortunately, they never did learn how to turn them off again.

The sixteen millimeter color film that we'd taken in Mexico arrived at long last from the Eastman laboratories. We got out our projector, pulled down the shades in the apartment, and Dan threaded up the first reel with shaking fingers.

The first reel was good. "Try the next," I said, hardly daring to breathe. That was good too. I'm afraid we weren't very critical. If we could see what was on the film, we were satisfied.

286

Absolutely correct exposure, depth of focus, and composition were unimportant to us.

Dan edited the film and then took it to Mr. Lee Keedick, a lecture agent of whom we had heard glowing reports. Mr. Keedick didn't go into the ecstasies we'd hoped over our pictures, but he agreed to handle us. A week later, Mr. Keedick called us to say that we were to speak at Columbia University that Saturday evening.

Dan and I had arranged to talk alternately. I would give the "woman's view" of our trip while Dan confined himself to talking about hunting with Aguila. We were very proud of our films and had worked out a very nice talk. So we headed for the university that evening with no misgivings.

The chairman in charge of lectures met us and ushered us through a small door. I glanced up casually and suddenly found that we were standing on the stage of an enormous auditorium. This coliseum was packed with people who promptly broke into optimistic applause. Our chairman announced us and said cheerfully that he was sure everyone was in for a delightful experience. Then he left us.

Dan crossed an acre or two of stage and stood unhappily in front of the microphone. Then he coughed nervously to clear his throat and produced a sound that rang through the auditorium like a cannon shot. Horrified, Dan got so far away from the mike that nothing he said was audible. The frantic sound man turned his amplification unit on full in a desperate attempt to pick up Dan's muttered remarks. No sooner had he done so, than Dan promptly stepped out to the mike and bellowed into it. The resulting roar didn't do the building any permanent damage but it so frightened Dan that he carefully avoided the mike from then on. The people in the first row may have heard him, but if so they had to strain their ears.

At last the time came for me to talk. At first everything went well. Then I too bogged down. Our talk had to be co-ordinated with the pictures on the screen. I thought I knew every frame of those films as well as I knew the letters in my name, but I was

287

standing directly below the huge screen and the degree of distortion was so great I couldn't tell what the pictures were. After futilely trying to talk into the mike and at the same time puzzle out what was on the screen, I gave up the struggle and just went ahead with my talk. As a result, I found out later that I was discussing housekeeping problems in Taxco while the film showed Wriggles in a battle to the death with a giant iguana.

Dan and I were pretty discouraged after that lecture and so was Mr. Keedick. So we went to see Mrs. Hazel Muller, who is in charge of the lecture series at the American Museum of Natural History in New York, to ask for a booking. Mrs. Muller said that she'd caught our Columbia lecture and didn't think we had enough experience to talk before a museum audience.

To our astonishment, she pulled out a large, loose-leafed notebook full of notes about every lecturer in the business. Three pages were already devoted to us.

That evening, we went over Mrs. Muller's criticisms carefully. The next day, we examined our film and ruthlessly eliminated all the out-of-focus shots, badly exposed pieces, and shaky bits that she had objected to. Our pictures had seemed quite good when shown on a small screen in our living room, but when projected on a giant screen in a large auditorium every little defect appeared with horrible distinctness.

As we continued to lecture, we were constantly making new changes, depending on our audiences' reaction. We soon found out that Wriggles got more applause than the wild birds and animals we had spent so much time photographing. Wriggles had personality. We added more footage of Wriggles and discovered that audiences got to expect her and began to laugh as soon as she appeared on the screen. People also liked the coatis. Poncho and Pedro were so popular that we decided to take them around to lectures with us. From then on, our career as lecturers was assured. People would far rather see the coatis trying to open a pop bottle than they would watch the rarest of Mexican birds sitting on their nests.

Taking the coatis on tours was a lively business but at that it was better than leaving them in the apartment. We had a large, very substantial cage made for them, and whenever we left the apartment, Poncho and Pedro were firmly put inside while they screamed, bit, and scratched. That cage could have held a bull elephant, but it didn't hold the coatis for long. One day we returned to be met at the apartment door by a despairing janitor, a furious model who lived in the apartment below us, and the owner of an art store located on the ground floor of the building. While we were gone, the coatis had managed to get the door of their cage open. They had promptly gone into the bathroom and turned on the water in the bathtub. Unfortunately, the plug was in and as the coatis never bothered to turn the water off after they'd finished with it, the tub soon overflowed. The water had poured down in the model's apartment below us, ruining her dresses, and then had gone on down into the art dealer's store. Luckily it didn't hurt any of his paintings, but it made a mess of his rug.

We got Poncho and Pedro back in their cage, feeling that we'd be spending the next twenty years paying for the damage they'd done. But neither the art dealer nor the model would accept a cent. Both of them said the whole disaster had been an accident and that they didn't want us to lose by it. The model claimed she could dine out on the story for the next month and if anyone asked her why her dress was stained, she'd merely say, "Oh, a couple of anteaters poured water on it." The art dealer said the rug would dry out and no real damage was done, although he did suggest that in the future we disconnect the plumbing before leaving the apartment.

CLOSE-UP OF A MANTA RAY

W E HAD never thought of trying to sell our films to a motion-picture company. But after Dan's article on our Mexican adventures called "Hunting Dragons with an Eagle" appeared in the *Saturday Evening Post,* we began to get calls from Hollywood. One of these calls resulted in a contract to return to Mexico to make a short film of Aguila hunting iguanas for Universal Pictures.

We telegraphed Natalie Scott to have Casa Riding ready for us, and when we pulled up in front of the familiar door, Maria and Chon were waiting to greet us. I felt as though we had come home.

When the picture was finished, Dan and I decided to prepare another lecture before returning to the United States.

Poncho and Pedro had been the hit of our first lecture. We were both determined that our second lecture would have plenty of pet animals in it. Then to "sell" the picture to lecture chairmen we also needed some spectacular sequence to take the place of the eagle and lizards combats. One afternoon, two Americans who were passing through Taxco dropped in to see us. They described themselves as "Old Mexican hands" and talked knowingly of remote villages far off the ordinary tourist routes.

The couple had just returned from Acapulco, which at that time showed little promise of ever being the internationally known resort that it has now become. "Of course, most Americans who go to Acapulco stay at the Mirador Hotel," the lady explained to us condescendingly. "But that's very expensive . . . eight dollars a day with meals. We discovered a delightful little place that is only half that much and has so much charm. You see, we enjoy getting off the beaten track."

"And you really get to know the natives," her husband added. "We met some Indian boys who, for a few pesos, will actually dive off a hundred-foot rock into a little gully that's fed by breaking waves. When the waves recede, the gully is almost empty so the boys have to time their dives to correspond with the breaking waves."

"Yes, the natives there are absolutely fearless," said the lady. "They swim out in the surf and fight sharks and giant manta rays with nothing but knives."

I didn't know what a manta ray was, so the assembled company had to explain to me that a manta ray is a huge fish, shaped somewhat like a gigantic bat, that measures twenty feet across his "wings." They are sometimes called "devilfish" because, according to an old story, a ray will envelop a swimmer with his huge wings and drown him. Dan and I couldn't believe that a man could fight such a creature with nothing but a knife, but when our visitors produced snapshots of the Indians making magnificent swan dives off a cliff that seemed towering, we were convinced.

"Jule, here's our next lecture," said Dan, wildly excited. "We'll make up a story about these boys, ending with a big hand-to-hand struggle between one of them and a giant manta ray."

Our guests explained that we'd really have to get Hugo to help us. "Hugo is a young German who lives in a little thatched cottage by the beach," the lady explained. "He's a perfectly wonderful person. He's done everything . . . diving for sunken treasure, running a trading schooner up and down the coast, and exploring the jungles of South America. He knows the natives intimately and he'll make all your arrangements for you."

Our visitors were hardly out the door when Dan and I started making feverish arrangements for our departure. We were both very confident. This picture would be easy.

When we reached Acapulco the small hotel recommended by our friends turned out to be a sort of tourist court, carefully located in a hollow that kept out every breath of air. The place was alive with mosquitoes. However, it was cheap and we felt

291

that as old travelers, we should be able to rough it a bit for the sake of the picture.

The next morning, we looked up Hugo, the picturesque young German of whom we'd been told.

When Dan explained why we'd come to Acapulco, Hugo eagerly volunteered for the job.

"I know all the diving boys," he told us hopefully. "I can get one of them to act for you very cheap. How much commission can you pay me?"

Dan hesitated, so I hurriedly spoke up. "Would a hundred pesos be all right?"

"Done!" said Hugo quickly.

We hoped to sell our Acapulco film to Universal as a short, as well as using it in our lecture. To make the picture more acceptable for commercial release, Dan had written a scenario for it . . . a very simple story about an Indian fisherman who sees his little brother attacked by a manta ray and dives off a cliff to rescue him. The picture ended with a fight between the manta ray and the fisherman; the man using only his knife. Hugo approved the script until Dan came to the ending. Then he burst into laughter.

"Why, none of these Indians would go anywhere near a manta," he assured us. "They're scared to death of them. Where did you ever get such an idea as that?"

We both explained that the couple we'd met in Taxco assured us that the fishermen fought mantas and sharks for fun. Hugo laughed until he could hardly sit up.

"Oh, I know that couple," he managed to gasp out. "They were only here a few days. Indians killing manta rays with knives! Oh, this is really too good."

It might have been funny to Hugo, but it certainly wasn't funny to us. When I saw how distressed Dan was, I was furious at the American couple. Posing as great authorities on Mexico and sending us off on a crazy trip like this! And they'd been so positive about the whole thing, even behaving as though we were idiots to doubt their story.

292

Finally I remarked gloomily that there didn't seem anything for it but to return to Taxco. That sobered Hugo quickly. He didn't want to lose the hundred pesos.

"Wouldn't just the dive be enough?" he asked. "The Indians really do that and it's very dramatic."

Dan and I both shook our heads. The dive would be over much too quickly. Then Dan began to question Hugo about mantas. Hugo explained that the great fish float very close to the warm surface of the water. An Indian can get right on top of a manta in a canoe. Harpooning them is comparatively simple. But if a man got into the water with one, the ray would stun him with a blow of its great wings. "I know all about mantas and there's no possible way it can be done," Hugo concluded.

Dan had been listening carefully. He said, "Suppose you used a harpoon with a very small, detachable head . . . a head so light that it would hold the ray without injuring him. Then you used some fine wire for the harpoon line. By keeping a strain on the line, you could prevent the ray from turning on the man. Couldn't it be done under those circumstances?"

Hugo thought for a minute. Then he said, "With a setup like that, it could be done."

At that time, there were three boys who did the dramatic dive off a great rock known as the Quebradas. The Quebradas form part of the cliff on which the Mirador Hotel is built and the boys performed this difficult and dangerous feat for the hotel's patrons. Afterwards, they'd pass the hat and usually took in half a dozen pesos . . . about a dollar. I found it hard to believe that anyone would risk his life for such a small sum but Hugo explained that by making several dives a day, the boys did very well . . . certainly better than the average Indian. "Also, the dives only take a few seconds so the boys have the rest of the day off," Hugo pointed out.

Hugo went off to find the diving boys and see if they were willing to do the fight. He returned that evening to say that one of the boys had consented to try it. The boy was perfectly willing to make the hundred-foot dive from the Quebradas as many times as we wanted for ten pesos, but he wanted three hundred pesos for the fight with the ray. Dan and I did some rapid budgeting and decided we could just afford it.

We also needed a little boy to play the part of the diver's younger brother. As Dan had originally written the script, the boy had a friend who went with him on his fishing trips . . . a sort of Indian Tom Sawyer–Huckleberry Finn combination. Hugo brought in two boys, both about twelve years old. One of them was a pure-blooded Indian. The other boy was more Negroid. As there is a considerable mixture of blood among the natives of Acapulco, there was nothing incongruous in this combination and we liked the contrast.

Hugo arranged for the renting of a small fishing boat and the use of two canoes. Dan was to be in one canoe with the hand-held camera getting close-ups of the ray. I would be in the fishing boat with our heavy cine-special mounted on a tripod taking a "master" shot of the whole affair. The other canoe was for the two little boys who were supposed to paddle around at a safe distance from the ray while our native diver was struggling with the animal.

We delayed several days to make positive of getting absolutely faultless weather. Acapulco weather is generally beautiful but there were big, fluffy clouds in the sky that might happen to float across the sun at a crucial moment, thus suddenly changing the exposure in the middle of the fight.

Finally the perfect morning dawned. The water was as smooth and green as the top of a billiard table. I sat in the bow of our little boat, between the two canoes which had been tied on either side like inverted fenders, basking in the sun and thinking this was the nicest possible way to make a picture.

But as our boat reached the mouth of the bay, the water grew rougher. Great swells came rolling in and our boat rose to meet them like a horse to a jump. Hugo came forward. "These swells make it good for ray fishing," he told me. "The waves raise the fish up so they're more apt to lift their wings above the surface

294

and you can see them more easily." Everything seemed to be working out perfectly.

But before we'd cruised more than a couple of miles along the coast, everybody began to get horribly seasick. Even the native crew were taken ill. Our diver became so sick that he wanted to turn back. The little Negro boy was simply a forlorn bundle of misery in the cabin, and at last even the captain had to lean over the side.

Suddenly one of the crew, who had been hanging over the bow in agony, gave a shout and pointed ahead. Some thirty yards in front of us a great swell was slowly beginning to build up. As the hill of water gradually rose, I could see on its side a great, dark, diamond-shaped form. As the swell grew higher, the water seemed to grow clearer and suddenly we could see the entire fish. He was longer than the boat and I had a sinking feeling that the whole idea of this trip had been a horrible mistake. Nobody but an idiot would ever dream of sticking a harpoon into that monster. For a man to try leaping on the creature's back would be simple suicide.

Instantly everyone forgot all about being seasick. The captain grabbed the wheel and swung the boat towards the ray. Dan and I tumbled over each other to get the cameras. By then the ray had disappeared. As there aren't any landmarks in the ocean, locating the exact spot where he had submerged was very difficult. The captain cut the engines and then, as the boat drifted forward under its momentum, turned the wheel over to a member of the crew. Running to the bow, he snatched up the harpoon. Bracing one foot against the gunnel, he stood with the harpoon upraised, carefully studying the water as the boat drifted on.

When there was no sign of the ray, the captain motioned the man at the wheel to start the engines. As he did so, the ray's wing tip broke water a few feet to our left. The man at the wheel started to swing the boat over when the ray's other wing tip broke water on our right. We were passing right over the partially submerged fish.

"Cuidado!" shouted the captain and drove his harpoon straight down in front of the boat's bow. Suddenly the whole ocean exploded around us. The broken handle of the harpoon shot past my head and ricocheted off the cabin. We were soaked with spray. I clung to my camera with one hand and to Dan with the other. The harpoon line was hurling itself out of the bucket so fast that the loops didn't have time to straighten out. Everyone was yelling, *"Donde estas el manta?"* . . . a good question, as sometimes a ray will leap clear out of the water and come down on top of a boat.

Dan was desperately trying to take pictures of the struggle although the lens of his camera looked like Niagara Falls. The ray had surfaced now and was beating the water with his wings. The great flippers hit the surface with reports like a shotgun fired off in a tunnel.

"He may break loose," gasped the captain. "Hurry with your pictures."

We started launching the canoes in almost hysterical haste. Two of the crew swung into the first canoe and Dan dropped in between them. I handed him down his camera and the Indians shoved off.

Instead of going directly towards the fish, they began to paddle around him in a great arc. The ray was fighting desperately to throw out the harpoon head. At one moment, he would leap nearly clear of the water like a hooked salmon . . . if you can imagine a salmon twenty feet across and shaped like a flounder. Then he would start swimming in a straight line, towing the heavy boat behind him. An instant later, he would dive and the captain would have to throw the harpoon line off the stanchion to let it run. The men in the canoe had only a vague idea where the ray was, as the heavy swells concealed the creature and when the fish dove he was completely invisible. The line was of no help in keeping track of the monster's whereabouts, for it might be leading directly forward over the bow and the ray suddenly surface astern of the boat.

The captain said desperately to Hugo, "The fish will throw

296

that harpoon head in a few minutes. Why doesn't that fool gringo take his pictures instead of paddling around the ocean?"

Hugo repeated the question to me. I had no idea what Dan was doing. I tried to scream at him, but he was too far away. Then I decided to take pictures myself. As soon as I looked through the camera finder, I saw at once what the trouble was. The boat had swung so that we were facing directly into the sun. Dan had realized this and was making the paddlers take him around the ray so he'd have the sun at his back.

I explained this to Hugo, who told the captain who used a brief Spanish expletive that I'm glad I couldn't understand. Every minute was precious now and Dan and his two paddlers seemed to have set off for a pleasant little cruise along the Mexican coast that was taking them farther from the ray every second. At last they got into position and I saw Dan taking pictures. He finished his roll, reloaded the camera (all this seemed to take hours), and then waved to me.

I said to Hugo, "He wants the canoe with the two boys next."

We didn't have the slightest intention of allowing the children to get within reach of the fish. Dan wanted them to paddle past the ray at a safe distance so he could get their canoe and the struggling manta in the same frame. Unfortunately, no one had gotten this idea across to the boys. As far as they were concerned, we'd paid forty pesos apiece for them and now obviously considered them expendable. The little colored lad sat down on the deck and positively refused to budge. In desperation, I turned to the Indian boy.

"Will you do it?" I asked him.

The child drew himself up. "Death means nothing to an Indian," he said proudly.

This was horrible. But the crew had already launched the second canoe and the boy leaped into it. Snatching up the paddle, he headed straight for the ray.

With the most marvelous skill, the boy shot his rickety craft right over the partially submerged monster. Then he circled the

297

ray several times, and finally came in so close that he was actually able to lean out of the canoe and touch one of the ray's thrashing wings. Then he swung the canoe away and headed back for the boat while the entire crew cheered him. He was pulled on board and stood there grinning happily while the crew beat him on the back.

Now was the moment for the climax of our film. The Indian diver with a knife between his teeth would swim out and battle the fish. I shouted to Hugo to get the diver.

"I can't!" Hugo shouted back. "The man's helpless with seasickness. He can't move."

I rushed to the cabin. The diver was lying groaning on the floor. "Get me ashore!" he kept moaning. "Get me ashore!"

The captain appeared in the cabin door. "What's delaying you?" he bellowed. "The manta is pulling us too far inshore. We'll be in the surf in another few minutes. Hurry, or I'll cut him loose!"

"Don't you dare cut him loose!" I screamed back. Then I said to Hugo, "Tell that man that unless he stops lying around on that floor, we'll go out to sea and roll around there for the rest of the day."

That did it. The diver staggered to his feet and reeled out of the cabin. One of the crew shoved the knife into his hand. The diver put it between his teeth and sprang over the side.

The water seemed to revive him. While Dan and I poured film through the cameras, he swam towards the ray. The fish was tiring now and floating just flush with the surface. The diver treaded water until the manta's back was towards him. Then he gave a quick kick and, grabbing the ray by the head, pulled himself up on the broad back.

The ray instantly brought both his great wings down on the water with a crash that hurled spray ten feet into the air. Then he reared up until his white belly was plainly visible. For an instant, I thought the fish was going over backwards but the weight of the man on its head kept the manta down. The manta rolled on its side, and tried to wipe off the man with one of its

298

wings. Then the fish dived. For a split second both man and fish vanished under the water. They had hardly disappeared before the ray came shooting up again and tried to jump. Again the man's weight pulled the fish down.

The captain grabbed my arm. "Look!" he said, pointing inland. The boat was drifting towards the most terrible breakers I've ever seen. They were at least fifteen feet high. For the last few minutes, I'd been vaguely conscious of a drumming noise like heavy thunder but I'd been too excited to notice it. Now I realized the noise came from these terrible waves.

"We must get out to sea," said the captain abruptly. "I'll start the engines."

I knew he was right, but I didn't know what would happen when the boat took up the slack on the harpoon line. I continued running off film while the captain struggled with the engines and the boat drifted steadily towards the breakers. Suddenly the motor began to throb and jets of smoke and spray rose astern. Slowly, we began to pull away from the shore.

When the ray felt the tug on the harpoon line, he really began to fight. He jerked back and forth and then dove again. This time the diver had to let go. As the man came up, the ray turned over on its side and struck at him with one of its wings. The man dove to escape the blow. Then he was left behind as we moved out to sea, towing the ray behind us.

Dan came up alongside in his canoe. He was almost incoherent with rage. "What's the idea of stopping the fight?" he yelled.

"We had to," I screamed back. "We were getting too near the shore."

Dan turned around and noticed the breakers for the first time. He reluctantly had to admit the captain was right. "Well, the diver'll have to fight the ray again out here," he called.

The diver had swum over to the boat by now. He climbed on board and announced that there wasn't enough money in Mexico, or the United States either, to induce him to get near that ray a second time.

Dan looked at the footage scale on his camera. "How many feet have you got, Jule?" he called.

"Ninety feet," I shouted back.

"I've got eighty." Dan considered. "Well, with the filling shots we can just make it."

The Indians brought the canoe alongside the boat and Dan clambered aboard. The captain supervised the securing of the canoes. Then he turned to Dan. "Is that all?"

"That's all," Dan said reluctantly.

The captain picked up a spear with a very long shaft and a stubby, knife-sharp head. "We'll bring the boat in close to the manta. I'll kill him and get the harpoon head back," he explained.

Dan and I looked at each other. After all, sport fishermen come to Acapulco every year by the hundreds and catch scores of sailfish and marlin. No one considers it cruel. We had not hesitated to harpoon the ray in the first place for the picture was very important to us. Just the same, we both hated to see him killed. We'd given the poor creature a hard-enough time without that.

"Can't you cut the harpoon line and let him go?" asked Dan.

The captain looked at Dan as though he considered him crazy.

"It'll cost you ten pesos for the harpoon head," he told us.

"We'll pay the ten pesos," Dan decided.

The captain put down the spear and got a pair of wire-cutting pliers from the cabin. The steersman brought the boat close to the ray. The captain leaned over the side and cut the line near the manta's head. Then we swung away. The ray continued to float on the surface for a few minutes. Then he suddenly dived and disappeared.

This very slight act of charity brought us in an unexpected return. Dan wanted to try taking some pictures of pelicans on the way back. He put a plate holder loaded with color film in his Graflex. Then he opened the lens as far as it would go, set the shutter to the maximum speed for the light, and turned to focus the camera on a spot about fifty feet from the boat. Suddenly the ray broke water in the exact spot where his camera was focused. In an ecstasy of relief at finding himself free from the nagging restraint of the line, the great fish soared up like a huge bat. As he rose out of the water, Dan pressed the camera trigger. The ray fell back and was gone.

Dan turned to me, his face shining as though he'd seen a vision. "Jule, if that picture comes out, it's one of the damnedest photographs anybody ever got."

It was, too! *Life* featured our manta ray picture in full color and described it as "One of the most remarkable fish pictures ever taken."

A NEW PET, BABY JULE

PEARL HARBOR had come while we were in Mexico, and as soon as we returned to the United States, Dan applied for a commission in the Navy. Almost at the same time, I made another important discovery. I was going to have a baby.

The Navy, on checking Dan's record, decided that he could best be put to work making training films. So he was stationed at the Photographic Science Laboratory in Anacostia, just outside of Washington, D. C. We managed to rent a small house in Georgetown and I moved in with Wriggles and Aguila. Poncho and Pedro we reluctantly gave to the Philadelphia Zoo.

I went home to be with Mother when my baby was born. She was a little girl and we named her Jule after me. I thought she was the nicest pet I'd ever had. As soon as the baby was old enough to travel, I took her to Washington.

Occasionally, Dan would have some of his Navy friends in to dinner. I found that entertaining in United States was very different from entertaining in Taxco. There, I had only to tell Maria how many we expected for supper and she quietly arranged everything. Here, I had to do all the cooking myself, although Dan did help clean up afterwards. During one of these evenings, Dan decided to amuse his friends by giving them an exhibition of sword swallowing and fire eating. Not unnaturally, he was a sensation. Afterwards, everyone wanted to know how he'd ever learned these stunts.

Now as far as Dan was concerned, there'd been nothing particularly humorous about learning to swallow a sword or eating fire. The people in the carnival had been his friends and he had accepted them for what they were. So Dan, as seriously as if he were discussing the Marshall Plan, began to describe the correct technique for swallowing a giant corkscrew and sewing buttons on your eyelids.

In two minutes, our guests had dissolved in helpless laughter. Dan was at first astonished. Then, showman that he is, he began to play up to them. Before the evening was over, he had developed a sort of dead-pan delivery that had even me laughing and I'd heard all the stories many times before.

When our last guest had left, Dan said to me in thoughtful amazement, "Why, Jule, this carny stuff is funny. When I wrote my book on the side show, I handled it as though I were putting out a treatise on mathematics. I'm going to try again."

We'd almost forgotten about Dan's rejected manuscript that he'd written during the first months of our married life. Now we dug it out of the trunk. He planned to write a series of articles on the different side-show stunts, handling each in the same dead-pan way that he'd told the stories that evening.

His first article was called "How to Swallow a Sword" and sold at once, promptly picked up by the *Reader's Digest*. In the next few weeks it was reprinted all over the world . . . we were even sent a copy of the *Bagdad Gazette* with the article translated into Arabic. Dan did another on fire eating and soon had a series launched. At long last, we were getting some good from that poor, rejected carnival book.

At last on that glorious day of August 14, 1945, the war was over. Dan was discharged from the service a few weeks later and we prepared to resume our interrupted lives.

I had almost forgotten my ambition to be an actress. Ever since I'd been married to Dan, I'd had too many other things to think about. Then one day our agent called us from New York. John Beck, a producer at International Pictures, had seen our lecture film and wanted me to come to Hollywood for a screen test. Dan was even more excited than I was. He told our agent to telegraph Beck that I was on my way. Dan would stay in Washington and look after baby Jule while I was gone.

I left by plane with very mixed feelings. I hated to leave Dan and Julie even for a few days. If by some miracle John Beck did like me and I signed a contract, it would mean that I couldn't go on any more trips with Dan. Still, it seemed like such a great opportunity I couldn't turn it down.

The test was scheduled for eleven o'clock in the morning. I was so nervous the evening before that I couldn't get to sleep until shortly before dawn. I had hardly closed my eyes when I was awakened by the frantic ringing of the telephone. I stumbled out of bed and managed to get the receiver off the hook. Mr. Morley, a young executive who was handling my test, was on the phone.

"What are you doing in your hotel?" he yelled. "We only have three hours before the test."

Bewildered, I got a taxi and sped down to the studio. Morley was waiting at the gate. He rushed me to the make-up department where the experts were already impatiently waiting for me. They sat me down in a big chair like a barber's chair and the head make-up man started putting on the grease paint.

When he finally finished, Morley hurried me across the hall to the hairdresser's. The girl there grabbed me as I came in the door. "You're awfully late," she complained, starting to work on me before I could sit down. When I emerged from the drier, I'd never seen my hair look so lovely. I would have liked to have sat and admired myself. But the hairdresser twisted a net over my hair and Morley rushed me off to the wardrobe room.

Two girls helped me to dress. Then with the hair net still over my hair and the fitter trotting along beside me making last-minute changes with my suit, I headed for the sound stage.

After each take, the make-up man would run on the set and retouch my face and the hairdresser would pat my hair back into shape.

I returned to the hotel late that afternoon feeling as though I'd just come through a painful operation. After taking a hot bath, I called Dan. He had news for me.

"Jule, I was at the Academy of Natural Sciences in Philadelphia and met Charles Mohr there. He's a well-known authority on bats. It seems that vampire bats in Mexico have been biting cattle and may be spreading disease. The bats live deep in a system of caves, some of the caves are apparently miles long and have never been explored. Charlie is going down there to investigate and I thought that I'd go with him."

Going back to Mexico again seemed like heaven. "Wonderful! When do we start?" I asked.

Dan hesitated. "Well, Jule, I thought I'd better do this alone. With this big opportunity, you'd be wiser to stay in Hollywood. After the Mexican trip, I can join you there."

Dan and I had never been separated for more than a few days and I knew this trip might take three months. I'd miss him horribly and already I was getting bored with Hollywood. Also, I wanted to explore those caves. It sounded wonderful.

So, feeling very restless, I waited to hear the results of the test.

Two days later, the studio called me in. They had been testing me for a definite part in a new picture, but the studio heads had decided that I wasn't quite the type and didn't have enough experience. However, they were willing to give me a job as a contract actress. I would get seventy-five dollars a week as a start and play in whatever roles they selected for me.

Seven years before, I'd have jumped at such an offer. Now, I never even considered it. The thought of sitting in Hollywood while Dan was off exploring caves seemed horrible to me.

There was another reason why I felt that I couldn't accept a job under contract . . . a reason that I wasn't even going to tell Dan until after we'd come back from the cave-exploration trip. I was going to have another baby. I knew that if Dan found it out, he wouldn't let me go and I was determined to be with him. I hate the feeling that I'm being left out of things.

MEXICAN CAVES AND VAMPIRE
BATS

T HE plane seemed to take an eternity to fly back to Washington. Dan and I had never embarked on an enterprise that we both hadn't carefully discussed for long hours beforehand . . . until this cave-exploration business had come up while I was away in Hollywood.

I was the first one out of the plane. I looked around and there was Dan with Julie and Wriggles.

For a while all we could do was hug each other. I said over and over, "Never again! Hollywood or no Hollywood!"

At once I was plunged into the details of the cave-exploration trip and the problems of catching and keeping vampire bats, for Dan was counting on trying to tame some of the uncanny little creatures so he could photograph and study them. To work in the caves, we needed miners' helmets with headlights and batteries. We had to get Dietz lamps and extra flashlights. We needed carrying boxes for the bats. Mother had agreed to take care of Julie while we were gone and she was also allowing Aguila to stay in her old room over the garage.

In Philadelphia, I met Charlie Mohr. Charlie was an authority on cave exploration and all the strange animals that inhabit caves. He was secretary of the Speleologist Club, a group of men who devote all their spare time to exploring the underground world which most people hardly know exists.

I hadn't told anyone that I was pregnant and I didn't intend to, but when I saw the amount of equipment we'd have to carry into the caves, I knew that I could never lug my share of the equipment for the next three months. So I asked mother if Joe, my fourteen-year-old brother, could go with us.

Joe was delighted, so after a wild week of packing, checking cameras, and getting booster shots, we were ready to leave.

With Charlie and Joe in the back of our station wagon and Dan, myself, and Wriggles in the front, we started south.

In the excitement of preparing for the trip, I hadn't thought much about the bats. But as Charlie talked about the weird beasts, in his calm, detached, scientific way, I began to feel squeamish.

"Vampires seem to prefer living in the deepest, darkest caves that they can find," Charlie told us as we sped south across Oklahoma. "They sleep during the day, and then at dusk fly out to look for their prey. They must feed on fresh blood every twenty-four hours. They apparently eat nothing else. It doesn't have to be human blood. Any kind of blood will do. After they've gorged themselves, they fly back to the cave and sleep off their feast. The next evening, they're off again."

The first cave we explored was near the village of Los Sabinos, about two hundred miles south of the border. It consisted of half a dozen thatched huts, a well, a score of chickens, two cows, and some twenty Indians. The Indians were very much impressed to think that we'd come all the way from the United States to explore their cave. Everyone in the community knew the location of the cave but only two men . . . a father and his son . . . had ever been inside. They offered to act as guides.

I'd taken for granted that the cave was only a few steps from the village. Actually, it was several miles through the densest jungle. The entrance looked like the partly opened mouth of an old, toothless man. Vines overhung it like a straggly mustache. We climbed through the opening into a great entrance hall seventy feet high, filled with gigantic boulders. We began feeling our way down a long incline in utter darkness except for the puddles of light from our head lamps.

The long slope finally ended and we came out in a great room as big as Grand Central Station. The cave seemed to end here. We ran our lights around the walls. There were innumerable black pockets among the stones. Some of the passageways only went in a few feet and then stopped. Others kept on going. Our guides had stopped in front of one hole that seemed no different from any of the others, and started to writhe through the narrow tunnel. Charlie followed and then Joe and Dan. I went last.

The tunnel through the rock was much narrower than I'd realized. It was like crawling through a sewer pipe. I couldn't even get up on my hands and knees. I had to wriggle on my stomach. Finally I came out in another room, where the others were already standing.

Here, at last, I could stand. We were on the edge of a steep slope composed of mud as slippery as grease. The slope fell away into a vast black hole so deep that not even our powerful flashlights could reach the bottom of it.

The guides started working their way down the slope, kicking footholds in the soft mud as they went. We followed them cautiously. Only one person moved at a time, the rest holding their flashlights so the climber could see the footholds. Bats had begun pouring out of the hole below us like a black blizzard. Charlie said that these bats weren't vampires but the little, insect-eating kind. They rushed past over our heads like a pulsating cloud, keeping up a constant, shrill, chittering cry.

The guides stopped on a ledge of rock. We could see them playing their flashlights back and forth along an overhang which projected out over nothingness. One after another we joined them on the ledge and looked over into the abyss. "This is where we use a rope," the older man explained.

They doubled the rope so we could use one strand as a safety line and climb down the other length. Charlie went first. It seemed to take him forever to descend. I was next. I wrapped my feet around the climbing rope, and, gripping the safety line, slowly inched backward over the edge. I went down seventy feet and there the rope ended.

"I've come to the end, what shall I do?" I called up.

A hasty conference was held above me. At last Dan called back, "The guides say you're on the floor of another cave. Just let go."

I was in no mood for joking. "I'm not on the floor, I'm hanging in mid-air," I screamed back. "I won't let go."

Fortunately, Charlie Mohr came back from a little exploring trip he'd been making and flashed his light on me. I was hanging only six inches above the floor. Thankfully, I let go and sat down on a stone while Dan started down.

We moved forward slowly into a big room with passageways branching off on all sides. They were separated from the main hall by fringes of stalactites hanging like draperies around the openings. Getting down on our hands and knees we crawled under a strip of the stone teeth. Ahead of us was a series of great, billowing terraces like monster fountains turned into stone.

We began to climb the terraces. The rock was as smooth and as slippery as ice, but there were occasional hollows where we could sit and rest. Suddenly, on the wall ahead, we saw little shapes running and leaping among the formations. The long shadows thrown by our lamps added to their height. They looked exactly like little men rushing frantically about, trying to decide what to do. Every now and then, one of them would crane himself up to look down at us.

These were the vampires. Running on their hind feet and the elbows of their wings, they could go as fast as a four-footed animal. They kept turning their enormous ears about as a rabbit would, to pick up the noise we made. As we came closer, several ran to the edge of the ledges and sprang into the air. Others ran up the walls, hooking themselves up with two long thumbs growing out of the elbows of their wings. These thumbs are amazing instruments. Each one ends in a curved nail, like a squirrel's. Turning up our lights, we could see dozens of vampires hanging head down on the wall above us.

We found three young vampires in a pocket in the rock. They were all huddled together and their weird little bulldog faces peered out at us anxiously. Every time they saw the long bellows of the camera coming towards them, two of the little devils would grab the third and shove him forward while they hid behind him. I pulled them apart and lined all three up on a stalagmite, but before Dan could press the flash gun one of them had kicked another and the fight started all over again.

When we got back to the Indian village, it was late in the evening. Our first job was to try to feed our captured vampires. Charlie assured us that unless the weird little bats ate at least once every twenty-four hours, they would die. We bought a chicken from the villagers and Dan and Charlie killed it while I looked the other way. But the blood began to coagulate almost at once and the bats couldn't drink coagulated blood.

Here was an unforseen difficulty. Charlie came up with a valuable suggestion. "I know Dr. Alfredo Tellez Giron, chief of the Animal Pathology Laboratory in Mexico City," he told us. "I'm sure that Dr. Giron will have liquid blood in his laboratory. Blood can be kept from coagulating by certain processes but we don't have the apparatus to do it here."

We jumped in the car and raced for Mexico City. All during the long ride, I kept thinking, "Less than a month ago, I was taking a screen test in Hollywood, surrounded by directors, make-up men, and hairdressers. Here I am driving at breakneck speed over twisting mountain roads trying to get fresh blood for vampire bats." It did seem crazy, but I couldn't say that I hadn't asked for it.

Dr. Giron was most pleasant and very co-operative. He did have the blood we needed and Dan tried to feed the bats with an eyedropper, as by this time they were too weak to eat by themselves. I hadn't intended ever touching one of the vampires again, but Dan is rather clumsy when it comes to feeding animals. Finally, I begged him to let me try.

The bats weren't really mean. They were just frightened and upset. I'd have been upset too if I'd been a bat. I talked to them, scratched their heads, and finally persuaded them to drink from the eyedropper. I could never get really fond of them. But after a short time, I didn't mind their looks. In a way, they were quite handsome . . . rather like gargoyles. I was also very proud of the way they'd all line up for their blood every evening and eat until their little tummies were round as ping-pong balls.

For the next month, we explored cave after cave under the guidance of Charlie Mohr. The caves varied from two to ten miles in length, but two miles in a cave is very different from two miles along level ground. We had to climb up and down underground cliffs, wade streams, and crawl through holes. Often we spent hours wandering up and down dead-end passages trying to find the one that led into the main body of the cavern.

In the few weeks we spent creeping through caves, I began to realize dimly the terrible fascination of this underground world. Until humans succeed in reaching another planet, they will never find as weird a place as the interior of a great cave. Often the entrances were so small we had to crawl on our hands and knees to get in. We might crawl ten feet. We might crawl several hundred yards. Then we would come out in a room that might be as big as a closet or as big as the capitol at Washington. One of the caves had a room so huge that it contained mesas . . . flat-topped hills . . . at least a hundred feet high.

When we finished the cave exploration, we drove back by easy stages to Philadelphia and rented a small apartment near Bryn Mawr College. I settled down there with Julie and Dan to await the arrival of the new baby. Aguila, as usual, stayed in her room over mother's garage.

Since we had a little girl, I hoped this baby would be a boy. I'd always wanted a son. I was lucky. Our baby was a boy. We named him Danny. For the next few months, Dan and I lived in Bryn Mawr with our little family. I thought the children were the nicest "pets" I'd ever had, and Dan was delighted with them.

CAPRI INTERLUDE

AFTER Danny was born, we got a wonderful break. Dan's agent wrote him that a publisher wanted him to do a book about his life in the carnival. Writing the book would take nearly a year, so the publisher was giving us an advance on royalties. For the first time in our lives, we didn't have to go to some specific place to collect material for Dan had all the information in his head. We were in our element. We got tourist circulars, travel books, and tried to decide where to go. At last we decided on the fabulous Isle of Capri. It sounded like a perfect place to spend a year and we could take the children.

We sailed for Europe on the Ile de France in September. The crossing only took five days and I was sorry it wasn't twice as long. There was a swimming pool, a sun deck, dances in the evening, and motion pictures.

But I must admit we were a little disappointed in Capri. The town was charming but not as charming as our beloved Taxco. Little, twisting streets paved with cobblestones were no longer a novelty to us. Although the Bay of Naples was lovely, I thought Acapulco Bay was even lovelier. I missed the white-sand beaches, the long lines of palm trees, and the brilliant tropical birds. Also, the weather was terrible. It rained constantly during the first five days we were there and although the temperature never went down to freezing, it seemed to stay at a cold, damp fifty degrees that penetrated your bones.

We took a year's lease on a house that was a marble palace set in a series of terraced gardens an emperor would be proud to own. The rent was two hundred and fifty dollars. I thought the palace was the most beautiful home I'd ever seen. The gardens were ideal for the children and we were only a few minutes walk from the beach.

We moved in and Dan settled down to write his book in a

room that had a glass-sided alcove overlooking the bay and the garden. Unfortunately, he nearly froze to death. His fingers got so cold he couldn't hit the typewriter keys. The rains started again and before long, I began to feel less like a Roman empress and more like Sadie Thompson. The palace did have central heating . . . we'd carefully checked that item before moving in . . . but the furnace didn't work. We called the landlord and insisted that it be repaired. The landlord reluctantly consented, although as he angrily pointed out, "It never becomes cold enough in Capri to need more than a small fire in the fireplace." He was standing in the living room of our palace when he made this remark, clad in a heavy overcoat, rubber boots, a fur cap, and two suits of long, woolen underwear. I could see the ends of the underwear sticking out of the coat sleeves. We gave him cognac to stop his teeth from chattering and begged him to do something about the furnace.

The furnace was finally repaired and we joyfully started a fire. The old wreck was capable of generating enough steam to get the battleship Missouri underway. Eight hours later, every radiator in the place was red-hot but the temperature of the house had scarcely risen two degrees. Unable to understand this contradiction, we gave our beautiful home a more careful examination. The lovely leaded glass windows didn't fit within three quarters of an inch of their marble sills. You could have shoved your hand through the cracks in the carved, hand-colored twelfth-century doors. When we lit the furnace, we weren't heating the house. We were heating half of southern Italy.

There are some writers who can lock themselves up for six months or so and come out at the end of that time with a completed manuscript. Dan wasn't that kind. He'd work hard for a few hours a day and then he'd begin to get cramped sitting at a typewriter and want a break. To Dan, a break had always meant some form of exercise. There wasn't much you could do on Capri for exercise. Dan likes to walk and I think we walked over every square foot of that island. We saw Tiberias' castle and the Blue Grotto and Axel Munthe's house and finally Dan was even reduced to climbing up and down the side of the great cliff that composes Anacapri. But the almost constant rains interfered with walking and there wasn't anything else to do.

At long last, spring came to Capri. The slopes of the hills burst out into such masses of flowers that they seemed to be dyed red, blue, and yellow. Great bunches of purple wisteria hung over gateways and the sea turned, if possible, an even deeper, richer blue. Dan and I discovered the island all over again. Everything seemed different now that spring had come. The old Roman ruins, which had been somewhat bleak and forbidding in winter, took on a new beauty. We wandered through them by the hour, lamenting that in the past so many of the original mosaics had been carted away to museums or to private homes. Even so, enough remained to thrill us when we looked at a stained fresco and realized that other people had admired and loved that fresco two thousand years ago.

Then the summer season opened with a bang. Tourists began to pour into the island by the tens of thousands. The piazza was so packed it was impossible to force your way through it. Prices soared. The heat became suffocating and there was hardly standing room on the beaches. There were no screens in our house and the mosquitoes were everywhere. If you shut the windows, you smothered. If you left them open, you were eaten alive.

Dan's writing came to a standstill and looking over what he had accomplished during our six months on the island, we both had to admit that it wasn't very good.

One evening while we were sitting in our sweltering living room, swatting mosquitoes, we at last had the courage to come to a decision. Capri wasn't for us. We were desperately homesick for the United States. So we packed up and took the first boat back to America.

We moved in with dear, long-suffering Mother. Dan's first act was to take a trip to New York and show our agent his partially completed manuscript. The agent read it in silence. When he had finished, he looked up and said simply, "Dan, you know as well as I do, it's not right."

Delivery date to the publishers was sixty days away. Dan returned to Mother's feeling completely defeated. We had almost no money left and he couldn't face having to do a rewrite. For two days, he sat around moping while I tried to think of something to cheer him. Then one evening, Dan started to laugh. "Jule, I've just remembered a very funny thing that happened with the carnival while we were playing Newark." As he started talking, his face lit up with the interest and excitement I hadn't seen there all the time we were on Capri. When he finished, Dan jumped up and said, "I'm going to write that up before I forget it."

He went up to our bedroom and I heard the click of his typewriter . . . not the slow, hesitant sound I'd listened to in Capri but a fast, machine-gun beat. When I went up to bed at eleven, he was still working. It was dawn when he stopped. He got a few hours sleep and started again.

The typed pages began to pile up beside him. Dan virtually ignored the work he'd done in Europe. The book, *Step Right Up,* was completed two days before the dead line. A month after publication, it hit the *Herald-Tribune*'s best-seller list. An English publisher, Hamish Hamilton, brought it out in Great Britain and the *Evening Standard* published it serially. Bantam Books bought the paper-cover rights and *True* bought several articles based on incidents in the book.

When the first check for royalties came in, Dan sank down in a chair and said, "Well, Jule, we finally made it."

We certainly had.

WE ACQUIRE A CHEETAH

BOTH Dan and I had returned from Capri with a strong desire to resume our old way of life. For over two years, we hadn't done any work with animals, and working with animals was in our blood. We decided to base our new lecture on a camping trip with some strange, new pet.

"Jule, ever since I was a kid," Dan said one day, "I've always wanted to hunt with a pet cheetah."

"How wonderful! Let's get a cheetah and go hunting with it."

"Do you know what a cheetah is?"

"No, but I'm sure it's just what we want for our next lecture." I didn't really care what a cheetah was. I only knew it was some sort of an animal and we could get out of doors again instead of being cooped up in a house.

Still, I was a little taken aback when Dan explained that a cheetah was a hunting leopard. Dan, however, assured me that cheetahs were very nice animals. In India, the rajahs keep trained cheetahs to run down antelope and the big cats sleep in the same beds as the trainer's children. Cheetahs are the fastest four-footed animals in the world . . . reaching a speed of seventy miles an hour. Dan wanted to take a camping trip and see what a cheetah could do on the open plains of the West.

Our first problem was where to get a cheetah. Dan called a number of animal dealers he knew, and finally learned that Warren Buck, who is a wild-animal dealer in Camden, New Jersey, was expecting a shipment of rare beasts from Africa. We drove out to Mr. Buck's farm, hoping that there might be a cheetah in the collection.

"I've got one cheetah . . . a year-old kitten," Mr. Buck told us. "He's never been handled but I think with a little care you can tame him."

From the way Mr. Buck spoke, I expected to see something the size of a domestic tabby. Instead, Mr. Buck showed us a

316

spotted monster that looked as big as a lioness. The cat was throwing himself against the bars and sweeping his paw through the feeding slot trying to grab anything that ventured too close. He weighed about one hundred pounds and measured more than six feet, including his long tail.

I began to have an uneasy feeling that my husband was preparing to bite off more than he could chew. If we'd had our own home with a large cage where we could keep the animal I didn't doubt that eventually Dan could tame the cat. But obviously we couldn't let this creature go galloping around the house as we'd done with the coatis and he wouldn't sit on a perch like Aguila.

"Dan, where will we keep him?" I asked anxiously.

"In our bedroom, naturally," said Dan, clearly surprised by such a foolish question.

"But he isn't tame, dear," I squeaked helplessly.

"Oh, he'll tame up in no time," said Dan optimistically. Then, after thinking a few moments, he added, "I think we'd better keep him away from the children for a few days, though."

Mr. Buck said the cheetah cost nine hundred dollars. Dan and I looked at each other. Then Dan said, "Look at it like this. We have nine hundred dollars and what do we want more than a cheetah?" I couldn't answer logic like this, so I said nothing while Dan made out a check.

Four powerful cagemen forced the spitting, biting cat into a shipping crate and helped us load it into the back of our station wagon. Then we drove back to Mother's with our new purchase.

The shipping crate was much too small to keep the cheetah in but we didn't have anything else. We had planned simply to turn our bedroom over to the animal and sleep elsewhere until he tamed down. I thought it would be wiser to wait a few days and let the cat get accustomed to his new surroundings, but Dan was as eager to start playing with his new toy as a child is to open his Christmas stocking.

Sometimes I can talk Dan into being a little more cautious with animals, but this time his mind was made up. All I could do was get him to wait while I went down to the hardware store and got the biggest, heaviest collar they had and a strong chain. When I got back to the house, Dan had put on a heavy, leather, hunting jacket and equipped himself with a kitchen chair. He took the collar and chain up to the bedroom while I waited outside, furious with my husband and wishing desperately that I was inside the room and could see what was going on.

There were loud thumping noises and cries from Dan of "Easy, boy, down! Down!" Finally I couldn't stand it any longer and opened the door for a peek.

The cheetah was crouched in one corner while Dan, holding the chair in front of him, was talking to the animal. As soon as the cheetah saw me, he made a great bound for the door. Dan stopped him with the chair. The cat rolled on his back, playing patty-pat with the chair legs and even I could see he wasn't trying to attack Dan. He was playing. Dan put the chair down and scratched the cat's neck. The cat seized Dan's wrist in his jaws. I went sick and started to rush into the room but Dan easily extracted his hand and rubbed the cheetah's ears. In the next few minutes we satisfied ourselves beyond all doubt that the cheetah wasn't vicious. He had been cooped up in cages for months and this was his first chance to get a little exercise.

We named the cat Rani. We really should have called him Rajah, but we thought he was a female. The next day, we got Rani's collar on him and took him for a walk in the garden on a leash. Our cheetah behaved like a big dog being taken out for the first time in months. He rolled on the grass, and tried to chase every squirrel he saw. We gave him the run of the house and within a month he became such a member of the family that even Mother didn't object when the children pulled his tail or tried to ride on his back. Neither did Rani. He purred away like a twin-engine bomber warming up and licked the children with his sandpaper tongue.

When we were satisfied that Rani was as tame as he was ever going to get, we prepared for our trip to the West. We had a special cage built for Rani that fitted into the back of the station

318

wagon. Dan tied our tent and camping equipment on the roof of the car and we fitted Aguila's old perch into place. We'd decided to take the eagle with us and give the bird a chance to stretch her wings again in open country. Wriggles sat up front with us as usual.

We had taken for granted that Rani would ride peacefully in his cage all the way West. Rani, however, positively refused to stay in the cage. He cried constantly, giving a curious little bird-like chirp and was so fretful that at last we took him up in the front seat with us. Rani rode beautifully. Like a dog, he loved to stick his head out of the window to drink in the air. The only trouble was with other motorists. A car would start to pass us and then the driver would catch sight of Rani. Instantly he'd let go of the wheel and start gesticulating while he shouted to his passengers, "Look folks! They got a tiger in that car." Several times we almost had a collision while Dan shouted to the man either to pull ahead or drop behind us. Finally we had to put Rani in his cage when passing through towns or on roads where there was heavy traffic.

When we reached Texas, we were in open country. Dan was crazy to see what Rani could do with jack rabbits. I was less crazy. I could just see Rani . . . all nine hundred dollars' worth of him . . . vanishing over the horizon at seventy miles per hour after some rabbit. However, we'd gotten Rani because we could hunt with him, not simply to keep the cat locked up in a cage, so I reluctantly agreed to make the attempt.

Driving along a stretch of straight, almost deserted road, we saw a big, white-tailed jack rabbit leap up beside the highway. The rabbit raced the car and then suddenly bolted into a culvert under the road.

Dan slammed on the brakes and fell out of the car, followed by Wriggles. I hung on to Rani's collar. Rani hadn't seen the jack, but as the rest of the party raced for the culvert, the big cat nearly went wild trying to join them. At last I thought, "Well, if Dan wants to lose Rani the first week out, I suppose that's up to him," and I turned the cat loose.

319

Rani bounded out of the car and loped along behind Dan and Wriggles. I followed.

Dan had picked up Wriggles to keep her from charging into the culvert. Rani was sniffing at the mouth of the tube but not having much of a sense of smell, he still didn't know that the rabbit was inside.

"Jule, you stay here with Rani," Dan said. "I'll take Wriggles to the other end and put her in."

I took hold of Rani's collar so he would not follow Dan and Wriggles as they crossed the road. I could hear Wriggles roaring through the culvert, sounding like a lion in a tunnel. Then the jack suddenly shot out at my feet and sailed across the plains like a blown bit of thistledown.

I had no idea that jack rabbits could go so fast. I hated to turn Rani loose after that disappearing speck. But Rani was frantic at the sight of the rabbit. He pulled out of my hands and sped after the jack, moving so fast he seemed like an image on the screen when the projector is run too rapidly.

The rabbit hadn't been running at full speed but when he saw Rani he really did let himself go. He fled over the desert like a richocheting bullet. Fast as he went, he seemed to be standing still compared with the cheetah. Rani was on top of the rabbit when the jack suddenly doubled. Throwing out his long tail as a counterweight, Rani spun with the jack. The rabbit came racing back towards the road, with Rani gaining at every bound. A drainage ditch ran alongside the road. The rabbit turned, ran parallel to the ditch and then suddenly jumped across it. Rani tried to follow. He plunged head foremost into the ditch, turned a somersault, and landed on the bottom with all the breath knocked out of him. The clever jack vanished over the plains.

For the rest of the summer we camped out with our animals . . . setting up our tent any place that looked attractive and moving slowly through New Mexico, Utah, Wyoming, and Montana. We tried Rani on several different kinds of game . . . jack rabbits, coyote, and once, by mistake, on antelope. Rani overtook the antelope but made very little attempt to pull the animal down. Rani was really more of a pet than a killer, which was just as well for us.

Although we were always very careful to make sure that there was no one about before we turned the cat loose, Rani nearly got us in trouble several times. I remember one incident especially that could have been serious. Rani was running ahead as he usually did and Dan was following more leisurely when a man on a motorcycle appeared, whizzing along a dirt road we hadn't noticed. Rani stopped, fascinated by the strange sight and then, obviously deciding that the motorcycle was some strange, new kind of animal, took out after it. The rider saw the cheetah suddenly burst out of the sagebrush and come streaking towards him. He took one horrified look, and then pressed his foot down on the pedal, obviously confident he could leave this weird beast far behind. But he hadn't counted on Rani's speed. The racing cheetah easily pulled up alongside of the cycle while its frenzied rider tried desperately to coax a little more speed out of his vehicle. Rani was clearly puzzled by the machine and didn't quite know how to deal with it. He struck out at the cycle several times, but the noise of the cutout daunted him and he stopped. When Dan came up, Rani was standing in the middle of the road watching the motorcycle vanish over the next rise, the driver leaning forward like a jockey coming in on the homestretch.

When Dan got back to camp and told me what had happened, I was horrified and wanted to pack up and leave immediately. Dan was more casual. "When that fellow tries to tell people what he saw, nobody will believe him," he assured me.

After that experience, Dan and I tried never to let Rani get out of sight. Tame as Rani was, he was still a powerful animal and we didn't want any accidents to happen.

When autumn came, we drove westward to California. After shopping around a bit, we rented a lovely beach house at Malibu. The house was right across from a canyon in the Malibu hills, a wild spot where no one ever seemed to come. This canyon was an ideal place to exercise Rani and also to fly Aguila, so we rented the house and sent East for the children.

Dan, of course, was still writing articles. He did a piece about gem hunters . . . those strange people who wander through the desert looking for precious and semiprecious stones . . . and one about Homer Snow, a remarkable man who traps wild seals and trains them for circuses. But Dan was particularly interested in doing an article about Grace Wiley. Dan had known about Grace Wiley for years and often corresponded with her, although they had never met. Grace Wiley was a woman with a passion for poisonous snakes. She was the only person in history who had ever succeeded in taming hamadryads . . . the great, king cobras of India which reach a length of over eighteen feet and are by far the most aggressive and deadly of all snakes. In her home near Cypress, California, Grace kept rattlesnakes, cobras, water moccasins, Egyptian asps, mambas, European vipers, and many other reptiles. All of these creatures were tame and Grace was reputed to be able to handle them as easily as we could handle Rani and Aguila. Dan was crazy to do an article about her, so one day we drove out to Cypress to introduce ourselves. Neither of us had the slightest idea that this article was to end in a ghastly tragedy that made headlines throughout the country.

A GOOD STORY ENDS IN TRAGEDY

D AN had told me so much about this remarkable woman
that I'd expected to see an elaborate establishment, at
least as large as the reptile house in a zoo. Instead, there was
only a little, clapboard cottage and behind it a low, rambling
barnlike building. A tiny woman, scarcely five feet two and
weighing less than a hundred pounds, came out to meet us.

Dan explained the purpose of our visit and Grace beamed.

"I'm so glad, because I need publicity very much," she assured us. "You see, almost my only source of income comes
from people who want to see my snakes. If my place were only
better known, I'm sure it would make all the difference."

The barn was a long, narrow structure and rather dark. The
walls were lined with glass-fronted boxes, wire-mesh cages,
aquariums with wire tops, and every conceivable kind of con-
tainer that could hold a snake. Down the center ran a line of
tables, also full of cages. Obviously, Grace was hard pressed for
room in which to house all her collection.

"Now we'll start at this end and work down," Grace called as
she trotted up the aisle. "Don't step on a crocodile." At this
thoughtful warning, I hurriedly looked down. I could see several
large shapes lying on the floor or protruding half out from under
the tables. At least a dozen crocodiles and alligators lay sprawled
on the floor, varying in length from three feet to one monster
nearly fifteen feet long.

Dan threaded his way unconcernedly among these creatures.
After taking a deep breath and gritting my teeth, I followed him.
None of the saurians paid any attention to me, except for one
six-footer who opened his mouth and hissed as I went by. I carefully circled him and joined Grace and Dan.

"Aren't they handsome?" Grace asked me, referring to the
mixed crocodiles and alligators. "And so smart too! Each of
them knows his own name, and comes when I call him."

Now Dan knows quite a little about reptiles. He had often

told me that no reptile is smart enough to know its name or come when called. Obviously intending to warn Grace that we weren't completely gullible, Dan said politely, "That's very remarkable. In fact, this must be the first time in history such a thing ever happened."

Grace was preparing to open a cage but she stopped abruptly and turned to face Dan.

"You don't believe me, do you?" she asked.

Dan didn't answer her.

Grace gave a little sigh. Then she became brisk again. "Well, I'll tell you their names. Now the Chinese alligator over there is Mr. Ferocious. The Egyptian crocodile is named Jackie, the American alligator under the table is Bill . . ." and she went through the whole lot. "Now, you tell me which one you want me to call, and I'll bring him over."

I felt horribly embarrassed for the poor lady because, like Dan, I knew the half-sleeping saurians wouldn't pay any attention to her. I was sorry Dan had called her bluff.

Dan pointed to Mr. Ferocious. "Call him," he suggested.

Grace went down on her knees and called, "Here, Mr. Ferocious! Here, baby!"

Almost at once the alligator reared up on his stumpy legs and crawled rapidly across the floor. He lay down at Grace's knees and she scratched his head.

I glanced at Dan. He was staring popeyed.

"What's the grift?" he asked bluntly.

Grace looked puzzled, not understanding Dan's carnival lingo. Dan pointed to a crocodile. "Try that one," he demanded.

"Here Jackie!" called Grace. The crocodile was a little slower than Mr. Ferocious, but by the third call, he came also.

I've seldom seen Dan so excited. We stood there for an hour while Grace called those grotesque creatures to her and then moved to the other end of the barn and called them back again. Finally even Dan had to admit that the assorted saurians knew their names.

"Grace, this is the darndest thing I've ever seen and I've been

324

playing around with animals for twenty years," he told her. "Everybody says you're a miracle woman, but they've underestimated you."

"I'm not a miracle woman in the slightest," she told him gently. "People have never given reptiles the credit due them, that's all."

Then Grace began to show us the snakes. She stopped at each cage, lifting out its occupant and explaining the snake's fine points to us with the air of a connoisseur showing off a priceless art object. In silent awe we watched her carefully but easily handle copperheads from New England, Gabor vipers from the Congo, the terrible little karait from India, the Australian tiger snake and the slender Egyptian cobra. Grace made no attempt to hold the snakes behind their heads so they couldn't bite. She talked to each snake for a moment or so, stroked it gently with her hand, and then lifted it in her arms as you might pick up a puppy.

Then Grace stopped in front of a very large cage that seemed to contain nothing but newspaper. "These little fellows only arrived a short time ago so they're still very wild," Grace explained indulgently. She quietly lifted the paper. Instantly a forest of heads sprang up in the cage. Grace moved the paper slightly and the heads suddenly began to spread and flatten. Then I saw that they were not heads. They were hoods. I was looking at the world's most deadly creature . . . the Indian cobra.

Cobras kill twenty-five thousand people a year in India alone. Unlike rattlesnake venom which affects the blood stream, cobra venom strikes at the nervous system and is therefore much more deadly. If a rattlesnake bites you, you can cut open the wound and squeeze out much of the poisoned blood but cobra venom runs immediately through the nerves, causing paralysis and death within a comparatively short time.

While Dan and I were staring in fascinated horror at this nest of hoods, we suddenly realized that Grace was going to put her hand into the mass of cobras. Dan grabbed Grace's arm.

325

"Don't do it, Grace," he begged.

Grace looked amused. "Why, I handle the cobras every day when I clean their cage."

Not believing my eyes, I saw Grace slide her hand into the box. The nearest cobra reared up even higher than before and began to vibrate his rigid body like a tuning fork. He was gauging his distance before striking. Grace held out her hand, palm to the snake. The cobra swayed for an instant and then struck so rapidly I could hardly follow the movement. I saw him hit Grace's palm. I gave a little gasp of horror but Grace was perfectly composed. She let the snake hit her palm several times and then, raising her hand, began to stroke the top of the snake's head. The cobra twisted around, trying to reach her hand but Grace kept talking to the snake and continued to stroke him until the threatening hood slowly collapsed. Then Grace quietly lifted him out of the box and held him in her arms, the cobra watching her intently but not offering to strike. I made a slight movement and instantly the snake reared up again, threatening me.

I turned to Dan to see if he was as thrilled as I. Dan had his head turned the other way. "Has she been bitten yet?" he asked in a strangled voice.

"Oh no. Look, she has the snake in her arms and is playing with him," I said.

Dan turned slowly around and stared at Grace. Grace, obviously anticipating what he would say next, remarked wearily, "No, I don't have their fangs extracted. See here." Very gently, she forced the snake's mouth open. We could see the fangs with the light-yellow venom dripping over them as the cobra struggled to free himself.

Once the snake was again in the box, Grace explained how she was able to handle cobras. Dan and I were more impressed by her exhibition than ordinary persons would have been because we knew something about snakes and how dangerous they can be. However, we had never worked with cobras, only with the North American pit vipers, such as the rattlesnakes, copperheads, and water moccasins. We had more or less taken for granted that all poisonous snakes behaved in somewhat the same manner and we knew that it would be fatal to try to pick up a semiwild rattler as Grace had handled that cobra. So Grace explained the difference between the two snakes, illustrating her points by alternately handling the cobras and some diamond-back rattlers she kept in a near-by cage.

A rattlesnake does not "bite" when he strikes. His fangs are very long and when the snake strikes, he throws back his head and stabs forward with his fangs, like a man striking with a dagger or, rather, with a hypodermic needle for the fangs are hollow and connect with the poison glands on either side of the head. A cobra, on the other hand, actually bites just like a rat or a mouse does. His fangs are comparatively short and he must even chew the wound to force the venom into it. A cobra has a small mouth, so he cannot get a grip on a flat surface. He must fasten on a fold of skin or on some part of the body where his open jaws can find a hold.

When Grace extended her hand towards a nervous cobra, she kept the palm towards the reptile. When the snake struck, Grace met the blow with her flat palm. The snake couldn't get a grip on the palm and after several attempts, grew discouraged. Then, moving slowly, Grace was able to pick him up. Of course, while she was holding him the snake could, at any moment, turn and get her in the finger or in her face but apparently a snake, once he is picked up, does not readily bite if he is gently handled. He is used to seeing enemies approach him from a distance and he does not connect the person holding him with danger. This was Grace's theory, as she explained it to us. Before we'd been with her an hour, Dan and I were so convinced that we were even holding the cobras and rattlers ourselves.

Before we left Grace's home that afternoon, Dan and I had virtually forgotten that any of her snakes were dangerous. Dan would say casually, "Grace, will you pick up that horned viper and move him over where the sun strikes him?" or, if Grace didn't happen to be there at the moment, either Dan or I would move the snake ourselves. None of the reptiles paid any attention to us. I felt only annoyance rather than fear if I happened to trip over one of the alligators or crocodiles. Grace's home seemed like a tiny Garden of Eden where fear and mistrust were nonexistent.

Dan could have written his article after that first visit, but he was so fascinated by Grace and her pets that we drove out to Cypress many times, either to photograph some rare reptile that had just arrived or simply to chat with Grace and her mother, a wonderful old lady in her eighties.

When the article was finished, Grace checked it. There was one small detail still left. We hadn't been able to get a picture of a cobra with a spread hood. Dan hadn't taken any pictures of the batch of newly arrived Indian cobras that first day and by the time we got around to it, the cobras had all become so tame they refused to spread no matter how they were teased. Grace was very upset over this omission as she was proud of her cobras and without the spread hoods they looked just like our native black snakes. But after waiting several weeks, Dan finally decided to send in the piece without the cobra picture.

The manuscript was already sealed in its envelope and the pictures wrapped for shipment, when our phone rang. Grace was calling, very eager and excited. "A new shipment of cobras has just come in," she told us happily. "They're all wild and they spread beautifully. I've only taken them out of their cage once or twice so they won't get too tame. If you come right over, I'm sure you can get your picture." So we piled into the car once more and drove out to Grace's home.

"The new cobras are marvelous," she told us proudly when we arrived. "One of them has markings on the back of his hood that form a perfect *G*. I call him My Snake."

Grace took one of the cobras out of the box, using the technique we'd watched so often, and held him in her arms. Then she removed her glasses as she always did for pictures and held the snake up, teasing him a little so he would spread his hood. The snake, weaving back and forth only a few inches from her

328

face, spread perfectly and Dan got the picture. Although by this time we took for granted that Grace could do anything with snakes, we were both relieved when Grace returned the cobra to the box and went on to the simple task of putting a cobra down on the grass in the yard so Dan could get a close-up of the spread hood. As long as Grace was holding the snake, Dan didn't dare to get near enough with his flash gun for an extreme close-up of the hood.

Grace selected the cobra with the curious *G* on his hood. She carried the snake out on the grass and laid him down. The snake reared, partly spreading his hood. Dan was on his knees a couple of feet from the snake watching him through the finder of his Graflex. Grace teased the snake to make him spread, catching his blows on the flat of her palm as we had seen her do literally scores of times before.

Suddenly Grace said, "Will my face be in this picture?"

Without looking up from the Graflex, Dan said, "No, I'm just trying to get a shot of the hood. But you might be in the background."

"Then I'd better take off my glasses. I look terrible with them on."

Grace removed her glasses a second time. She was very short-sighted without them, but neither Dan nor I gave this a thought. We had seen Grace work with cobras so much that it never occurred to us that she could be bitten.

The snake had turned and was crawling away. Grace put out her hand in front of him to make the snake rear again. Suddenly the cobra struck at her.

I waited to see the cobra go back into position after striking Grace's palm. But the snake didn't go back. He remained clinging to Grace's hand. Even then, I didn't realize what had happened. I just thought, "Why is the snake doing that? Cobras always rear up again after a strike."

Dan had clicked the shutter of the camera as the cobra struck. He remarked casually, "Well, I got that . . . spread hood and all. That winds up the piece." Then he looked up.

We both saw at the same instant that Grace hadn't caught the snake's blow on her palm. The cobra had seized her by the middle finger. He was chewing the finger to force in the venom. Grace said in her usual, quiet voice, "Oh, he's bitten me."

Dan tried to take hold of the cobra by the back of the head and force his mouth open, but Grace shook her head and said, "No, no! Please let me do this." She took the cobra's head in her other hand and carefully worked his fangs loose. Then she stood up and carried him back to the barn.

She was perfectly calm. "Jule, will you please call Wesley Dickinson. He's a herpetologist and a friend of mine. He'll know what to do." She gave me the telephone number. I went to a telephone on the wall of the barn and called Wesley Dickinson. He said not to worry. He would be over in a few minutes. "I know exactly what to do," he assured us.

Dan had gotten out the snake-bite kit. "Where's the serum, Grace?" he asked.

Grace said quietly, "I don't keep any serums. I have so many different kinds of snakes and each requires a different serum. I couldn't afford them all and they go bad in a few months. I just never thought this would happen."

Dan and I knew well, in theory at least, how to treat a snake bite. We started getting out the different parts of the kit. I tried to work as easily and calmly as though I were simply getting out camera equipment.

Grace said suddenly, "I'm feeling a little faint. I'll pass out in a few minutes and I want to show you where everything is before I do." In a businesslike way, she went to the cabinet with Dan running alongside trying to hold a tourniquet in place. Grace got out a hypodermic syringe and several needles. "When I pass out, you'll have to give me injections of strychnine, dear," she said to me. "That will keep my heart going until Wesley gets here."

As cobra venom is a nerve poison, its first action is to paralyze the heart. Strychnine tends to counteract this effect for a short time. Grace gave me some of the tiny glass vials containing the strychnine and then sat down again to keep as quiet as possible to slow down the absorption of the venom. After a minute, she said, "I think I'd better lie down. Will you put a newspaper under my head so my hair won't get dirty?"

I arranged the newspaper and Grace lay back. As Dickinson hadn't arrived yet, I called the Long Beach Hospital. The nurse at the desk told me that Dickinson had already called and was on his way over with an ambulance. The hospital authorities were desperately trying to find some serum for cobra bites but there wasn't any in the West. "We're calling Washington to see if they have any," she added.

Grace said, "I think someone had better give me the strychnine now."

I gave her the injection and then we waited until Wesley Dickinson arrived with the ambulance. It was just nineteen minutes after Grace had been bitten. As she was lifted into the ambulance, Grace called back, "Please remember to cut up meat for my frogs. Mother will feed the snakes until I can get back."

We sat down and tried to think. We felt that now the worst was over. No one who knew Grace could believe that she would ever actually die of snake bite.

After a little while, Dan called the hospital. He hung up the receiver slowly and I knew it was bad news. Dan said, "Grace is in an iron lung. They're keeping her heart going with stimulants, but the nurse says it's hopeless."

When Dan called the hospital again, Grace was dead. She had died within ninety minutes of being bitten.

Dan and I moved about in a daze. We couldn't believe what had happened. I believed, and still believe, that if Grace hadn't taken off her glasses, the tragedy would never have occurred. She could have seen what she was doing and have caught the blow on her palm.

Grace's collection had to be broken up and sold. Mrs. Wiley could not take care of them. Wesley Dickinson tried to have some zoo purchase the entire collection for a Grace Wiley Memorial Reptile House, but without success. The snake that killed

JULE MANNIX

Grace was purchased by a roadside zoo in Arizona and huge signboards bearing an artist's conception of the incident were erected for miles in both directions.

Grace Wiley was the most remarkable person we have ever known. I do not believe that there was ever anyone like her before in history. I do not believe that there will ever be anyone like her again.

332

AFRICAN INTERLUDE

ONE morning, a letter arrived from our agent marked airmail, special delivery. He wrote that a Mr. John A. Hunter, one of the best known of the famous East African white hunters, was considering doing a story of his life. Mr. Hunter had sent in a sample of his autobiography but it said very little about his own emotions, personal life and background. Our agent felt that if Dan went to Kenya, he and Mr. Hunter could do a book together that would be the life story of a very remarkable man as well as an exceptionally fine account of big-game hunting. Also, we would be able to prepare a new lecture, this time about adventures in the African bush with big game, for Mr. Hunter had agreed to help us get pictures of rhinos, elephants and hippos in the country he knew so well.

We had taken the children with us to Capri and California, but I knew it would be impossible to take them to Africa. Of course, they could stay with Mother, but for some time now Dan and I had felt that we should have a permanent home. We were tired of living in rented houses. I wanted to get a place near my family so Mother could supervise things if we were suddenly called away on a trip. So we gave up our Malibu house and traveled east again to Pennsylvania.

We finally bought a lovely little farm with an old stone house, built by one of Washington's generals, a few miles from Valley Forge. Dan put up a really magnificent enclosure for Rani and we got a small, prefabricated house for Aguila. Aguila also had her own flying pen so the animals were quite comfortable and the children were delighted to have their own home. Under the capable management of their governess and with Mother near-by, I felt the household would run smoothly during the three months we planned to be away.

We left the International Airport in New York and seventy-

333

two hours later landed at the airport in Nairobi. David Hunter, John Hunter's son, met us at the airport. He told us that his father was at his hunting lodge at Makindu, one hundred and fifty miles from Nairobi, laid up with a bout of malaria but sent word that he hoped to come up to Nairobi within a few days. David drove us to his parents' home in Karen, a suburb of Nairobi. The house was very neat and modern, resembling a California ranch house, with white walls and a red-tiled roof.

Standing on the Hunter's porch, watching the bees buzzing around the Bougainvillaea that grew in great masses on the white trellis and listening to the whir of a grass cutter on the neighboring property, I felt that the plane had been flying in the wrong direction and we had ended up in Malibu. A native, looking exactly like the ordinary colored "handy man" at home, walked by with some gardening tools on his shoulder. He asked David some question about the work and then smiled at us. We smiled back. "Hard to believe that his parents may well have been cannibals, isn't it?" David remarked as he led the way into the cool living room.

Hard indeed, but even harder to credit your senses today when you pick up your morning paper and read that in Uplands, another suburban district near Karen, a gang of Mau Mau terrorists attacked a settlement and killed one hundred and fifty men, women, and children, cutting their victims to pieces and drinking the fresh blood.

A few days later, John Hunter and his wife, Hilda, came up from Makindu by train. We drove to the station to meet them, using David's car which he kindly lent us for the day. We had never seen a picture of Mr. Hunter so we had no idea what he looked like. But everyone connected with the book . . . the agent, the publishers, and ourselves . . . had done a lot of guessing. We had decided that Mr. Hunter must be at least ninety, probably had a long, white beard and walked with a cane. After reading the account of his life, it seemed incredible that anyone could have crammed so many adventures into any less time; after being tossed by rhinos, trampled by elephants, and chewed by lions, Mr. Hunter must be a doddering wreck. We were considerably surprised to meet a hearty, robust man in his middle sixties with a sweet-faced, delicate wife who wasn't much taller than I was.

Almost at once, he and Dan started going over the material for the book. Often he would say, "I cannot talk well here. Now my hunting lodge at Makindu . . . that's a fine place. When I'm a bit stronger, we'll go there. Hilda, do you think that to-morrow or maybe the next day . . . ?" And Hilda without looking up from her clicking needles would smile a little and say, "When you're at Makindu, John, you're always out in the bush. I think a few days' rest would be an excellent thing."

We all went to Makindu a week later. John was warden of the game reserve there . . . an area especially famous for rhino. Compared to their Karen home, the Hunter's house had almost no modern facilities. There was no electricity and no plumbing. But when you sat on the porch in the cool evenings, you could hear the hysterical laughter of hyenas and often the distant throbbing of native drums at some village dance. In Makindu, John chatted with his native scouts, bustled around the house checking equipment and supplies, and was miraculously transformed from a rather tired, older man to an energetic individual in the prime of life.

Dan and I could hardly wait to see some of the famous Makindu rhino, so the next day John took us out to the reserve. In his heavy truck . . . called a lorry in Kenya . . . John drove through the bush, twisting in and out among the flat-topped thorn trees, seeming to know by instinct how to avoid stumps and hollows hidden by the knee-high, yellow grass. Dan and I rode in the cab of the lorry with John while his native scouts stood up in the back which gave them an uninterrupted view of the country.

We drove until noon but still no rhino. John was skirting the edge of a thick patch of brush when suddenly his head scout tapped on the roof of the cab, the agreed-on signal when a rhino was sighted.

335

We tumbled out of the lorry, John taking his double-barreled rifle and Dan and I clutching cameras. We had only gone a few yards when John held up his hand to stop us. Through the bush, a great, brown shape was moving. It was the rhino.

I had often seen rhinos in zoos and never considered them particularly impressive. They'd looked like overgrown pigs. This animal didn't look a bit like a pig. It looked gigantic and dangerous.

The rhino hadn't seen us. He was strolling along, grazing as he went. I heard Dan's motion-picture camera begin to purr and I began to focus on the animal with the Graflex. As he went by, I could see two little tick birds riding along on his back. These tiny birds, no bigger than a chickadee, are wonderfully intelligent little things. They live on the ticks that get between the folds of the rhino's hide and in return, act as sentinals for their huge patron. Rhinos have very poor eyesight, but the tick birds can see splendidly and they make sure that nothing happens to their rhino. Through the finder of the Graflex, I could see the tick birds stretch up as though standing on tiptoe to get a better look at us. Then they suddenly took off, screaming their alarm note. The mean little things flew towards us and then back to the rhino, obviously to show him where we were.

The rhino stopped dead and lifted his great head to study the movements of the birds. Then he swung around with amazing nimbleness and trotted down-wind of us to get our scent. When the scent struck him, the great beast slammed on his brakes so hard he actually seemed to skid. Then he turned and came slowly toward us.

The rhino didn't stop until he was almost on top of us. I could have reached out and touched his horn with a fishing pole. Dan's camera kept up its steady whir while the rhino was watching him. Then I pressed the trigger of my Graflex. At the sudden click, the rhino gave a little start and swung around to face me. I started to change the film and at the motion the rhino dropped his head and charged.

Instantly both John and his head game scout shouted and

waved their aims. The rhino whirled like a polo pony. He crashed through the heavy thorn bush as though it were paper. A moment later we saw him galloping across an open stretch, his tail held high in the air and his two tick birds hovering over his broad back and probably telling him what they thought of him.

Of all the animals in Africa we particularly wanted to photograph elephants. The African elephant is the largest land animal in the world and, in John Hunter's opinion, by far the most intelligent. John had told us wonderful stories about elephants . . . how, when a road is cut through elephant country, the elephants will often pull down branches and use them to cover the ugly scar through their jungle, and how an elephant that knows he is being hunted will often double back and stand motionless by the trail to ambush his pursuer. The best elephant country in Kenya is at Voi, some two hundred miles southeast of Nairobi. Mr. Mervyn Cowie, the director of the Royal National Parks of Kenya, very kindly made arrangements with David Sheldrick, the warden of the eastern section of the area, to show us some elephant herds.

Sheldrick met us at the railway station at Voi. He was a slender, quiet man in his early thirties who had spent several years as a white hunter and served as a major in the British army. Dave and his twenty-two-year-old assistant, Bill Woodley, patroled an area of five thousand square miles with a few native game scouts. After lunch, they took us out in a light lorry with some of their native game scouts to look for elephants.

I don't think that there is anything more exasperating than animal photography. It is hard on the photographers but to a third person who, after all, has no personal interest in the business, it must be perfectly infuriating. Dave and Bill certainly fulfilled their promise to show us elephants. We saw herd after herd of the magnificent beasts. But always something seemed to go wrong. Sometimes the elephants were between us and the sun. Sometimes they were so deep in brush that we couldn't get a clear picture. Sometimes, just when everything was perfect, the wind would shift and the whole herd would vanish like a conjuring trick into cover that didn't seem high enough to hide a large dog.

Finally Dave located a small elephant herd grazing in some open bush that was ideal for photography. We sneaked up on the animals as silently as possible, for elephants, even though they have poor eyesight, have excellent hearing. At last we got within camera range and started taking pictures.

The next hour was the most thrilling, wonderful time Dan and I have ever experienced in all our adventures. The herd seemed to be all around us. Later, Dave explained that the animals were never actually down-wind, or they would have scented us, but they *seemed* to be all around us. In some places the bush was very thick; in others, quite open. The elephants for all their great size moved absolutely noiselessly. While we were photographing one animal, another would suddenly loom up through the bush almost at our side, as quietly as a ship drifting through a fog. Then Dave would touch us and we'd quietly retreat whi.. Bill or one of the game scouts brought up the rear. Sometimes an elephant would stop and study us intently with his tiny eyes, his great ears swung forward to catch the slightest sound. At such times, we would stand motionless until the animal made up his mind that we were simply tree trunks and moved away.

We still hadn't gotten the perfect picture and I was beginning to grow discouraged, when a cow elephant appeared and came towards us. We were standing by an opening in a line of high brush. Dave motioned us to retreat and we did, stopping again a few yards away.

The cow came up to the opening in the brush and started through it. She was only about twenty yards away and I was following her every motion through the finder of the Graflex. The cow reached up with her trunk to gather some brush and as she did, I clicked the shutter. The noise frightened even me. It was a startling, mechanical sound that was completely out

338

of place in the stillness of the jungle. The cow stopped, petrified, and then she saw us.

No one moved. The cow stood regarding us, a perfect picture, but I didn't dare move. Then she started slowly towards us, holding her trunk out in front of her like a circus elephant asking for a peanut except this animal was trying to get our scent.

She was moving over the ground where we'd just been. Suddenly, she dropped her trunk and began to run it back and forth over the earth, picking up scent from our footprints. Instantly, both Dave and Woodley quietly moved in front of me and lifted their rifles.

The cow feverishly swung her trunk around. Then she whirled with amazing speed and disappeared into the bush. She made no sound and gave no warning cry, but instantly every elephant in the herd also turned and began to run. Many of them were too far away to have seen her but by some curious telepathic process they all sensed danger. Within a matter of seconds, we were alone in the jungle.

Then, as both our time and our film were running out, we returned regretfully to Nairobi.

We flew back to the United States, leaving most of our heavy luggage to follow later by boat. Mother met us at the New York airport with the children. We had only been gone for three months, but I felt as though we'd been away for years when I saw their dear faces.

Our next trip was an easy camping jaunt through the Southwest so the children could and did go. They were able to watch Rani and Aguila in action, fish in mountain lakes, and swim in the Pacific. When autumn came, we returned to the farm again in time for their school.

Hunter, the book that Dan and John had done together in Kenya, was a great success. It was a Book-of-the-Month Club selection and a best seller for many months. As I am writing this, we are planning to go again to Kenya to do a sequel. Then we will continue on around the world, stopping in India and Australia on other assignments.

Looking back over my twelve years of marriage, I don't see how I could have had a fuller or more interesting life if I had become a second Katherine Cornell or Lana Turner. When Dan and I first started off for Taxco with Aguila and Wriggles, we had no real idea what we wanted to do in life . . . except that we both wanted to do interesting things. Dan, like Kipling's elephant child, had a "satiable curiosity." He still does. Last night, we sat up until almost dawn discussing the Mau Mau uprising with a noted anthropologist. We are expecting a cable that will send us down to Venezuela for a three weeks' trip to photograph natives hunting with blowguns. Tomorrow, I am going to the commencement exercises at Julie's school to hear my daughter give a piano recital, and tonight I have to do something about lengthening Danny's trousers.

When I was in school, I remember speculating with the other girls as to whether it was possible to combine marriage with a career. With me, marriage, children and a career have been inexorably blended. I wouldn't want it any other way. I hope it always remains so.

Cress
Delahanty

JESSAMYN WEST

CHAPTER I

WHILE her mother and father awaited the arrival of Mr. and Mrs. Kibbler who had called asking to speak to them "about Cress and Edwin Jr.," Mr. Delahanty reminded his wife how wrong she had been about Cress.

"Not two months ago," he said, "in this very room you told me you were worried because Cress wasn't as interested in the boys as a girl her age should be. In this very room. And now look what's happened."

Mrs. Delahanty, worried now by Mrs. Kibbler's message, spoke more sharply than she had intended. "Don't keep repeating, 'in this very room,' " she said, "as if it would have been different if I'd said it in the back porch or out of doors. Besides, what has happened?"

Mr. Delahanty took off his hat, which he'd had on when Mrs. Kibbler phoned, and sailed it out of the living room toward the hall table, which he missed. "Don't ask me what's happened," he said, "I'm not the girl's mother."

Mrs. Delahanty took off her own hat and jabbed the hat pins back into it. "What do you mean, you're not the girl's mother? Of course you're not. No one ever said you were."

Mr. Delahanty picked up his fallen hat, put it on the chair beside the hall table and came back into the living room. "A girl confides in her mother."

"A girl confides in her mother!" Mrs. Delahanty was very scornful. "Who tells you these things, John Delahanty? Not *your* mother. She didn't have any daughter. Not me. Cress doesn't confide in anyone. How do you know these things, anyway, about mothers and daughters?"

John Delahanty seated himself upon the sofa, legs extended, head back, as straight and unrelaxed as a plank.

"Don't catch me up that way, Gertrude," he said. "You

343

know I don't know them." Without giving his wife any opportunity to crow over this victory he went on quickly: "What I'd like to know is why did the Kibblers have to pick a Saturday night for this call? Didn't they know we'd be going into town?"

Like most ranchers, John Delahanty stopped work early on Saturdays so that, after a quick clean-up and supper, he and his wife could drive into town. There they did nothing very important: bought groceries, saw a show, browsed around in hardware stores, visited friends. But after a week of seeing only themselves—the Delahanty ranch was off the main highway—it was a jaunt they both looked forward to.

"Five minutes more," said Mr. Delahanty, "and we'd have been on our way."

"Why didn't you tell Mrs. Kibbler we were just leaving?"

"I did. And she said for anything less important she wouldn't think of keeping us."

Mrs. Delahanty came over to the sofa and stood looking anxiously down at her husband. "John, exactly what did Mrs. Kibbler say?"

"The gist of it," said Mr. Delahanty, "was that . . ."

"I don't care about the gist of it. That's just what you think she said. I want to know what she really said."

Mr. Delahanty let his head fall forward, though he still kept his legs stiffly extended. "What she really said was, 'Is this Mr. John Delahanty?' And I said, 'Yes.' Then she said, 'This is Mrs. Edwin Kibbler, I guess you remember me.'"

"Remember her?" Mrs. Delahanty exclaimed. "I didn't know you even knew her."

"I don't," said Mr. Delahanty, "but I remember her all right. She came before the school board about a month ago to tell us we ought to take those two ollas off the school grounds. She said it was old-fashioned to cool water that way, that the ollas looked messy and were unhygienic."

"Did you take them off?" Mrs. Delahanty asked, without thinking. As a private person John Delahanty was reasonable and untalkative. As clerk of the school board he inclined toward

344

dogmatism and long-windedness. Now he began a defense of the ollas and the school board's action in retaining them.

"Look, John," said Mrs. Delahanty, "I'm not interested in the school board or its water coolers. What I want to know is, what did Mrs. Kibbler say about Cress?"

"Well, she said she wanted to have a little talk with us about Cress—and Edwin Jr."

"I know that." Impatience made Mrs. Delahanty's voice sharp. "But what about them?"

Mr. Delahanty bent down and retied a shoelace. "About what Cress did to him—Edwin Jr."

"*Did* to him!" said Mrs. Delahanty aghast. "Why, what could Cress do to him? He's two or three years older than Cress, fifteen or sixteen anyway. What could she do to him?"

Mr. Delahanty straightened up. "She could hit him, I guess."

"Hit him? What would she want to hit him for?"

"I don't know," said Mr. Delahanty. "I don't know that she did hit him. Maybe she kicked him. Anyway, Edwin's got teeth out. I don't know how else she could get them out, do you?"

"I'm going to call Cress," said Mrs. Delahanty, "and ask her about this. I don't believe it for a minute."

"I don't think calling her will do any good. She left while I was talking to Mrs. Kibbler."

"What do you mean, left?"

"Went for a walk, she said."

"Well, teeth out," repeated Mrs. Delahanty unbelievingly. "Teeth out! I didn't know you could get teeth out except with pliers or a chisel. I don't believe Cress did it or that that boy's teeth are out. Anyway I'd have to see them to believe it."

"You're going to," Mr. Delahanty said. "Mrs. Kibbler's bringing Edwin especially so you can."

Mrs. Delahanty sat for some time without saying anything at all. Then she got up and walked back and forth in front of her husband. "Well, what does Mrs. Kibbler expect us to do now?" she asked. "If they really are out, that is?"

"For one thing," replied Mr. Delahanty, "she expects us to

pay for some new ones. And for another . . ." Mr. Delahanty paused to listen. Faintly, in the distance, a car could be heard. "Here she is now," he said.

Mrs. Delahanty stopped her pacing. "Do you think I should make some cocoa for them, John?"

"No, I don't," said Mr. Delahanty. "I don't think Mrs. Kibbler considers this a social visit."

As the car turned into the long driveway which led between the orange grove on one side and the lemon grove on the other to the Delahanty house, Mrs. Delahanty said, "I still don't see why you think this proves I'm wrong."

Mr. Delahanty had forgotten about his wife's wrongness. "How do you mean wrong?" he asked.

"About Cress's not being interested in the boys."

"Oh," he said. "Well, you've got to be pretty interested in a person—one way or another—before you hit him."

"That's a perfectly silly notion," began Mrs. Delahanty, but before she could finish, the Kibblers had arrived.

Mr. Delahanty went to the door while Mrs. Delahanty stood in the back of the room by the fireplace unwilling to take one step toward meeting her visitors.

Mrs. Kibbler was a small woman with a large, determined nose, prominent blue eyes and almost no chin.

Behind Mrs. Kibbler was Mr. Kibbler, short, dusty, soft-looking, bald, except for a fringe of hair about his ears. Behind Mr. Kibbler was Edwin Jr.

Edwin Jr. was as thin as his mother, as mild and soft-looking as his father; and to these qualities he added an unhappiness all of his own. He gave one quick look at the room and the Delahantys through his thick-lensed spectacles, after which he kept his eyes on the floor.

Mr. Delahanty closed the door behind the callers, then introduced his wife to Mrs. Kibbler. Mrs. Kibbler in turn introduced her family to the Delahantys. While the Kibblers were seating themselves—Mrs. Kibbler and Edwin Jr. on the sofa, Mr. Kib-

bler on a straight-backed chair in the room's darkest corner—
Mrs. Delahanty, out of nervousness, bent and lit the fire, which
was laid in the fireplace, though the evening was not cold enough
for it. Then she and Mr. Delahanty seated themselves in the
chairs on each side of the fireplace.

Mrs. Kibbler looked at the fire with some surprise. "Do you
find it cold this evening, Mrs. Delahanty?" she asked.

"No," said Mrs. Delahanty, "I don't. I don't know why I
lit the fire."

To this Mrs. Kibbler made no reply. Instead, without pre-
liminaries, she turned to her son. "Edwin," she said, "show the
Delahantys what their daughter did to your teeth."

Mrs. Delahanty wanted to close her eyes, look into the fire, or
find, as Edwin Jr. had done, a spot of her own on the floor to
examine.

Very slowly, as if it hurt him, Edwin opened his mouth.

His teeth were white, and in his thin face they seemed very
large, as well. The two middle teeth, above, had been broken
across in a slanting line. The lower incisor appeared to be missing entirely.

"Wider, Edwin," Mrs. Kibbler urged. "I want the Delahantys
to see exactly what their daughter is responsible for."

But before Edwin could make any further effort Mrs. Delahanty cried, "No, that's enough."

"I didn't want you to take our word for anything," Mrs.
Kibbler said reasonably. "I wanted you to see."

"Oh, we see, all right," said Mrs. Delahanty earnestly.

Mr. Delahanty leaned forward and spoke to Mrs. Kibbler.
"While we see the teeth, Mrs. Kibbler, it just isn't a thing we
think Crescent would do. Or in fact how she *could* do it. We
think Edwin must be mistaken."

"Tell them, Edwin," said Mrs. Kibbler.

"She knocked me down," said Edwin, very low.

Mrs. Delahanty, although she was already uncomfortably
warm, held her hands nearer the fire, even rubbed them together
a time or two.

347

"I simply can't believe that," she said.

"You mean hit you with her fist and knocked you down?" asked Mr. Delahanty.

"No," said Edwin even lower than before. "Ran into me."

"But not on purpose," said Mrs. Delahanty.

Edwin nodded, "Yes," he said. "On purpose."

"But why?" asked Mr. Delahanty. "Why? Cress wouldn't do such a thing, I know—without some cause. Why?"

"Tell them why, Edwin," said his mother.

Edwin's head went even nearer the floor—as if the spot he was watching had diminished or retreated. "For fun," he said.

It was impossible not to believe the boy as he sat there hunched, head bent, one eyelid visibly twitching. "But Cress would never do such a thing," said Mrs. Delahanty.

Mrs. Kibbler disregarded this. "It would not have been so bad, Mr. Delahanty, except that Edwin was standing by one of those ollas. When your daughter shoved Edwin over she shoved the olla over, too. That's probably what broke his teeth. Heavy as cement and falling down on top of him and breaking up in a thousand pieces. To say nothing of his being doused with water on a cold day. And Providence alone can explain why his glasses weren't broken."

"What had you done, Edwin?" asked Mrs. Delahanty again.

"Nothing," whispered Edwin.

"All we want," said Mrs. Kibbler, "is what's perfectly fair. Pay the dentist's bill. And have that girl of yours apologize to Edwin."

Mrs. Delahanty got up suddenly and walked over to Edwin. She put one hand on his thin shoulder and felt him twitch under her touch like a frightened colt.

"Go on, Edwin," she said. "Tell me the truth. Tell me why."

Edwin slowly lifted his head. "Go on, Edwin," Mrs. Delahanty encouraged him.

"He told you once," said Mrs. Kibbler. "Fun. That girl of yours is a big, boisterous thing from all I hear. She owes my boy an apology."

348

Edwin started to speak—but had said only three words, "Nobody ever wants," when Cress walked in from the hall. She had evidently been there for some time, for she went directly to Edwin.

"I apologize for hurting you, Edwin," she said.

Then she turned to Mrs. Kibbler. "I've got twelve seventy-five saved for a bicycle. That can go to help pay for his teeth."

After the Kibblers left, the three Delahantys sat for some time without saying a word. The fire had about died down and outside an owl softly hooted.

"I guess if we hurried we could just about catch the second show," Mr. Delahanty said.

"I won't be going to shows for a while," said Cress.

The room was very quiet. Mrs. Delahanty traced the outline of one of the bricks in the fireplace.

"I can save twenty-five cents a week that way. Toward his teeth," she explained.

Mrs. Delahanty took the poker and stirred the coals so that for a second there was an upward drift of sparks; but the fire was too far gone to blaze. Because it had not yet been completely dark when the Kibblers came, only one lamp had been turned on. Now that night had arrived the room was only partially lighted; but no one seemed to care. Mr. Delahanty, in Mr. Kibbler's dark corner, was almost invisible. Mrs. Delahanty stood by the fireplace. Cress sat where Edwin had sat, looking downward, perhaps at the same spot at which he had looked.

"Edwin has a collection of bird feathers," Cress said. "The biggest is from a buzzard, the littlest from a hummingbird. They're all different colors. The brightest is from a woodpecker."

"Does he kill birds," Mr. Delahanty asked, "just to get a feather?"

"Oh, no!" said Cress. "He just keeps his eyes open to where a bird might drop a feather. It would spoil his collection to get a feather he didn't find that way."

Mr. Delahanty sighed and stirred in his wooden chair so that it creaked a little.

"Edwin would like to be a missionary to China," said Cress. Some particle in the fireplace as yet unburned, blazed up in a sudden spurt of blue flame. "Not a preaching missionary," she explained.

"A medical missionary?" asked Mr. Delahanty.

"Oh, no! Edwin says he's had to take too much medicine to ever be willing to make other people take it."

There was another long silence in the room. Mrs. Delahanty sat down in the chair her husband had vacated and once more held a hand toward the fire. She didn't turn toward Cress at all or ask a single question. Back in the dusk Cress's voice went on.

"He would like to teach them how to play baseball."

Mr. Delahanty's voice was matter-of-fact. "Edwin doesn't look to me like he would be much of a baseball player."

"Oh he isn't," Cress agreed. "He isn't even any of a baseball player. But he could be a baseball authority. Know everything and teach by diagram. That's what he'd have to do. And learn from them how they paint. He says some of their pictures look like they had been painted with one kind of bird feather and some with another. He knows they don't really paint with bird feathers," she explained. "That's just a fancy of his."

The night wind moving in off the Pacific began to stir the eucalyptus trees in the windbreak. Whether the wind blew off sea or desert, didn't matter, the long eucalyptus leaves always lifted and fell with the same watery, surf-like sound.

"I'm sorry Edwin happened to be standing by that olla," said Mr. Delahanty. "That's what did the damage, I suppose."

"Oh, he had to stand there," said Cress. "He didn't have any choice. That's the mush pot."

"Mush pot," repeated Mr. Delahanty.

"It's a circle round the box the olla stands on," said Crescent. "Edwin spends about his whole time there. While we're waiting for the bus anyway."

"Crescent," asked Mr. Delahanty, "what is this mush pot?"

350

"It's prison," said Cress, surprise in her voice. "It's where the prisoners are kept. Only at school we always call it the mush pot."

"Is this a game?" asked Mr. Delahanty.

"It's dare base," said Crescent. "Didn't you ever play it? You choose up sides. You draw two lines and one side stands in the middle and tries to catch the other side as they run by. Nobody ever chooses Edwin. The last captain to choose just gets him. Because he can't help himself. They call him the handicap. He gets caught first thing and spends the whole game in the mush pot because nobody will waste any time trying to rescue him. He'd just get caught again, they say, and the whole game would be nothing but rescue Edwin."

"How do you rescue anyone, Cress?" asked her father.

"Run from home base to the mush pot without being caught. Then take the prisoner's hand. Then he goes free."

"Were you trying to rescue Edwin, Cress?"

Cress didn't answer her father at once. Finally she said, "It was my duty. I chose him for our side. I chose him first of all and didn't wait just to get him. So it was my duty to rescue him. Only I ran too hard and couldn't stop. And the olla fell down on top of him and knocked his teeth out. And humiliated him. But he was free," she said. "I got there without being caught."

Mrs. Delahanty spoke with a great surge of warmth and anger. "Humiliated him! When you were only trying to help him. Trying to rescue him. What gratitude."

Cress said, "But he didn't want to be rescued, Mother. Not by me anyway. He said he liked being in the mush pot. He said . . . he got there on purpose . . . to observe. He gave me back the feathers I'd found for him. One was a road-runner feather. The only one he had."

"Well, you can start a feather collection of your own," said Mrs. Delahanty with energy. "I often see feathers when I'm walking through the orchard. After this I'll save them for you."

"I'm not interested in feathers," said Cress. Then she added, "I can get two bits an hour cleaning blackboards at school. That would be two fifty a week at least. Plus the twelve seventy-five. How much do you suppose his teeth will be?"

"Cress," said her father, "you surely aren't going to let the Kibblers go on thinking you knocked their son down on purpose, are you? Do you want Edwin to think that?"

"Edwin doesn't really think that," Cress said. "He knows I was rescuing him. But now I've apologized—and if we pay for the new teeth and everything, maybe after a while he'll believe it."

She stood up and walked to the hall doorway. "I'm awfully tired," she said. "I guess I'll go to bed."

"But Cress," asked Mrs. Delahanty, "why do you want him to believe it? When it isn't true?"

Cress was already through the door, but she turned back to explain. "You don't knock people down you are sorry for," she said.

After Cress had gone upstairs Mrs. Delahanty said, "Well, John, you were right, of course."

"Right?" asked Mr. Delahanty, again forgetful.

"About Cress's being interested in the boys."

"Yes," said Mr. Delahanty. "Yes, I'm afraid I was."

CHAPTER II

IT WAS a hot August morning, Saturday, six-thirty o'clock, and Mr. and Mrs. Delahanty still lingered at the breakfast table. Six-thirty is midmorning for a rancher in summer; but Mrs. Delahanty hadn't finished talking about the hat.

"It's perfectly clear why she wants it," she said.

It wasn't perfectly clear to Mr. Delahanty. Besides, he thought it would be interesting to know what one woman thinks of another's reasons for buying a hat, even though the second is only thirteen and her daughter.

"Why?" he asked.

"Edwin," said Mrs. Delahanty.

Mr. Delahanty put down his coffee which was too hot, anyway, for a hot morning. "Edwin!" he exclaimed.

"Oh yes," Mrs. Delahanty assured him.

Mr. Delahanty decided to drink his coffee. After drinking, he asked, "How does the hat figure in it?"

"I think Cress thinks this hat would make Edwin see her in a new light. Frail and feminine."

"Better let her have it, hadn't you?" asked Mr. Delahanty. "Not that I like the idea of encouraging Edwin in any way."

"This hat," Mrs. Delahanty said, "wouldn't encourage anyone. This hat . . . Oh, Cress," she cried, "don't slip around that way. You gave me a start. What are you doing up this hour of the day anyway?"

During summer vacation Cress, unless she had projects of her own afoot, had to be routed from bed.

"I couldn't sleep," she said. She could tell from their faces that they had been talking about her. "And I wanted to ask Father something before he went out to work." She sat down at the table and turned toward her father as if they were two together, though seated unfortunately at a table with a stranger.

353

"Can I call the store and tell them that if they'll hold the hat, you'll come in and look at it with me?"

"I've looked at it, Cress," said her mother.

"Mother," said Cress very sweetly, "I was speaking to Father. May I?"

"You don't have to ask permission of me, Cress, to speak to your father."

"Thank you, Mother," said Cress. She leaned toward her father. "Daddy," she said—she hadn't called her father Daddy for years but somehow the word seemed right and natural to her this morning—"Daddy, if you thought a hat was beautiful and becoming, I'd know it was beautiful and becoming. Or if you thought it was ugly and unsuitable, I'd know it was ugly and unsuitable. Do you know what, Daddy," Cress said, leaning toward her father. "Do you know what?"

"No, Cress," said Mr. Delahanty, "I don't. But I'm waiting to be told."

"I think you probably have instinctive taste."

Mrs. Delahanty laughed, quite loud and long for so early in the morning.

Cress looked at her mother with a mingling of shock and disapproval on her face. "Were you laughing at me or Daddy, Mother?" she asked politely.

"The two of you," said Mrs. Delahanty. "You and your daddy. Your daddy, Cress, can't tell a bonnet from a bushel basket. Not if the basket has a flower on it, anyway."

"Well, Gertrude," said Mr. Delahanty, "I may not be an expert on hats. I grant you that. But I think I know a pretty hat when I see one."

"That's why I want you to see this hat, Daddy," cried Cress. "It's so downright beautiful."

"That hat, Cress," said her mother, "is the most unsuitable object for a girl of thirteen years to put on her head I ever laid my eyes on."

"Just what do you mean by unsuitable, Gertrude?" asked Mr. Delahanty.

"I mean that hat was never intended for a thirteen-year-old girl. It's for an older—woman," concluded Mrs. Delahanty, wasting irony.

Mr. Delahanty poured himself a glass of milk. "You mean it ties under the chin?" he asked. "Or has . . ." he took a drink of milk, visibly running out of what suggested to him the hat of an older woman.

"Or has a black veil?" Cress helped him.

"No," said Mrs. Delahanty, "it hasn't got a black veil and it doesn't tie under the chin. But every single other thing on this earth that hat has got."

"Now, Gertrude," said Mr. Delahanty, "maybe you'd just better tell me what this hat is really like."

Mrs. Delahanty had a musing look in her eyes. "John, do you remember the chamber of commerce dinner last fall? In Santa Ana? Do you remember the table decorations?"

"No," said Mr. Delahanty, "I can't say I remember the table decorations."

"Well, it's a pity you can't, because then you would know what this hat looks like."

Cress did not like the way her mother had of being funny about serious matters. It was objectionable in anyone, and particularly so in a mother. When I have a child, Cress thought, I'll be serious and understanding the rest of my days.

"The table decorations," said Mrs. Delahanty reminiscently, "were horns of plenty, made out of straw mats. And out of them came spilling every fruit, grain, and flower ever grown in Orange County. Cress's hat would look right at home on that table."

"Oh Mother!" cried Cress.

"Except," said Mrs. Delahanty, "that those horns of plenty were of natural-colored straw, while this hat . . ." she paused, searching the room for some object with which to compare it, "while this hat," she concluded, "is an indescribable color."

"Oh Mother," cried Cress again. "It isn't. It's flamingo red."

"I've always considered red a nice warm color," said Mr. Delahanty.

"This is the warmest red, if it *is* red," agreed Mrs. Delahanty, "you ever laid eyes on. And its size! It's just unbelievable," she said, shaking her head.

"Which all adds up to saying, I gather," said Mr. Delahanty, "that this hat Cress wants is large and flowered. Is that right, Cress? Is that the way it strikes you?"

The way the hat struck Cress was so overwhelming that she felt she might search the whole world over and still not find any word, any comparison which would explain it or the way she felt about it. The hat was summer time. It was deep and broad like summer. It caused soft scallops of shadow, like summer shadows under the densest trees, to fall across her face. The person wearing it would be languorous, gentle, and delicate. Looking at herself in the store mirror with that hat on, she had heard herself saying to Edwin, "If you'll be kind enough to give me your arm I think I'd like a stroll a little before the dew comes out." And she had seen how she would look, saying that, glancing appealingly upward at Edwin from under the brim of the shadow-casting, summery, flower-laden hat.

"Well, Cress?" asked her father.

"Oh, yes!" said Cress. "That's how it strikes me. May I call the store and say you'll come in tonight to look at it?"

"There's no rush, is there?" asked Mr. Delahanty. "Could look Monday as well as tonight, couldn't we?"

"The rush," said Cress, "is because I want it to wear to the beach tomorrow. That is, if you approve of it, Daddy."

"What's the idea, Cress?" asked her father. "A hat to the beach? You usually put on your bathing cap before we leave the house."

"Tomorrow," said Cress, "I'm not going to go thrashing about in the water. I'm going to walk about and observe."

"You're not going to be able to observe much, Cress," said her mother, "with that hat hanging down over your eyes."

Cress ignored this. "Father, may or may not I call the S.Q.R.? You don't have to promise to buy it or like it. Only to look at it."

"I guess looking never did any harm," said Mr. Delahanty.

"Now you've gone and done it," said Mrs. Delahanty, when Cress had gone.

"Done what?" asked Mr. Delahanty, innocently.

"Promised her that monstrosity. And all in the world she wants it for is to parade around Balboa in it tomorrow hoping Edwin will catch sight of her."

"Is Edwin at Balboa?"

"His family is. And as far as I know they haven't abandoned him."

"I didn't promise to buy the hat," protested Mr. Delahanty. "All I said I'd do was look at it."

Wearing the hat, Cress felt just as she had known she would: gentle and fragile and drooping. Beautiful, too. Running, with it on, would be utterly out of the question. Even sitting with it on had its difficulties, for the hat with its burden of fruits and flowers had to be balanced just so.

"Father," she called from the back seat, "will you please roll up your window? It's blowing my hat."

"Cress," said Mr. Delahanty, "it's at least ninety in here now and I'm not going to roll this window up another inch. We're barely getting enough fresh air to keep us alive as it is."

"It's blowing the flowers off my hat," cried Cress.

"A few will never be missed," said Mr. Delahanty.

Mrs. Delahanty leaned across her husband and rolled up his window.

"Steer for me for a minute, will you, Gertrude?" Mr. Delahanty said. "I want to get out of this coat before I have a heat stroke."

How ridiculous! Cress felt just right. Warm, summery warm, of course, but though the car windows were tightly closed she could feel the freshness of the sea breeze which was bending the brown grass by the roadside. She could smell the strange salt freshness of the sea, the far, non-land scent of its never-quiet water; and suddenly, in a little gap between two brown hills, she saw the sea itself, blue in the hot air, rippling and glinting under the sun. Cress sighed so deeply with pleasure that her hat rocked unsteadily and she righted it, holding it for a minute with both hands at just the angle which she hoped it would have when Edwin saw her.

Because Edwin would see her, of course. It was impossible to believe that she, having become the owner of the most beautiful hat, should be in the same town with Edwin, without his seeing it and her.

After her father parked the car, he got out his own and her mother's bathing suits; then the two of them stood for a time looking at her.

"Well, times change," said Mr. Delahanty. "Times change. I never thought I'd live to see the day, Cress, when you'd elect to tramp up and down the boardwalk on a hot day instead of going swimming with us."

"I'm going to walk and observe," said Cress holding onto her hat which was hard to control in the stiff sea breeze. "I'm getting a little old for just sporting around in the water."

"Observe," said Mr. Delahanty, seriously regarding her. "I can only hope, Cress, the shoe won't be too decidedly on the other foot."

"Now, John," said Mrs. Delahanty, and though she wasn't ordinarily a mother much given to kissing, she managed to get sufficiently under the brim of Cress's hat to give her a loving kiss.

"You're all right, Crescent," she said. "That hat's a little unusual, but I don't know that I'd want a daughter of mine trigged out like everyone else. Have a good time. And I hope you see Edwin."

"We'll meet you at Tiny's at four," said her father, "and have some ice cream before we go home."

At first, Cress was so certain of seeing Edwin that she walked along the boardwalk, really observing and truly enjoying the sights and smells of the town and the sea. Now and then in front of a plate glass window which served her as mirror she stopped to

admire her hat, to get it on straight again and to poke up the
stray hairs which kept dangling down from her not very solid
kid-curler curls. Her mother had tried to persuade her not to
wear a middy and skirt, saying they didn't go well with her hat.
She was glad she hadn't listened to her. A middy was a nautical
costume, and what, unless you actually went to sea, was more
nautical than the shore? She was glad she had worn her high-
heeled patent leather pumps, too. They made her teeter a little,
but a swaying gait, she thought, suited the day, the hat, and her
own personality; besides denying in the sharpest way possible
the tomboy she was afraid Edwin thought her.

What with observing, keeping her hat on straight, and practicing on occasional strangers the look of melting surprise with
which she planned to greet Edwin, the first hour went by quickly.
After the quietness of the ranch, the sights and sounds of a
beach town on a Sunday afternoon were almost too exciting to
be borne.

First, there was the strange light touch of the penetrating wind
off the sea on her warm inland body. Then there was the constant, half-heard beat of the surf, hissing as it ran smoothly up
the sand, thundering as it crashed against the rocks of the break-
water. There were all the smells of salt and seaweed, of fish and
water and wind. There were all the human smells too of the
hundreds of people who filled the boardwalk: ladies in print
dresses smelling like passing gardens; swimmers with their scents
of sun-tan oils and skin lotions; there were the smells of the
eating places: of mustard and onions, of hamburgers frying; and
the sudden sharp smell of stacks of dill pickles, as brisk in the
nose as a sudden unintended inhalation of sea water. There was
the smell of frying fish from the many fish grottos. And outside
these places, in the middle of the boardwalk like miniature, land-
locked seas, the glass tanks, where passers-by might admire the
grace and color of their dinners before eating them.

For the first hour this was enough for Cress: being a part of
this abundance and knowing that at any minute she would see
Edwin. For in a town of one street how could she miss him?

Then suddenly the first hour was gone by; it was past three and already the wind seemed a little sharper, the sun less bright, the boardwalk less crowded. More of her hair had come uncurled; her hat took more righting to keep it straight; her neck ached from holding her head high enough to see out from under the hat's brim; occasional stabs of pain shot up the calves of legs unaccustomed to the pull of high heels. A thought, with the swiftness of a stone dropping through water, settled in her mind: he isn't coming.

It was fifteen after three. At first she had been willing that Edwin see her first. Now, she searched every figure, every slight, short man or boy's figure, for as great a distance as she could make them out, saying, "Be Edwin."

It was three-thirty. It was fifteen of four. Her hat was on one side, her mouth weary from practicing her smile on strangers, her feet mere stumps of pain. Still, she would not give up. "Edwin, appear, Edwin appear," she willed.

Edwin did appear, crossing the street a block away, small and neat and thin in white duck pants and a white shirt. He crossed and turned toward Cress, walking steadily toward her. In two minutes or three he would see her, and see the hat and notice her new gentleness. All tiredness and pain left Cress. She had just time to arrange herself, resettle her hat, give her now completely uncurled hair a quick comb upward. To do this she took her hat off, stood on tiptoe, and with fingers which trembled with excitement managed to get it up onto the top of one of the rectangular glass aquariums which by chance stood conveniently before her in the middle of the sidewalk.

Before she, herself, understood what had happened someone was jovially yelling, "Hey, sis, bread crumbs is what you feed them," and there was her hat, slowly, gracefully settling among the startled fish of the aquarium.

The man who had yelled was a short fat man, wearing pants, but no shirt or undershirt. He had sand in the hair on his chest; like dandruff, Cress thought wildly, unable for shame to raise her eyes to his face. "What's the idea, sis?" he asked.

Forcing her eyes away from the sandy dandruff, Cress saw that her hat, still gradually, gracefully floundering, was bleeding flamingo red into the aquarium, so that the amazed fish now swam in sunset waters.

"I thought it had a top," she whispered.

"The hat, sis?" asked the shirtless man.

"The glass place for the fish," Cress whispered. "I thought it had a top. I was resting my hat on it while I fixed my hair."

"You was resting your hat on air, sis."

"It dropped," said Cress. "It fell right out of my hands. Will it make the fish sick?"

"Make 'em die, sis, in my opinion. Make 'em all puke and throw up their shoestrings I should think."

Cress wanted to die herself. She willed it very hard, but she couldn't. She couldn't even faint, though she held her breath and willed her heart to stop beating. But a sort of numbness did come over her, making all the voices blurred and indistinct, making all the people, and there were dozens, hundreds it seemed to Cress, now pressed about the aquarium, distant and hazy.

It was a field day for fish and humans. It was a great occasion for fish, who had had nothing more exciting to look forward to than death in the frying pan: a big blunt-nosed fish swam at the hat as if to ram it; smaller fish circled it curiously. It was a glorious moment for humans, too, a sight they had never expected to see. Someone, a worthy man dedicated to service, brought out the fish grotto proprietor. He came in his white apron and tall chef's hat, brandishing a long-handled ladle and happy at first to see his fish arousing so much interest. He shouldered his way through the crowd, his blood-shot eyes bright with pleasure, until he caught sight of vermilion waters, frantic fish, and the heart of summer, still partially afloat among them. He had had a long hard day frying fish. This was the last straw, fish dying without frying.

"In God's name," he cried, sadly, "who is murdering my fish?"

361

Cress was too frightened to reply.

"She is," said the fat man, pointing. "Sis, here, done it. She was resting her hat on the top of the aquarium."

"There ain't no top," said the fish grotto owner. "Is she blind?"

"More or less, I reckon," said the fat man. "You kind of blind, sis?" he asked kindly.

Cress was able only to moan a little. With a long shudder, like a capsized ship coming to rest, her hat settled to the bottom of the aquarium. Flowers and fruits were now adding their colors to that of the flamingo red straw. Streaks of purple from pansies and violets, puffs of sulphurous yellow from the daisies, veins of green from stems and flowers richly marbled the general red of the water. And the hat, in form as well as color, was suffering a sea change. It was softening up, flattening out. Each minute it looked less and less like a hat.

Cress finally found her voice. "Save my hat," she whispered.

"It's too late," the fish grotto proprietor said, "to speak of saving anything. Hat or fishes. They are all goners. Let 'em die together."

"Die?" asked Cress.

"Poisoned," said the fish proprietor, pointing to his frantic fish, the vari-colored water. "What've you got agin fish, kid?"

"I like fish," Cress whispered.

"She likes fish," said the fat man. "Hate to consider what she might do if she didn't." Those who had gathered about the aquarium laughed. The laughter was not malicious; it was lazy Sunday afternoon laughter. But it might as well have been malicious; it shamed Cress to the bone. It was unthinkable that anyone after such public humiliation could live.

"Poisoned," declared the fish proprietor again, gloomily, "deliberately poisoned."

"I think you're mistaken about their being poisoned."

It was impossible, Cress thought, that anyone should be defending her: let alone Edwin—Edwin, who was always a victim himself.

"I think that color is probably from pure vegetable dyes," said Edwin. Edwin's face was as white as his shirt and Cress could see that his upper lip trembled. But he was defending her, defying the fish grotto proprietor, not ashamed to be on the side of a person who had been publicly laughed at.

"It might even be good for the fish," suggested Edwin, "that pure vegetable dye."

"Good for them!" cried the fish proprietor. "Them fish have been scared to death at the very least, poison or no poison. Hats descending on them! I wouldn't feed them fish to a cat now. You related to this girl?"

"No," said Edwin.

"Well, someone," said the fish proprietor, coming to the crux of the matter, "has got to pay for my ruined fish."

"That'll be me, I reckon," said Mr. Delahanty who, without enthusiasm, was pushing his way through the crowd. He took the ladle from the fish owner's hand, and being a tall man was able, by stretching a little, to fetch up the hat, heavy and dripping from the bottom of the aquarium. He held the hat toward Cress, who without a word took it. Then Mr. Delahanty handed the ladle back to its owner.

"I'll pay ten dollars," he said.

"Twenty-five," said the fish grotto proprietor. "Not a cent less. Those were fancy fish and not to be picked up every day in the week."

"Eleven," said Mr. Delahanty.

"I was fond of those fish," said their owner. "They were pets, so to speak."

"Twelve," said Mr. Delahanty.

They settled for fifteen, Mr. Delahanty getting the fish.

Cress, the hat, and the fish, in an oversized kettle loaned by the fish man, occupied the back of the car on the trip home. It was a slow trip because speed tended to slosh the water in the kettle, together with a fish or two, out on the floor. It was a silent trip because Cress was thinking, and because up in the front seat, while Mr. and Mrs. Delahanty had plenty to say, they didn't want to be overheard by Cress.

They were nearly home before Mrs. Delahanty said, very low, "What a terrible thing to happen! It might mark her emotionally for life."

Mr. Delahanty agreed. "It wouldn't have been so bad though if that Edwin hadn't had to turn up in time to see it all."

"I know. She wanted to be such a lady—for him. That hat . . . and the curls . . . and then the hat in with the fish, the curls gone, and all those people laughing. I'm a grown person, John, but I just don't think I could live down such a thing. I think I might just stick my head in that bucket of fish and end everything."

As if her own words had put an idea into her mind, Mrs. Delahanty looked quickly around.

"Cress," she cried, "what have you got that hat on your head for?"

"It'll shrink if I don't," said Cress very calmly.

"Well, let it. Let it shrink. And you've got all those colors dribbling down your face and neck."

"I'm trying to keep them mopped up," said Cress, mopping some more.

"Throw that hat away," ordered Mrs. Delahanty. "Toss it out the window, Cress. You don't ever have to wear it again. We'll get you a new one."

"Oh no," cried Cress, "I love it. I'm going to keep it all my life to remember today by."

"Remember today," repeated Mrs. Delahanty, who was beginning to feel increasingly that she and her daughter were not speaking of the same day at all. "Why in the world do you want to remember today?"

"Because of the brave way Edwin defended me," said Cress. "He was really wonderful, Mother. He defied that man. And I was stricken, Mother, really stricken. It was the first time Edwin ever saw me stricken. He didn't even know I could be. He's always been the stricken one so far. The most I'd dared

364

hope for was to be gentle. Then," said Cress with great satisfaction, "stricken."

There was complete silence in the car for some time. "Don't you think I was, Mother?" Cress asked anxiously.

"Yes," said Mrs. Delahanty with conviction, "I think that's about the word for it."

"And whenever I wear this hat, he'll remember."

Mrs. Delahanty took her husband's handkerchief from his pocket and handed it back to her daughter. "Tuck this around your neck, Cress. It'll keep those colors from staining your middy."

With one hand Cress tucked the handkerchief about her neck, with the other she kept her hat in place.

CHAPTER III

THEY were both in the side yard when Cress got home, her mother cutting zinnias, her father holding them and complaining about the coming wind. Cress heard him as she rounded the house. Looking at her over the top of his armload of flowers he called out, "I suppose you ordered this weather, Cress?"

This was an old pleasantry and Cress didn't bother to reply to it. Instead she asked, "Is it all right if I start taking music lessons on Monday?"

"Music lessons!" her father echoed, as if she had suggested lessons in sword-swallowing. "At your time of life?"

Cress had been urged toward music lessons since the age of six. But she would have none of it. Sit on a piano stool hour after hour going tink, tink, tink, with the ends of her fingers. What a crazy idea! How could people waste their lives that way? Now she had to overcome their disbelief in her seriousness.

"I never *heard* music until recently," she told them. "I had no idea what music was, *really.*"

"Where would you take lessons?" her mother asked.

"From Mrs. Charlesbois. She's going to give lessons. There's an announcement in this evening's *Star.*"

Mr. Delahanty handed Cress his zinnias and walked over to the edge of the front lawn. He picked up the *Star,* unrolled it and turned to the back page.

"It's not with the want ads," Cress told him proudly. "It's on the society page."

Mr. Delahanty turned back to the society page, searched a second, then read aloud: "Mrs. Luther Charlesbois announces the formation of classes for instruction in the art of piano-playing, beginning on September 17th. Mrs. Charlesbois, a former pupil of Levinsky, is recently of Los Angeles where she made frequent appearances on the concert stage. She has been guest soloist with such well-known organizations as the Southern California Orpheus Club and the Los Angeles Lyric Society, and is a valued and distinguished addition to Tenant music circles. Mrs. Charlesbois is prepared to accept both beginning and advanced pupils. To contact her phone 153."

Mr. Delahanty re-rolled his paper and took a swing at a low flying swallow. "I wondered how long it would be before she'd have to take a hand at supporting that rundown ranch. One job in the family wouldn't turn the trick."

"It's probably more the loneliness than anything else," Mrs. Delahanty said. "Up there on the edge of the hills with nothing but coyotes and buzzards for company a good deal of the time."

Mr. Charlesbois worked in the city, a job on the Los Angeles *Times* of some kind, no one seemed to know just what. Certainly not a reporter, for he was the exact opposite of a news-hawk in appearance, being dumpy (this in spite of the fact that he was not short), with a round, worried face. The Charlesboises had no car and Mr. Charlesbois cut across the Delahanty ranch each morning on his way to catch the 7:10 Pacific Electric, and again each evening, on the evenings when he came home, after getting off the 6:20.

"Why didn't Charlesbois ask somebody who knew something about ranching before buying that place?" Mr. Delahanty asked, as if Mrs. Delahanty had never mentioned loneliness.

The Charlesbois ranch had been planted in the late '20's when orange prices were so high that all land in Tenant which was not straight up and down and to which at least a little water could be piped had been cleared and planted. Now the shallow foothill soil, together with a decade of insufficient fertilizing and spraying had resulted in a grove, yellow-leaved, and overproducing, as dying stock will.

"Maybe it was more to get out of the city, than get a producing grove?" Mrs. Delahanty suggested.

Cress, uninterested in why the Charlesboises had located in Tenant, said again, "Is it all right if I start taking lessons Monday?"

Cress had first met Mrs. Charlesbois two weeks ago in the hills back of the Charlesbois ranch. She often went up there at sundown, for the wonderful, sad, alone-in-the-world feeling it gave her to look out over the darkening valley at that hour.

Mrs. Charlesbois had had on white shorts that first afternoon and a white blouse; but Cress had never seen her in shorts again and certainly never thought of her that way. She always wore white, though, white dresses that to Cress's mind were old-fashioned. They reminded her of dresses she had seen in her mother's snapshot albums, dresses with puffier sleeves and fuller skirts than women wore nowadays; they were always freshly washed and ironed and had that sweet smell garments sun dried and newly ironed have. Though that was far from being Mrs. Charlesbois' only scent: she used perfume and lots of it— *Quelques Fleurs,* which was perfect for her. How terrible if she had been attracted to—though with her taste she couldn't have been, of course—something unsuitable like *My Sin* or *Shocking.* No, *Quelques Fleurs* with its fragrance, almost, of ripening fruit as well as of flowers, *was* Mrs. Charlesbois.

Music lessons were fully as awful as Cress had imagined and the worse the better, for they proved that there was nothing she wouldn't do to be near Mrs. Charlesbois. It was the afternoon of her fourth lesson and she was having the half-hour of super-vised practice which followed it. There was no light, quick tink, tink, tink, when she practiced—as once she had imagined there would be, but a slow heavy tunk. Tunk. Tunk.

"You are the worst of my pupils," Mrs. Charlesbois would declare, fondness in her voice. "I have never seen your like."

"Worse than Linton Matthews?" Cress would ask. Linton was a boy her own age, taking piano lessons to help his stammering.

"No comparison at all."

"Worse than Don Rivers?" Don Rivers was a grown man, though a young one, a road superintendent who was taking, of all things, lessons on the accordion.

"Beside you, Crescent Delahanty," Mrs. Charlesbois had said, "Don Rivers is a great artist, a second Liszt."

Cress had laughed at this exaggeration. Mr. Rivers left his accordion, an enormous thing, almost as large as a bale of hay, at the Charlesboises' between lessons. The tent at the road camp where he lived with the other men who were working on the Imperial Highway Project was not a safe place to keep so expensive an instrument.

"When does he practice?" Cress had asked.

"Here, after lessons. Like you."

"But I practice at home, too."

"Mr. Rivers isn't a beginner like you. He doesn't really need practice. All he needs is a place to play where people understand a taste for music—and don't make fun of a grown man who loves it—the way they do down at the road camp."

"In the movies," Cress had said, "men on jobs love music. They always sit around campfires at night singing and playing. Railroad gangs and cowboys and miners. And the like."

"Not the kind of music Mr. Rivers plays and understands. Not serious music."

"Maybe not," Cress had admitted. She really didn't know, and she liked Mr. Rivers. He had his lesson just after hers. Five to six. Her lesson was late because of school, and his, because of his work, was still later. After dinner would've been even better for him, Mrs. Charlesbois said, but it was too much to expect Mr. Charlesbois to put up with the eternal sound of music.

Mr. Rivers was a dark, beak-nosed young man, smiling, but not very talkative. He was going to have dinner tonight with her and Mr. and Mrs. Charlesbois. Cress would have preferred to have been the only guest, but she knew quite well that Mrs. Charlesbois couldn't show preference for any one pupil.

At seven o'clock Mrs. Charlesbois took Mr. Charlesbois' plate off the table. He was obviously not coming home on the 6:20 and there wasn't another car out from the city until 9:47. "He hates being pinned down to any particular hour," Mrs. Charlesbois explained. "And actually he can't always tell. Things come up." She lit the candles in the branched crystal holders, brought in the iced fruit cups and the three of them sat down at the round table. Cress couldn't keep her eyes off Mrs. Charlesbois. She had on one of her usual white wash dresses, though this one was cut low enough in the neck to show the first firm upswelling of her bosom. Mrs. Charlesbois presided as if the dinner were very important; yet she was so laughing and girlish, her round brown arms passing food with all the grace of piano playing, that Cress felt, beside her, quite heavy and matronly.

Sometimes she felt sorry for Mr. Rivers, Mrs. Charlesbois left him so much out of the conversation; as if he were only an audience for her and Cress's talk. She would touch Cress when she got up to change course, give her shoulder a little squeeze or smooth one of her eyebrows with a delicate forefinger. She was almost incandescent, Cress thought, burning bright, like Blake's tiger.

After dinner they sat in the living room. Mrs. Charlesbois brought the candles from the dining-room table and put them on the piano. Then she lit two big chunky candles on the mantel. "We have a festival of lights," she said in a low excited voice. "Oh do look how they glitter."

Cress did look and it was true. There were only two small rugs on the floor, and the bare floorboards reflected all the wavering unsteady lights. There were no curtains at the windows and the black night pressed against the glass and bore the candlelight on the surface of its darkness.

After they had looked for a while Mr. Rivers said, "Won't you please play for us?"

"No, not tonight," Mrs. Charlesbois said. "With you two, music is my business. Let's visit, let's be friends. Let's have a festival of talk. You start, Cress."

Cress asked a question she had been wanting to ask for a long time. "Tell us about that picture," she said. "Please."

The picture, a large one in a narrow gilt frame, hung on the wall just above the keyboard of the piano so that Cress, when she practiced, often looked at it. The picture was of Mrs.

Charlesbois as a girl. She wore a purple (the picture was hand-tinted) velvet dress, with a train, and there was white fur, ermine, Cress believed, around the neck and the edges of the great bell-shaped sleeves. On her head—she wore her hair long even then—was a golden tiara, just large enough to encircle the mound of her up-piled hair. "Was that," Cress asked, "the dress for your coming-out party?"

"Coming-out party! Oh, Cress!" Mrs. Charlesbois' laugh was like her hair and skin, warm, a mingling of rosiness and darkness. She left the fireplace and took the picture off the wall and holding it in both hands peered down into it as if it were a mirror. "Coming-out party! Sweet little Cressy. What would I have come out of? Or to?"

She carried the picture over to Mr. Rivers and Cress was the audience now as Mrs. Charlesbois, one hand on the back of Mr. Rivers' chair, addressed her talk to him.

"Were you ever in Oilinda?" she asked. "A little oil town up in the stubble hills, the houses throbbing all night with the pumps and the coyotes coming down at dawn to steal the kids' pet rabbits?"

Mr. Rivers looked up from the picture, saying no by a shake of his head.

"You've missed nothing," Mrs. Charlesbois declared. "I was born there. I was born there and went to school there and was elected Queen of the County Fair there. And that is the picture of me, Queen of the Orange County Fair."

"They couldn't possibly have elected anyone else."

"They could have, but they didn't. Fifteen or twenty other girls were candidates, but I won easily. Oil men make big money, or did then—and they are easy spenders. You voted," she explained, "by buying tickets at a quarter each. One man, a driller, bought an even hundred. So I won. I reigned for the five days of the Fair. On the second night of the Fair, I was formally inaugurated, floodlights, a full band then, and so forth. They gave me this ring, that night. It was my prize for winning the election."

She held up her left hand and showed them the diamond she wore above her wedding ring. "It is small," she said, "but deep and true in color." Then, looking over Mr. Rivers' shoulder, and speaking objectively, "She was really quite a pretty girl then."

There was a small silence, before Mr. Rivers, as if the truth must be spoken, however awkward or difficult, said, "She was *beautiful,* Inez. She still is."

It was the first time Cress had ever heard Mrs. Charlesbois called by her first name. She looked at her as if, beneath the familiar outline, she might see emerging a new and more intimate personage. And for a minute that hidden person did partially emerge; that sweet, regal, newly crowned girl was there in the room, more real than the grown-up music teacher.

"Oh, Mr. Rivers," she said. "Thanks, thanks. I was seventeen then and that was seventeen years ago. Why, I'm old enough to be Cress's mother. Easily old enough."

At first, Cress thought proudly that Mrs. Charlesbois was saying, "Since I'm old enough, why don't I have a daughter like Cress?" But she wasn't sure, because the next words she said were, "Me, me, Inez Dresden."

She took the picture from Mr. Rivers and ran her finger over the glass of the picture, as if hunting for that lost fur and velvet. And diadem. "I met Luther the last night of the Fair," she said.

"Luther?" Cress repeated.

"Mr. Charlesbois. He came up onto the grandstand and played a duet with me. He'd had about one bottle of beer too much and some one had dared him to do it. We played Beethoven's *Appassionata* together."

Mr. Rivers, who knew about serious music, said, "The *Appassionata!*"

Cress said, "I didn't know Mr. Charlesbois played. I didn't know he even liked music."

"I don't think he does any more," Mrs. Charlesbois replied, taking the picture back to its place on the wall beside the piano.

Cress spent that night at the Charlesboises'. At ten thirty Mrs. Charlesbois asked, "Is there really any sense in your going home at this hour, Cress? Why don't I just call your mother and tell her you're spending the night here? There's no telling whether or not Mr. Charlesbois will be home and while I'm not afraid to stay alone here, I'm not exactly happy about it either."

Mrs. Delahanty of course said, "Stay," and after that Cress was often at the Charlesboises'. She would fall asleep in her room upstairs, listening to the sound of Mr. Rivers' serious music on the accordion. On the nights when Mr. Charlesbois came home there was, out of deference to his having grown away from music, no sound from the accordion.

Though Cress still felt considerable hardness of heart toward Mr. Charlesbois for what appeared to her to be his neglect of his wife and for his loss of interest in her music, this feeling was tempered some by a talk she had with Mr. Charlesbois himself. She had come home one Saturday afternoon at the beginning of December on the same Pacific Electric car as Mr. Charlesbois. She had spent the night before with her grandfather in Whittier and Mr. Charlesbois, through work early because it was Saturday, had taken the 4:10 out from town instead of the 6:20. Cress hadn't seen him on the car and was surprised when he alighted with her at the Tenant station.

They walked the mile to the Delahanty ranch together, talking as they went. Cress saw that, though Mr. Charlesbois was neither handsome nor commanding, she had been mistaken to think him nothing. His face *was* biscuit-shaped, round, rather doughy and biscuit-colored, too. And when he took off his hat, she could see, through his thinning, dun-colored hair, the faint pinkness of his scalp. But his eyes were a strong, flashing gray and when he looked at her she was aware of his thoughtfulness; aware that, as he talked, he thought of *her*.

When they reached the arroyo on the Delahanty ranch where their paths separated, Mr. Charlesbois stayed on for a few minutes talking. It was by now a clear, green winter evening. The rains were late and there was a summer warmness and dry-

373

ness in the air. Mr. Charlesbois put his hat back on his head, but to one side, and with his baldness thus covered and with his cocky inquisitive stance, feet apart and head tilted downward toward her, Cress saw, as she never had before, how this man could be the one who had volunteered to play duets with the soloist at the County Fair.

"I hear you've been kind enough to keep Inez company on some of the evenings when I've been away."

"Yes," Cress answered, "I have. But it wasn't kindness." She was caught between a desire for very strong words and a desire not to be silly or sentimental. "I dearly love Mrs. Charlesbois."

Mr. Charlesbois received this statement quietly. "I know," he said. "Me, too. For seventeen years." Then, as if he too feared the mawkishness Cress had tried to avoid, he swept his hat off once again and made her a stiff, stocky bow, "Us two great lovers," he said.

They both laughed at this: Cress at the idea of a man of Mr. Charlesbois' age being called a lover of any kind, let alone a great lover. The tension that the word *love* had set up being relieved by the laughing, Cress said, "I'm staying this Monday night too." Then she said self-consciously, "If you're home I can play my first real piece for you."

"What is it?" Mr. Charlesbois asked.

" 'Barcarole' from *The Tales of Hoffmann!* Simplified, of course," she admitted.

"Well," Mr. Charlesbois said, "that's real progress. No, I won't be home Monday, but you can play it for me some other time."

Monday night was the most beautiful night she had had, so far, at the Charlesboises'; and even though Mr. Rivers stayed for dinner too she had come not to mind him very much. In fact, once or twice when she and Mrs. Charlesbois had been alone for dinner some of the magic had been missing. The outward surfaces had been the same; the warm glowing skin, the fresh white dress, the usual kind graciousness; but Inez Dresden, the young queen, had been absent. And nothing Cress could say, no funniness or compliment could bring her back.

This was the first night they had had music after dinner. "Inez," Mr. Rivers said (Mr. Rivers and Mrs. Charlesbois, now that they knew each other better, were always "Don" and "Inez" to each other), "won't you play for us this evening?"

Mrs. Charlesbois, who had always before said no to this question, said, as if she had only been waiting to be asked, "Of course, Don, I'll play for you. Then you can play for me and Cress can play for both of us." And that was what they did, no questions asked about, "What do you want," or any nonsense of that kind. Mrs. Charlesbois went to the piano and began to play as if, long ago, it had been settled that whatever Mr. Rivers wanted, she wanted too.

Cress had no idea what was being played; and she saw clearly enough that this was no time—though she had a bent that way —for picking up musical facts, memorizing the names of composers and compositions. The sounds which Mrs. Charlesbois' strong pink-nailed fingers brought out from the piano were to be heard and felt, not labeled or pigeonholed. Mrs. Charlesbois was *so* beautiful! She had a kind of satiny sheen like plums or grapes, fully ripe but not yet touched. It was a winter's night but Mrs. Charlesbois put summer in the room. The scent of her perfume was as warm and gusty as if it came off a real garden where real flowers opened their trumpets to invite the sun's entry down to the last granule of golden pollen.

Mr. Rivers' playing was quite different, no summer sounds or scents came from that great instrument of his. What he played was night and storm and darkness, things anyone sitting in the dark would want music to blot out. The accordion, Cress supposed, was the nearest there was to a human lung, most able to cry and bewail and entreat. Stop, stop, she wanted to say to Mr. Rivers.

And he did stop, suddenly, with no sign given beforehand that a stop was coming, no flourish of any kind. Mrs. Charlesbois did not say a word to him—any more than he had spoken to her when *she* finished playing. But she helped him out of the harness of that crying instrument, before turning to Cress.

"Now it's your turn," she said.

Up to the minute of that command Cress had supposed that she would play, that she was waiting to play. But when the command came she was suddenly tired and sleepy. And she saw how absolutely crazy the notes of her simplified "Barcarole" would fall into a room still echoing with those other notes. "If you'll excuse me," she said, "I think I'll go to bed."

She went to sleep at once and awakened to the sound of Mrs. Charlesbois and Mr. Rivers playing together. The music much hushed by the time it reached the second story might have been dreamed. Cress rested on her elbow for a time listening. Listening, a line, then two lines of a verse she would like to write for Mrs. Charlesbois came to her mind. There was an empty place in her heart, which she would have to *do* something to fill. She turned on the light by her bed and got, from her school bag, paper and pencil. After she had put down the two lines, a third came by itself, and then a fourth. She made a fair copy of her verse and above it wrote, "A Few Lines for Mrs. Charlesbois." Looking at her verse she had a sudden impatience with waiting for morning to give them to Mrs. Charlesbois. The emptiness of the act unperformed wasn't filled simply by writing. And though she couldn't awaken Mrs. Charlesbois at that hour of the night to say, "Here is a poem, Mrs. Charlesbois, to say how much I love you," she could slide her sheet of paper under Mrs. Charlesbois' door where she would find it the moment she opened her eyes in the morning. Cress went down the stairs barefooted, filled with the happiness of doing.

Either Mr. Charlesbois hadn't come home at all on Tuesday and Wednesday nights, or he had come home on the late car. Cress had kept a sharp look-out for him but hadn't seen him. On Thursday night she walked into the Tenant station and was waiting in the shadow of the building when the 6:20 pulled in. She watched Mr. Charlesbois come heavily down the steps, noted that he was hatless and that he had pushed his newspaper, folded any old way, into his bulging coat pocket.

"Mr. Charlesbois," she called, "Mr. Charlesbois."

At first, all of her sorrow and pity had been for herself. She remembered hearing Mrs. Charlesbois telling everybody, one time when she had gone into town with her and her mother, "Oh Cress is *more* than a pupil. She stays with me almost every Monday night." "Yes, Mr. Charlesbois *is* away a good deal, but Cress stays with me when he's gone." "Oh no, I'm not lonely. I almost look forward to the nights Luther is gone, Cress and I have such good times."

And I was nothing to her, Cress thought bleakly. Nothing. She perhaps even loathed me, but she had to put up with me, I was so convenient for her. After a while she had stopped thinking of her own hurt and deception and thought of Mr. Charlesbois. What of him? He was still deceived. He still believed. "Us two great lovers." And we were nothing to her. Nothing. Me, a convenience and Mr. Charlesbois, a hindrance.

She ran out of the shadow calling in a louder voice, for Mr. Charlesbois, head down, was already walking away from the station. He turned at her call and came back toward her. "Why, Cress!" he exclaimed. "I didn't see you on the car. You been up visiting your grandpa again?"

"I wasn't on the car," Cress said. "I came especially to meet you."

Mr. Charlesbois looked at her with some surprise, but said only, "That was nice of you." They started their homeward walk in silence. It was a dark moonless night with only a handful of stars to be seen between the big threatening clouds. Cress, who had believed that her sense of duty was strong enough to make it easy for her to tell Mr. Charlesbois what she had to tell him, could find no words with which to begin.

Mr. Charlesbois himself said, "Well, did you play your 'Barcarole' Monday night? Simplified version?"

"No," Cress answered. After a while, she said, "They played, though."

377

"They? You mean Inez and Mr. Rivers?"

"Inez and Don," Cress said.

"Inez and Don. That's right. First names don't come easy to me. It's a wonder I'm not calling you Miss Delahanty."

Cress went on desperately, in spite of this playfulness. "I came down to meet you, Mr. Charlesbois, to tell you that Monday night—"

Mr. Charlesbois finished for her, "To tell me you had a fine shindig Monday night. Played music. Made fudge, maybe."

"No," Cress said, "oh no, it was nothing like that. It was the opposite of that. I came to tell you that afterwards, after I went to bed I came downstairs and—"

"And left Inez a poem," Mr. Charlesbois said. "I have it right here." He clapped a hand against his coat pocket. "I like it. I've thought what you say in it a lot of times myself, but I haven't your gift for words. I can say it by heart, if you want me to."

"Don't," Cress cried. "Don't say it. You wouldn't want to say it if you knew—"

"Knew," Mr. Charlesbois interrupted her. "Why I know everything, Cress. By my time of life there's nothing a man doesn't know—whether he wants to or not. All a man at my time of life can learn is new ways of saying things like this pretty rhyme of yours:

> *She had the dark and windswept beauty*
> *Of the hills from whence she came."*

"No," Cress insisted. "No, please don't say it." She made one more effort. "You and I, Mr. Charlesbois, we both—"

He once again completed her sentence for her. "We both love Inez."

"Did," Cress said. "We did."

"No," Mr. Charlesbois contradicted her, "we do. I know everything, and you know quite a lot. For a girl your age—," he said, and though it was too dark to see, his voice sounded as if his face might have that same crooked Jack O'Lantern smile she had seen when he said, "Us two great lovers"—"for a girl your age you're downright loaded with knowledge. And both of us love Inez. Only you can say it in rhyme and I can't. So long," he said. "It's late and it's going to rain before I get home if I don't hurry."

Cress stopped beside a lemon tree near the house for a while before going in. The light shone outward onto the waxy yellow fruit and she picked a lemon, rolled it between her hands until it was soft, then broke its skin with her thumbnail and began to suck it. A few drops from the coming storm spattered onto her forehead and hands. She wanted to stay out in the rain, be drenched, muddied, cold. She knew exactly what she had tried to do and why. It was perfectly clear to her and now she would like to stay out until she was half-drowned and worried about, then go in and be made the center of a considerable to-do, dried and warmed and comforted. She went in just as she was, however, scarcely dampened, pausing at the door only long enough to throw away her half-sucked lemon.

CHAPTER IV

"WHO is this Ina?" her mother asked Cress. "Where does she live? And I thought Honor Gallagher was your friend of the moment?"

"Honor is," Cress said, "but she can't be thinking of me every minute. And Ina's full name is Ina Inez Wallenius," Cress answered. Cress didn't care whether her mother said yes or no about this visit. Without telling her mother, she had assigned to her for the moment the role of Fate, and Cress was perfectly willing that Fate should know everything she knew about Ina, and then decide.

"As a matter of fact, she isn't even a friend," Cress added.

"Not a friend?" said Mrs. Delahanty, puzzled. "I thought you just said she was. I thought that was why you wanted to visit her."

"What I should have said," Cress told her mother, "was that Ina wants me to be her friend."

Cress didn't think it would be good taste to say just how much Ina seemed to want her for a friend, or of any use to try to explain to her mother the high school's complicated social structure—a structure upon whose upper level she was now located, but not established, and upon whose lower level Ina stood, reaching upward. A visit could put Ina up where she was, or just as easily put Cress down where Ina was. Cress thought it was her duty to give Ina her chance. This was one of the reasons she preferred to leave everything to Fate. There was more responsibility in the visit than she cared to assume.

"She's a nice girl, is she—this Ina?" Mrs. Delahanty asked.

"Oh, she's a very nice girl!" Cress said. She didn't say that in her opinion Ina was too nice. Ina's hair was yellow white and she wore it in heavy, sausage-like curls low on her neck. She had heavy white eyelashes and eyebrows, big, murky blue eyes, and a loose-appearing golden skin.

380

"She's an orphan," Cress said, thinking she should perhaps give Fate more to work on.

"An orphan," her mother repeated. "She surely doesn't live alone, does she?"

"I mean she's a half orphan," said Cress, for whom a mother was still the most of a family. "Her father's alive."

"Have you ever seen him?" Mrs. Delahanty asked.

"No, but he's a good old man, I know," Cress said with assurance. "Ina says he reads a chapter from the Bible out loud before every meal."

"Well," said Mrs. Delahanty, "I don't know a reason in the world why you shouldn't stay all night with Ina if you want to. Where does she live?"

"Kettle Hill," said Cress.

"Oh!" said her mother.

Cress knew what that "Oh!" meant. Kettle Hill, although only ten miles distant by road and six by the spur line down which the tank cars rumbled, carrying the hill's oil to the main tracks, seemed a world away from the valley, with its orange groves, where the Delahantys lived. It was off by itself, separated by its location and work from the ranches. Did anyone ever go there, Cress wondered, besides the drillers, the riggers, the pumpers, and their families? One evening when out for a drive, Mr. Delahanty had taken his family up the road to Kettle Hill and there, Cress had seen, the road stopped. It didn't climb on further into the brown, cactus-covered, snake-inhabited foothills, but ended in a loop among the derricks at the hill's top.

And, though the settlement was on a hillside, Cress always thought of it as being in a dark pocket. It *was* dark there, not only because the earth was oil-soaked and pocked with sump holes that shone like greasy bruises in the gray dust, but because the oil people, wishing for something green amid the barren forests of their derricks, had planted, years ago, pepper trees along their streets. Now that the trees were old, their foliage sprayed outward in dense, smothering cascades, setting the oil workers' homes in gloomy caverns of shade. And it was dark

381

there because the hill blotted the sun out early; while children in the valley below still played in the slanting light of afternoon, the houses of the oil workers would already be deep in evening shadows.

"Ina can't help living there," Cress said to her mother accusingly. "Where your folks are, there you have to be."

"Why, I never said she could help it," Mrs. Delahanty answered. "I never even suggested she would want to help it. And I think it would be a very nice thing for you to visit her."

Cress didn't know whether it would be a nice thing or not, but anyway the matter was now decided. She was going.

She felt very lonely, packing. On the evening before the day she was to leave, she started putting together what she would need for her visit. She was using a little satchel of her father's as an overnight bag. It was small enough not to be awkward to carry to school on the bus. She was packing things she couldn't possibly need, because in her mind the trip was somehow momentous. She had made a list and was checking off articles on it, like an overseas traveler. Her father watched her awhile from the doorway of her room. "Cress," he asked, "have you drawn up your will and taken out travel insurance?"

Cress looked up from the midst of the articles she was checking: bottles containing iodine, camphorated oil, attar of roses, hand balm, green ink; a package of band-aids; a comb cleaner; a spray of lavender tied with frayed silver gauze.

"Let's see," said her father. "Just how long is it you're to be away from us?"

"Till Thursday," said Cress bleakly.

"A whole day?" Mr. Delahanty asked. "Are you taking a calendar with you? I wouldn't want you to lose track of time while you're away."

Cress knew her father was being funny and she tried to smile, but her face seemed to have lost all of its springiness.

"Look here, Crescent," her mother said, coming into the room. "You know you don't have to visit your friend Ina if you don't want to. No one's forcing you to go, you know."

"Oh, I want to go!" cried Cress intensely. "Besides," she added, "I feel it's Fated."

Next evening, when Cress got off the school bus at the foot of the hill with Ina, she was in a mood to be a perfect guest and to see the best in Kettle Hill. For one thing, she felt contrite. She had talked to some of the girls that day at school rather as if her visit to Ina were a slumming trip.

"Going to see how the other half lives," she had said, and listened to the appreciative laughter. When the girls had asked her what she had in her valise, she had said, "My crude-oil-colored week-end wardrobe, so I won't spot," and was rewarded with laughter again.

If she had said these things in front of Ina, it wouldn't have been so bad, but she hadn't; she had been two-faced, said them behind Ina's back, and the girls had still been snickering when Ina came up to them. The memory of this two-facedness made a sore spot in her chest and, as she climbed the street under the pepper trees, caused her to link her arm through Ina's.

"It's a ratty little town," Ina said apologetically.

"Why, it's not either," said Cress, putting balm on the sore spot. "I think it's romantic."

In a way, a peculiar way, it really was. The fading sunlight came through chinks in the pepper trees and fluttered about upon the hard-packed earth, like a covey of yellow evening birds. The houses, though small, and almost all alike, because they were company-owned, were neat and whitewashed. Their porches were filled with large potted plants growing in cheerful red Hills Brothers coffee cans, or with smaller potted plants in green Del Monte peach cans. From under the pepper trees, the derricks were out of sight. It was only the smell of the oil—which was taste as much as smell—the sight of an occasional sump hole at the end of a side street, and the sound of the pumps that reminded Cress where she was.

"There's a book in the library," she said, "called *The Romantic Story of Oil.*"

383

"Is there really?" said Ina. Ina had worn one of her best dresses to school, showing how important she thought Cress's visit—a soft silk pongee middy suit. She stopped beside Cress now and clasped her pongee-colored hands. "Cress Delahanty," she said, "I think you are the most sweet and tactful girl I know. Oh, I could just about hug you for that!" she said, reaching out and taking Cress's hand inside her own soft, folding palm. "Most people," she confided, "just see the oil, and smell the smells, and miss the romance."

"Most people," said Cress, working her fingers out of Ina's hand, "are blind."

For some reason, Ina took her into the house by the back door. She said, "Here we are," and Cress, carrying her bulging valise, stepped over the threshold and into the kitchen.

There she was, at the end of her journey, and she looked about to see where that was; she was in a small, very neat room, she saw at once, the table ready set for supper, and chairs standing in front of each place. The room was close, with the smell a kitchen has which is left each morning the minute breakfast is finished.

Cress had never seen a more orderly room. Over the sink, can openers, egg beaters, potato mashers—all the kitchen implements—were hung with careful regard for their size. Half a lemon rested in the exact center of a saucer, and the saucer had been placed in the exact middle of the window sill. The chairs, ranged around the set table, were all pushed under it a uniform distance, and on the back of the stove was a stack of pot holders, the largest at the bottom, so that they formed a pyramid, calculated and orderly. The room was orderly in the way a sickroom is orderly, or the room of a person who has little time or is for some reason unsure of himself.

Ina, as if she knew what Cress was thinking, said, "Father likes everything very neat. He says he wants to be able to put out his hand in the dark and find whatever he wants."

Cress saw Ina looking at her, trying to discover if this seemed strange to her. "I expect I'm messy," Cress said.

384

"Oh, no!" Ina protested, leading the way into the living room. "That's the last thing I'd think of calling you."

Cress paused in the doorway to the living room. "Why, it's nice!" she exclaimed, and then worried for fear the surprise she felt had shown in her face or voice.

She had somehow thought of Kettle Hill homes as being faded, run-down, and dingy inside. This room was none of these things; it was a small, warmly colored, padded-looking room. The light, already dimmed by its passage through the pepper trees, was dimmed once again before it got into the room through the curtains, and Cress was startled when her eyes, coming to the room's final dark corner, saw that a man whom she knew by his resemblance to Ina to be Mr. Wallenius had been very calmly looking at her while she had been looking at the room. He sat bolt upright watching the two of them and when Cress's eyes discovered him, he rose very politely and spoke.

"Good evening, girls."

When Mr. Wallenius stood up, Cress saw that he was a large man, broad as well as tall, old but only old like a father, not like a grandfather, as the Bible reading had led her to believe. His hair was yellow white, like Ina's, not silvery with age, and he had a yellow-white mustache, very thick and soft-looking.

"This is my friend Cress Delahanty, Father," Ina said, and Cress shrank inside herself a little at seeing how proud Ina was to have a friend.

"Cress," said Mr. Wallenius. He had a pink-and-white skin, not a loose, golden one like his daughter's, but his voice, Cress thought, had rather a loose, golden sound, like a handful of rings clinked softly together.

"Well, well," said Mr. Wallenius, "so I'm to have two cooks tonight instead of one."

Supper-getting was very simple because Ina had planned it so carefully. Before she had gone to school that morning, she had boiled potatoes and made white sauce. Now she diced the potatoes and put them, together with pink, rubbery cubes of bologna, into the pan of white sauce and set the mixture on the stove. While this—whatever it was called—heated, she opened a can of beets, set them to cooking, too, and got a bowl of deviled eggs out of the icebox.

When the food was ready and they had carried it, dished up on three plates, to the table, Ina said proudly, "I tried to have different colors, and the hot food hot and the cold food cold."

Cress thought she had succeeded very well; the bologna-potato mixture was pink and white, the beets a dark, handsome crimson, the deviled eggs, in their green nests of lettuce leaves, gray and yellow. Steam rose above the helpings of heated food; the eggs shone with a cold and clammy sweat.

But the cold food was warmer and the hot food much cooler before they ate, for Mr. Wallenius came into the kitchen, and asked, "Will you read for us tonight, Miss Cress?" and placed an opened Bible in her hands. After they took their places, Cress read the chapter through. She was accustomed to the Bible and knew that it was right for her to speak aloud words found there which, elsewhere, it would be very wrong for her to whisper or even think about. So she was able to finish without stumbling or blushing, though she couldn't help feeling the chapter was a funny one to have chosen to be read aloud.

After the reading was finished and they had begun to eat, Mr. Wallenius asked, "Did you understand what you read?"

Cress wasn't sure whether she had or hadn't. If she said yes, she thought, she might be asked to explain, so she said, "No."

"Ah, so," said Mr. Wallenius. "An old-fashioned home, I expect."

Ina got up just then to put the tea on to steep and Cress ate steadily while she was gone, her face low over her plate. The clock in the living room struck half past five and she remembered how early that seemed at home—still afternoon—while here it was already evening.

It was strange to think that if the clock here and the one at home were both right (or both wrong in the same way), they were striking this half hour together. Remembering home, these things seemed stranger than they had even on first sight: the half lemon on the window sill had, in the kitchen's growing duskiness, a sort of misted light of its own; outside, the long, dangling leaves of the pepper trees moved together with the sound of dry fingers. At stove and sink, Ina was a long time setting the tea to steep, and the slight clatter she made sounded distant and muffled.

"Have you ever been kissed?" Mr. Wallenius asked suddenly. Keeping her eyes on her plate, she said, "No."

Finally, looking up, Cress saw that while Mr. Wallenius' eyes were blue, like Ina's, they were not at all murky, but had instead a shining glaze, like varnish, across their blueness.

"You're big enough, you know," Mr. Wallenius said, smiling.

"I guess it goes more by age than size," Cress said miserably, and was glad that just then Ina came to the table with the tea and dessert, and that there was no more talk of kissing.

When they rose from the table, Mr. Wallenius said to his daughter, "I'll take Cress out for a little walk while you do the dishes, Ina."

Cress's heart sank. "I wouldn't feel right, not helping," she said.

"Washing them alone," Mr. Wallenius told her, "is a little punishment I planned for Ina. A little reminder. Isn't that true, Ina?"

"Yes," said Ina, almost under her breath, and went quickly about the clearing up, so Cress could see no polite way of escaping the invitation. Mr. Wallenius put his hat on his head and took from behind the door to the living room a knotted and burly stick.

"In case we come across a snake or two," he said as they went down the kitchen steps. "I enjoy killing those fellows."

This made Cress feel better—a walk with a purpose, not just wandering about in the dusk with an almost total stranger.

"I killed a rattlesnake once," she told him.

"How?" asked Mr. Wallenius.

"Stoned it," said Cress.

"I can think of better ways."

So could Cress, but when you were alone and barefoot, what other way was there?

They came out from under the pepper trees, and turned down a side street. Overhead, the sky, which they could now see, still held considerable light and there was a streak of muddy yellow above the hills to show where the sun had set. At the bottom of the street, they came to a sump hole—not one of the big ones, no more than an eye, liquid and dark, reflecting the sky. It shimmered iridescently where water had seeped in with the oil and rose upward here and there in bubbles, as if it were an eye that could breathe as well as see.

Mr. Wallenius stirred it a little with the point of his stick, then went off to poke about among the straggling trees and bushes that grew at the sump hole's upper edges.

Sump holes always made Cress uneasy, whether they were large ponds or only small, ragged pools like this one. It seemed unnatural to find a pool of oil instead of water in the ground. This one was stranger than most, because, lying at the foot of a little arroyo down which there was a trickle of water in the winter months, it had stunted willows and elders, dusty castor-bean and tobacco-plant shrubs growing about it. Several birds, having seen the light reflected in it and mistaken it for water and dipping too low, had died there. Dragonflies and moths had darted down to drink and never risen again. It was a very strange place, yet peaceful—no sounds except the pumps, the dry, placid singing of insects in the faded grass, and Mr. Wallenius' quiet poking about in the elder clump.

"Ah, ha!" cried Mr. Wallenius. "What did I tell you?"

He came out of the elder clump with a heavy snake hanging across his walking stick. Fearful of falling, the snake balanced itself there, its head slightly lifted, its tongue flicking in and out.

Cress jumped quickly backward as Mr. Wallenius advanced. Then she saw, even in the fading light, that what he had picked up was nothing more than a poor gopher snake that had probably been out hunting a mouse for supper.

"It's nothing but a gopher snake," she said. "Nothing but a poor, harmless gopher snake."

"A fine fellow," Mr. Wallenius replied, as if agreeing. "Fat and sassy. I'll just put him in here to cool off a bit."

Then, with a gentle movement, Mr. Wallenius laid, rather than threw, the soft, brown, harmless thing in the sump hole.

Cress could not believe her eyes. So terrible a thing to do! Involuntarily, she took hold of Mr. Wallenius' wrist. "It will die," she told him.

"Maybe so, maybe not," said Mr. Wallenius. "It's too early to say. Sink—swim; sink—swim," he said. "Sink—swim."

It was almost as if the snake heard and obeyed. Oil-covered, eyes blinded, tongue motionless, it struggled, it rose and sank, rose and sank.

"Sink—swim," said Mr. Wallenius. "Up—down; in—out."

Behind the blunt, striving, blinded head making its horrible effort to rise, yet falling back again, the snake's body moved with such energy that against anything with less resistance than oil it would have broken free. Along the whole of her body, Cress felt the terror and effort of that struggle—the oil in her own eyes, the taste of oil in her own mouth.

"Save him!" she implored. "Save him! It's wicked to do that. It hurts him so!"

"Sink—swim," said Mr. Wallenius. "Sink—swim."

The snake's head lifted and fell; it kept time, it seemed, not only with the words Mr. Wallenius spoke but with the thud and suck of the pumps and with the rhythmical pressure of Mr. Wallenius' fingers on Cress's hand.

"It's dying!" Cress cried, her shrill voice disturbing all that orderly time-keeping going on so relentlessly about the sump hole, and, weeping not only for the snake but for herself, she plunged away from Mr. Wallenius and began, desperately, to run.

The last half-mile down the spur line, she walked, and she had stopped crying a mile or so before that. She stood on her own front porch, and it was so natural to be there and to see her mother and father sitting by the open window talking, that everything else, the whole visit—orderly kitchen, lemon that shone like a light, sweating eggs, snake, sump hole, even Mr. Wallenius—seemed objects she might have imagined. But when she opened the screen door, she realized that she had actually been away, for her mother, very startled, jumped from her chair and said, "Why, Cress Delahanty, how on earth do you happen to be here now?"

Cress didn't know what answer to make. It seemed foolish to say, "Because Mr. Wallenius drowned a snake in a sump hole." She thought of saying, "Because it's Fated, I guess," but that wasn't true. What had been Fated was for her to spend the night at the Walleniuses'. She had broken that by running.

"I guess I was homesick," she finally said.

She saw her father and mother look at each other. Her father stood up. "Well," he said, "I'm glad you were. I was just on the point of putting us together some kind of a bedtime snack. How does that sound to you?"

It sounded good, but Cress was silent. She sat down in her father's chair and nodded yes to him, because suddenly she was too tired to speak even so small and easy a word.

CHAPTER V

T HE sun blazed, fledglings flew, roses bloomed. But there was still, for Southern California, an indication of a lingering spring: green grass. There had been late rains and the yellow look had not yet come to the foothills and the grass in the Delahanty back yard was still February fresh. Now in later afternoon each bent blade carried on its hump a drop of water left over from the midday shower. The low sun, slanting through these drops, gave them jewel colors and Crescent, walking toward the house, put her feet down carefully. She was now fourteen years old and oppressed by the brevity of life, the fugaciousness of blossoms, and the evanescence of raindrops. Even words like evanescent and fugacious could set up, with their suggestive syllables, delicious tremors of sorrow in her heart. Ending, ending, everything is ending, she thought. In spite of her care, raindrops like emeralds and diamonds went flying down to nothing as she walked. She was even sorrowful about the box of tin cans she had just taken to the stack behind the barn. She had put them down with benedictory thoughts: finished and done with! Gone from the orderly kitchen shelves and the bright lights of the house into the cold earth.

There were tears in her eyes as she walked through the grass. She had more feelings than she knew what to do with, more emotions than her tranquil life permitted her to discharge. She had to invent sorrows and concoct dramas. She was capable emotionally of a woman's tragedies and, up to now, she had been unable to overtake any of these. Now, however, she loved and was not loved in return. No one, not even Calvin Dean, knew anything of this; though she could not believe it would matter if he did. That was a part of his appeal: his indifference. He didn't know Crescent Delahanty existed. Why should he?

With rubies and emeralds and diamonds transformed by her

feet into simple raindrops and the raindrops themselves shattered into the shapelessness of moisture she thought, I'm King Midas in reverse. I change jewels to water. I can touch gold and make it into a base metal, lead or tin. She stood ankle deep in the diamonds and rubies she had yet to ruin and figured what her name was. Midas in reverse was Sadim. I am King Sadim, she told herself, and the jewels I touch are water and the gold I touch is dust and the people I love hate me.

With these thoughts, she went into the kitchen, which was warm and fragrant with the tamale pie her mother was making. Her mother was at the sink shaking olives from a bottle. Cress watched her for a second or two, then said, "I am King Sadim."

Her mother, who did not turn around, asked in a cheerful voice, "Who's King Sadim, dear?"

"King Midas had a brother and Sadim was his name," Cress said, the relationship coming to her as she spoke. "This brother was not popular. He was King Midas in reverse. Everything he touched turned into dust. It may be bad to have everything you touch turn to gold—but it's a lot better than having everything you touch turn to dust."

Her mother, who had the olives out of the bottle, now began to stir them into her pie. She looked up from her stirring with amused interest, as Cress related this bit of unknown mythology. Cress regarded her mother dispassionately. The rain and the steam in the kitchen had made her new permanent too frizzy. There was a big splash of cornmeal mush across her apron. Her lipstick formed a dot at each corner of her mouth. She was smiling quite happily. Happy, Cress thought, on a spring evening of unutterable beauty, with nothing better to do than make a tamale pie. A pie that will be eaten tonight and forgotten tomorrow.

"Oh, Mother," she cried. "Poor, poor Mother." She dug an olive out of the pie and put it into her mouth. Under her closed lids she felt the happy smart of tears saying, You are alive and suffering. She took the olive seed from her mouth and pushed it deep into the well-watered soil about one of the African violet plants which her mother kept in pots along the window sill over the sink.

"What are you doing, Cress?" her mother asked.

"Giving it one more chance," Cress whispered, patting the soil in tenderly over the buried seed.

"Giving what one more chance?"

"The olive seed. It had given up. Into the bottle, into the pie, into my mouth. Like Jonah. Then when it thought all was over I spat it up. Rescue. Escape. It will be a tree again."

"It never was a tree, Cress. Any more than an egg ever was a chicken."

"It is an embryonic tree, Mother. It has leaves and limbs locked in its heart." All those surprising l's. *They* brought tears to her eyes, too.

"Leave them locked," Mrs. Delahanty said unfeelingly. "I don't want leaves and limbs in my kitchen. I want African violets."

"O.K.," Cress said, "if that's the way you feel about it." She began disinterring the seed. "The choice is yours. Life or Death. You choose Death." She opened the window over the sink and flung the olive pit out into the April twilight. "Die," she bade it in a tragic voice. "Cease to be. It is my mother's wish."

Her mother slid the tamale pie into the oven. "Cress," she said, "you have a bad case of spring fever. You need some vitamins or minerals or something."

Death in the world, spring passing, love never coming, and vitamins were recommended.

"Do you *know* it's spring?" Cress asked. "That this is a day that will never again be upon this earth? Never, never, never? And that it's the last day on earth a lot of people will ever see? There," she said, pointing to the fragment of pale sun still visible through the darkening leaves of the eucalyptus tree, "that sun is going down forever for someone at this very minute."

Something came into her mother's face, agreement, she was afraid. And she couldn't bear agreement or understanding just now. What she longed for was sorrow and contention, lasting

393

disorder and sudden death. She ran out of the kitchen slamming the door behind her. In her own room she flung herself onto the chair in front of her bamboo desk, put her arms on the open lid of the desk and her face on her arms. "Oh, Calvin," she whispered. Then, very daringly, "My darling." The word made a pulse beat on her cheekbone.

Cress sat up, so vigorously the desk rocked, and took from one of its pigeonholes a fold of adding-machine paper given her by the manager of the Piggly Wiggly store. She unfolded the long strip of paper, looked over what was already written there, picked up her pen and began where she had left off: "39. I love Calvin Dean. 40. I love Calvin Dean. 41. I love Calvin Dean." When she had written "I love Calvin Dean" one hundred times she intended to fold the paper to the size of a postage stamp and put it in the little chamois bag her mother had once used to carry her rings in. Then she would hang this bag around her neck, on a ribbon the right length to keep the words exactly over her heart. She would wear it night and day; she would never be parted from it; she would stand in Calvin Dean's presence, every thud of her heart lifting the words, "I love Calvin Dean," written one hundred times over, a fraction of an inch nearer him. Surely he would feel it, surely it would influence him.

She paused at "56. I love Calvin Dean" to think about him. He was eighteen years old, a big ruddy boy, blond-haired and supple. She thought he probably looked like Charlemagne and, like Charlemagne, he seemed born to command. He was the head of everything at school that had a head, from captain of the football team to president of the debating club.

Because of Calvin she had suffered agonies of shyness and hard work to win a place on the debating team. She was now first substitute and should any misfortune ever overtake Connie Bielefeldt, Calvin's partner, she herself would have to debate with Calvin, a possibility so overwhelming she tried not to think of it. Her try-out speech on the negative side of socialized medicine had been against her conscience, but since every word of it had been the truest cry of her heart, "Calvin see me, Calvin hear me," it had not been really hypocritical. And Calvin had seen and heard. And momentarily, and partially anyway, he had approved, for he had voted for her as first substitute.

Making the debating team had put her nearer Calvin, but this nearness had made her no more happy. His presence was too overwhelming. When the debating club met and Calvin presided she would fix her eyes on the picture of Longfellow which hung at the front of the room to keep from staring at Calvin. Once in the middle of a meeting Calvin had stopped the proceedings to address her directly. "Would you mind telling us," he had asked, "what you see in that picture, anyway?"

"Me?" she had whispered, nudged by a neighbor from her cultivated inattention.

Calvin had turned his back on the debating club to gaze up at Longfellow. Facing Cress again he had said, "I don't see the likeness myself."

"Oh no," Cress had explained as the laughter quieted, "I don't mean I see me in the picture." And too shaken for anything but the most literal truth she said, "What I mean is I don't see you."

Calvin had given her, at this, his long cold debater's stare with which he was wont to impress judges and paralyze opponents. "Delahanty," he said, practicing his university manner, "are you crazy?"

That had been his last word to her: "Crazy." She picked up her pen and wrote, to forget it, "57. I love Calvin Dean. 58. I love Calvin Dean."

At "59. I love—," her mother without a knock or a whistle came into the room. "Studying, Cress?" she asked.

"No," Cress answered. She didn't put away or try to hide her Piggly Wiggly strip of paper. In a way she did not understand, she wished her mother would pick it up, read it, and ask: "What's the meaning of all this 'I love Calvin Dean,' Cress?"

Then she would answer, tell her everything, say: "The meaning is, I love Calvin Dean and he doesn't know I exist except to think I'm crazy." It would be an excuse, if her mother picked it up, to tell her everything, of all the miseries of her life. How sad it was to die and to be a debater and to love the most outstanding boy in school.

But her mother, very honorably averted her eyes from the list and asked, diffidently: "I don't suppose you'd want to ride into town with us, would you?"

There was a time—could it be only last fall—when she would have been the first one out in the car at that invitation. But it was a dream-like time, vanished, remembered like a dream. "No," she said. "Thanks just the same, but I guess not."

Her mother lingered. Finally she said, "If your mind's made up I won't urge. Keep your eye on the tamale pie, will you?" Then, as if she had perhaps been too quick to accept Cress's refusal she turned back from the door. "Oh come on, Cress. It's a beautiful evening. We're just going in and back. Your father has to pick up something from the garage for the tractor. We won't be gone a minute. The tamale pie can take care of itself. Come on."

"No," Cress said, "I guess not."

"You used to love trips to town."

"I know I did."

"Want us to bring you anything?"

"There's nothing I want you can buy."

"O.K.," her mother said. "Good-bye then. We're going as soon as your father washes up."

When the door closed she began her writing again. "59. I love Calvin Dean. 60. I love Calvin Dean. 61. I love Calvin Dean." Her pen, as she remembered momentarily those trips to town, faltered.

There was first of all the pleasure of the change from the quiet of the ranch to the movement and noise of the city. She remembered the library, empty usually at this time of everyone but herself, the librarian and two old men reading papers. She remembered the hollow engulfed-cathedral echo of the six o'clock chimes from the Presbyterian church as it was absorbed and deadened by the rows of books.

She remembered the trip home from town, the library books on the back seat (among them perhaps the best book of her life). She remembered the hot popcorn which the three of them ate while they speculated about the people, fragments of whose lives were revealed to them through their lighted windows. Remembering all these pleasures they did not, after all, seem past. They *were* pleasure and they were hers right now for the taking.

She ran out of her room, down the hall, and through the dining room crying, "I've changed my mind." The car was just backing out of the driveway and she ran onto the side porch shouting, "Wait for me. I've changed my mind." But she was too late. They didn't hear her. The car rolled smoothly away without a sign from either of them. They were laughing and talking, with not the least memory it appeared of her.

She went back into the empty house, into her empty room, and there without bothering to sit down, picked up her pen and wrote "62. I love Calvin Dean."

What was she doing standing at her bamboo desk, writing "I love you" one hundred times to a boy who didn't know she existed? She was suddenly alone, not only in the house, but in the world.

"I am alone in the world," she said and the words had a terrible ring of truth which she had never intended.

THAT summer, Cress became a great lover of signs and portents—the summer she was fourteen, when everything was changing. Signs and portents didn't stop the changes, didn't even slow them down, but they did forewarn her. That was something. It was something to know that if you laughed before breakfast you would cry before supper, that Friday would be either the fairest or the foulest day of the week, that a pointed elbow is a certain sign of a sour disposition, and that a sweating glass brings rain.

Cress started her days that summer by counting buttons and ended them by counting one-eyed autos. One-eyed autos were called padiddles that summer, no one knew why. In between times, she counted white horses, loads of hay, tea leaves, bridges, beards, and mules. She wished on falling stars, over running water, and upon making accidental rhymes.

"Spit," she yelled at her father when a jack rabbit ran in front of their car.

Mr. Delahanty had learned that summer to spit first and reason later. "Why?" he asked, having spat.

"We'd been sure to've had a blowout if you hadn't."

Cress was shocked when her mother threw half of a too large pinch of salt into the sink.

"All the salt you throw away," Cress told her mother, "you have to come back after you're dead and pick up with your eyelashes."

Mrs. Delahanty rinsed away the salt that still remained on her hand. "Cress," she asked, "you don't really believe all this nonsense, do you?"

Wary as a witch doctor, Cress replied, "Why take a chance?"

That was the summer Cress saw Honor Gallagher again after Honor had been away a year, a meeting that didn't surprise

Cress. Hadn't it been foretold? Hadn't she dreamed of running water, and the day she saw Honor said her name not once but twice before eating?

A name that's spoken before eating
You'll use ere nightfall as a greeting.

The day she saw Honor again was a Monday, the day after the Fourth of July. Cress came to breakfast late and sat looking at her orange juice, not drinking it. After a day at the beach, she felt too passive and dreamy to eat, even to drink.

"Mother," she said, "is it O.K. with you if I go swimming in the Ditch this afternoon?"

The Ditch, which carried irrigation water to the orange groves, was nicer than it sounded, shoulder deep, wide as a narrow road, curving among the glossy-leaved trees.

"I don't know how you can stand any more water, Crescent," her mother said. Mrs. Delahanty's face, except for large white circles about her eyes, where her sunglasses had protected her, was raspberry-colored, and when she spoke, she tried to move her mouth as little as possible. Cress admired this way of talking. She thought it made her mother look a little like George Raft.

"I wish you could have given me a good, solid name," Cress said, "instead of Crescent."

"What do you mean, good and solid?" Mrs. Delahanty asked.

"Old-fashioned," Cress explained. "Like Faith or Abigail or Prudence."

"I once knew a girl named Abundance," Mr. Delahanty said. Mr. Delahanty, being dark, didn't sunburn and was able to speak heartily. "How'd you like that for a name, Cress?"

"Abundance is just as bad as Crescent," Cress said. "It's too unusual. My favorite name is Honor. I think it's the most distinguished name I ever heard."

This was not news to Mr. and Mrs. Delahanty. Before Honor had gone with her parents to Alaska, she had lived on a ranch adjoining the Delahantys' and had been, in spite of the five years' difference in their ages, Cress's best friend.

"Honor *is* a nice name," Mrs. Delahanty said. "But I like Crescent better. It's more romantic."

"Honor," Cress said, "is solid *and* romantic."

The first thing Cress heard from the other girls when she got to the Ditch that afternoon was that Honor Gallagher was back on a visit. Cress hadn't had many letters from Honor recently. Not that that mattered. After a lifetime of silence, it would still be the same between her and Honor.

"Honor and her mother got here Saturday," one of the girls said. "They're visiting Honor's grandmother, in town. They've bought a new car and are going to drive it back to Alaska."

"How swell!" Cress said. "How wonderful!" But all the time she was floating away from the others, slowly at first, then faster, around two bends, under Byfield Bridge, past the clump of acacias, until, finally, she was alone and, if missed, not missed enough to be shouted at by anyone or pursued. She drifted on, floating on her back, and overhead a white cloud like an opened parasol accompanied her. The cloud blotted out the sun, and the water was the color of a butcher-knife blade; the sun came out and the blade was first polished, then changed from steel to silver. Cress anchored herself by an overhanging bank where slanting willows shaded the water.

The water was high. It ran over the grass of the bank, extending it full length, so that it looked like soft, green hair being combed. The shouts of the swimmers were far away, so far that they were no longer human voices but only summery, afternoon sounds. "Honor is home," Cress thought.

It was at the Ditch that she had first met Honor Gallagher, two years before, the summer she was twelve and Honor seventeen. Cress had been practicing floating then. She could swim but not float. Sinking, as she always did, she looked up and saw a girl in a yellow bathing suit looking down at her from the bank above.

"Let go, let go," the girl above her said, and Cress did so and floated.

400

Honor was one of the big girls, full grown, one of the girls Cress had watched from a distance. She had a shape, beautiful, in and out like a flower on a stem. But she was hardy, too, like a boy. There were strong, swelling muscles in her brown legs and arms. Her yellow bathing suit was in one piece, not two wisps, like most of the big girls', with vacancies for their bodies to show through. Honor could swear like a trooper. She was the only girl in the Gallagher family, with older boys on one side of her, younger boys on the other. It was a tussle to stay alive in the midst of them, she used to say.

That first afternoon, she had dived down into the Ditch beside Cress. It takes pains and practice to dive into four feet of water. You can go too straight and break your neck, or flatten out too much and break yourself wide open. Honor went just right— under, then up, in a shallow arc. She had been with the big kids on a swimming party, but it had become a necking party, so she'd left. She stood up in the Ditch, water running down her fierce, pink face. "Those boys! So pinchy, so squeezy!"

After that, she and Cress were together for a whole year on Saturdays, Sundays, and after school. At first, Cress thought she was too young to be Honor's friend and was apologetic. But Honor liked her as she was.

She and Honor had been perfect together. That summer, they had discovered a shallow cave—a ledge with a roof over it, actually, in the hills. There was clean sand on the bottom, two bones —human or animal, neither of them knew which—at the cave's edge, and a view, on clear days, of the ocean. Cress and Honor had gone there that summer at every hour—at sunrise, at sunset, in between. They had imagined, sitting in the cave, that they were the last of the world's survivors. Looking out at the blue lip of the Pacific on the horizon, they had wondered how long it would be before the ocean gnawed inland to them.

They had often made fires in their cave and cooked food— hot dogs, usually. Sometimes they had a real meal—roasted potatoes and onions to go with their hot dogs, and served Hostess cupcakes for dessert.

401

Honor had been memorizing the records of all outstanding batters and pitchers that first summer. She carried with her a small, loose-leaf spiral notebook, a Beacon Wire-o, in which she kept these figures. She would bring her notebook to the cave and get Cress to test her knowledge.

"Why memorize them?" Cress asked her once.

"The mind is a muscle," Honor answered. "I want to exercise mine."

"But why on baseball?"

"I don't want to *guess,* I want to *know* what Lefty Gomez did and the year he did it."

Cress hadn't cared much about Lefty Gomez, but she hadn't been able to help learning about him that summer. What *she* really liked was poetry. She brought an anthology, "Star Points," to the cave, but it was Honor who did all the reading aloud. She could read so much better than Cress, who got carried away by the rhythm. What the words meant was always vivid and clear to Honor, to whom poetry, and even much reading, was new.

When Cress and Honor were not together, they left notes for each other at the Delahanty weir box, which they both passed on their way to catch their respective buses for school. Honor, who went earlier, would find a note put there by Cress the night before, and Cress, at eight-thirty, would pick up a note left there by Honor a half hour before. Honor's notes had been brief and businesslike: "See you tonight 5 P.M. Good luck in Geog. test. H. G." Cress's had been a good deal more flowery. Sometimes she had quoted poetry.

When Honor's father, who, Mr. Delahanty said, was a rolling stone if ever there was one, decided to roll on to Alaska after a year in California, Cress and Honor parted without any school-girl protestations of eternal devotion. What was the need? Even their names, Cress thought now as she floated quietly beneath a sky that was empty of clouds, had the sound of names that belonged together: Honor, Crescent—Crescent, Honor. One solid, square, an unchanging rock, the other curving, filled with light, but a reflected light.

Cress was in no great hurry to get home that afternoon. What was the need to rush? Honor would come as soon as she could. She would have to do a certain amount of visiting with her grandmother and other relatives in town; then she would drive out. When, at last, Cress started home, the sun was low; midges rose and fell above the yellowing roadside weeds. She was happy about Honor's return, but not excited, she thought. Then, when she saw the new yellow car in the driveway, she knew it was Honor's and began to run.

There was no one on the porch when Cress got there, no one in the living room. She walked into the dining room, paused, and called, "Honor! Honor!"

Mrs. Delahanty came in from the kitchen, wiping her hands on a paper towel. "Cress?" she said. "Honor's out in the orchard with your father."

This seemed strange. Honor had never been one to fall in with the boring trips of inspection suggested by grownups.

"She wanted to help him pick out some fruit to send back to Alaska," Mrs. Delahanty explained. "Some avocados and grapefruit, and oranges, too, I guess. She wants them to be absolutely perfect."

"Why don't you go brush your hair and put on a clean dress? Honor's all dressed up. After all, it's a holiday, you know." Mrs. Delahanty reached out a hand to smooth Cress's hair, which had dried into stiff, finger-width strands.

Cress put on a clean white dress and her new white moccasins, combed her hair, and tied it at the back with a blue ribbon. By the time she had finished, she heard her father's voice and knew that he and Honor had returned from the orchard.

The three of them were sitting about the table when she went into the dining room, a little pyramid of oranges in front of them. Her father was beginning to peel an orange in the methodical way he had, cutting the top off first with his knife.

"Honor," Cress said.

"Hello, Cress," Honor answered, stressing the second syllable

403

of "hello" in a way that was new to her. "How are you, anyway?"

"I'm all right," Cress said. Honor was as beautiful as ever. She had on one of those dresses in two parts, the parts not meeting—a short, tight bodice and a full, swirling skirt. The dress was apricot-colored, and between the bodice and skirt Honor's brown skin was smooth and supple.

"Your mother said you were swimming," Honor remarked politely. "Do you still like to swim?"

"Yes, I do," Cress answered. "I love to. Do you still swim, Honor?"

"Oh, no," Honor answered. "No, not any more." There was a pause in which no one said anything. Then Mrs. Delahanty said in an interested voice, "I expect you go skiing nowadays, don't you, Honor?"

"Yes," Honor answered, and went on eagerly, "It's so exciting I just can't tell you. It's the nearest thing to flying, they say."

"I was up at Arrowhead at Christmas," Cress said. "I wasn't much good on skis, but I tried."

Honor laughed, shook her head, and then spoke to Mrs. Delahanty. "She hasn't changed, has she?"

I'm right here, Cress thought. You can speak to me, Honor. But Honor went on talking to her mother. Here I am, Honor, Cress thought, but it was like those movies in which an invisible person tries to communicate with someone. She sat near enough to Honor to touch her, but she couldn't do that; there was something that separated them, something transparent and gauze-like that she could see through but couldn't understand and couldn't possibly break.

Mr. Delahanty handed an orange to Honor. "Eat this and see what you've been missing," he told her.

Honor began to peel the orange with her old-time quick, sure gestures. "These are really going to amaze Mike, Mr. Delahanty. I don't think he's ever eaten a tree-ripened orange in his life."

Cress looked inquiringly not at Honor but at her mother.

"Honor's engaged to Mike, dear," her mother said.

"Engaged?" Cress asked, as if it were a word she had never heard.

"To be married," Honor said, smiling.

"When was it you said the wedding was to be?" Mrs. Delahanty asked.

"In September. If Mike gets his leave then."

"Is Mike a soldier?" Cress asked.

"Oh, no, thank God," Honor said. "He's a flier, a commercial flier, but he was in the Army so long he always thinks of vacations as leaves, and so do I, now."

"Two months!" Mrs. Delahanty exclaimed. "That's not long, is it?"

"No, it's really terribly soon," Honor said. "That's the reason Mother and I are down here, actually. To buy me some clothes and get some household equipment. You have an electric stove, don't you, Mrs. Delahanty? Do you think I should get one?"

"I wouldn't have anything else," Mrs. Delahanty said.

"Does yours have its oven and broiler together?"

"Mine does, yes."

"Mike says that wouldn't be too satisfactory. Say you want hot biscuits and a broiled steak at the same time, for instance. How do you manage that?"

"Why don't you come look at mine?" Mrs. Delahanty suggested. "It's not new, but it's pretty good, I think."

The two women—that was how Cress thought of them now—went out of the room together, and Cress and her father were left alone.

"Sit down, Cress, why don't you?" Mr. Delahanty said.

Cress pulled out one of the chairs from the table and sat down beside her father.

"Have an orange," Mr. Delahanty said, rolling one toward her. Cress automatically cupped her hand to keep the orange from rolling off the table. On the table beside the oranges was a card, which said, "Michael J. Gates, Gates's Flying Service, Anchorage, Alaska, Box 1713."

"Is that his name?" Cress asked. "Gates?"

Mr. Delahanty nodded. "It's the address for the fruit."

"How terrible!" Cress said. "How terribly unlucky!"

"Unlucky?" Mr. Delahanty asked.

> *"Change the name and not the letter,*
> *Change for worse and not for better,"*

Cress explained.

But the minute she said the words, Cress knew they didn't matter, and that she would as soon walk under a ladder, throw salt away, put on her left shoe first. All these precautions, all this foresight, all these prophesyings! They were nothing. Countings and wishings and spittings were not going to change anything. In the kitchen she could hear Honor saying, "I should think this deep-well cooker would be pretty economical."

Mr. Delahanty smiled across at her. "There's a calmed-down tomboy for you," he said. "And I suppose it won't be long before you're thinking of steaks and stoves. And Edwin," he added thoughtfully. "How's Edwin," he asked. "I haven't heard you mention him for some time?"

Cress began slowly to peel her orange. She could not think of Edwin now. She could not think ahead to any coming time, only backward to the summer she had first seen Honor and to the summer that for her was already over, the summer of signs and portents.

CHAPTER VII

CRESS sat a little removed from Yolande Perrotti and Yolande's boy friend, waiting for the magic of the house party to bloom about her. The chief ingredients of that magic, as she had imagined it, were present: the sea and a boy. And though the Pacific, with its waves shattering from glass to foam and from green to white, was behaving as she had expected, Yolande and her boy friend were not.

The boy had come up out of the breakers fifteen minutes ago to join Yolande, and Cress had waited, at first excitedly, then unhappily, for the introduction which never came.

This was the first day of the house party; in fact, at nine in the morning, almost its first hour. For though they had arrived at the beach at dusk the night before, that flurry of unpacking, of eating peanut-butter sandwiches and making beds could not, surely, be called the "house party," any more than the arranging of a stage is called a play. So perhaps it was too early to judge or condemn the house party because it was so unlike the house party she had imagined, or the girls had planned. Or even the house party her mother had feared. Though all of these parties— the planned, the imagined, and the feared—were alike in one respect: what was most important in all of them had never been mentioned by anyone.

It had taken Cress two weeks to persuade her mother to let her go to the house party at all. At first, Mrs. Delahanty had said no because of Cress's age. At fourteen, she said, a girl was too young to go to a house party. Cress had countered this by naming a dozen fourteen-year-olds she knew who had gone to house parties. Mrs. Delahanty, at that, had shifted her ground. Fourteen might not be too young if the other girls were fourteen. But if the other girls were fifteen and sixteen and even, as in the case of that Perrotti girl, seventeen, Cress would be out of her depth, expected to know what she did not know, and interested in what didn't interest her; and she would hence have a miserable disillusioning time.

To this Cress had replied that she saw the five house-party girls every day at school, that they were all interested in the same things (what these were she had not said) and that she was never uncomfortable or out of her depth with them. Mrs. Delahanty had then changed her tack. She had become very practical. Cress, with her fair skin and no one to look after her, would surely have one of her terrible cases of sunburn. And indigestion. Many a woman she knew traced her chronic indigestion to girlhood follies in eating. And where were these follies more practiced than at house parties?

"You forget Miss Bird," Cress had said. Miss Bird was to be their chaperone. She was an aunt of Maribeth Dufour's, whose idea the house party was.

"Oh yes," Mrs. Delahanty had replied. "The biology teacher."

"And biology is about food," Cress had said, arranging biology to fit her needs. "Miss Bird probably has lists of balanced meals already made out and ready for us to follow."

Mrs. Delahanty had left off talking about indigestion at that. "What I really worry about, Cress, is drowning. Scarcely a summer goes by without my reading of a drowning or two at a house party."

Miss Bird is a wonderful swimmer. She is a little lame and can't go hiking or anything. So she swims."

"Like Byron," Mrs. Delahanty had said, unexpectedly. And then, in spite of the fact that Byron was surely the last person to hit on as a suitable chaperone for a girl's house party, she added, "I must say Miss Bird sounds like the perfect chaperone."

That was exactly the light in which Maribeth had presented her aunt. "Aunt Iris," she had assured the girls, "is practically a prefabricated chaperone. The minute she gets to the beach she will put on a kind of divided skirt outfit she has had since 1920 and which she has since shortened some, but not much. And she will sally forth with her specimen case to hunt marine specimens and we will scarcely ever see Aunt Iris again. She will, in fact, leave us perfectly free."

The house-party girls, when Maribeth had said this, had been eating lunch together in the high school cafeteria. Cornelia Samms, at whose parents' beach cottage the house party was to be held, had looked at Maribeth over a spoonful of trembling lime jello and asked, "Free for what, Maribeth?"

Everyone but poor Cornelia had known the answer to this question. They would be free for the word no one spoke. Cress had squirmed because of Corny's ignorance. And because Corny's question had demonstrated so perfectly why Cornelia was so lucky in possessing parents who owned beach and mountain cottages they were willing for Corny's friends to use. But Maribeth, without squirming and with her famous wide-open, violet-eyed stare unclouded, had answered, "Oh, free for whatever you like, Corny. Who am I to say what that is? Swimming in the nude, maybe."

Corny, at that, had clasped the big unsuitable alligator bag which she always carried to school to her matronly bosom, as if Maribeth's suggestion had already undressed her. "Oh, Maribeth," she had breathed, "I wouldn't think of such a thing."

"It was just a suggestion, Cornelia. The point is, with Aunt Iris for chaperone we'll be free. For whatever we want." And she and all the girls except Corny had looked at each other with understanding.

Even after her mother had said that Cress could go to the house party she had kept asking about it. Yesterday morning, though that seemed years ago now, her mother had brought orange juice in to her, and had sat on her bed while she drank it.

"Just exactly who are these girls you are going with, Cress?" she had asked. "Maribeth I know. Likewise Cornelia. And I've heard all about Yolande I care to. But who is this Mavis Avis?"

"Mavis Davis," Cress had corrected her mother. "And her sister, Avis Davis. They're twins, Mother, identical twins. They dress exactly alike, except for jeweled initial pins. They're the school yell leaders. They've trained themselves to talk in absolute unison like Jack Benny's Sportsmen. It's terrifically uncanny."

Mrs. Delahanty had made a sound in her throat. "In private conversation, you mean they do that?"

Cress had nodded with pride. "How can you stand them, Cress? Talking together that way?" her mother had asked.

Actually, although Cress had not known it yesterday morning, the twins, when separated from their official duties as yell leaders and drum majorettes, had almost nothing to say. Cress slept with Mavis. Aunt Iris had separated the twins because she believed it would help develop independence in them. Last night's separation had not helped Mavis much, Cress thought, since Mavis had spoken only twice and had both times said the same thing. "That goes double for me." Maribeth had declared when the house-party guest list was being planned that, with Mavis and Avis along, people at the beach couldn't help noticing them. Cress had been unwise enough to repeat this to her mother.

"People?" Mrs. Delahanty had repeated. "People?" For a minute the unsaid word of everybody's house party was on the verge of being spoken. For what Mrs. Delahanty had almost said of course was "boys." "*Boys,*" not "people," would notice the house-party girls with the twins along. *Boys* would see them as they tossed their shining hair in great exaggerated arcs after they took off their bathing caps; and *boys* would hear them when they ran back into the water, shouting and splashing. And *boys* would see them again, when they came out of the water and stood drying themselves with gestures slower and more deliberate than necessary in the slanting afternoon sun.

And they would not only be seen, they would see. They would see the big athletes and the track stars and the football players and perhaps even the Southern California Interscholastic Tennis Champion who lived at Balboa Beach. They would notice out of the corners of their eyes the showy handstands of these boys and their professional stance on the surfboards, as

410

they came racing shoreward on the crests of the largest breakers. They would also notice, or she would anyway, the boys of slighter build, the quiet boys who swam as if they liked the feel of water and picked up handfuls of sand and watched it trickle between their fingers. And one of these boys, his black hair dried in starfish points, would be somebody's cousin or brother's friend or ex-classmate; and he, after being introduced, and a little talk to everyone for politeness' sake, would toss a small shell in her direction and say to her alone, "Can *you* always tell when it's Sunday, because there's a Sunday shine in the air?" Something really personal, and about which they two alone would have any knowledge. And after that, a private world, like a great bubble, would settle down over the two of them.

When Yolande's friend had come up out of the water, Cress had thought for a minute that he was going to be this boy of the Sunday shine and the private world. But now he was leaving— without a shell, or even a word, tossed to her.

Just before supper Cress had to listen, once more, to the story of how this boy had come up out of the water to talk to her and Yolande and how she, mum as an oyster, had left to Yolande the whole burden of entertaining him. The girls, with Aunt Iris, were in the solarium, a big glass-walled room facing the sea.

Outside the low sun shone through the thinned top of the breakers, coloring them, as they broke, the pink of a raspberry soda; the nastiest pink in the world, Cress thought, waiting for the final, and by now familiar, line of Yolande's story.

She looked away from the sea to the room. Aunt Iris faced her at the other end of the big window, her head inclined over an old copy of *Scientific American,* unaware, it appeared, of anything but what she was reading.

The twins, in T-shirts and short white pleated drum majorette skirts, silently practiced a cheerleader routine in the arch of the doorway, dip, dip, dip, leap. But their faces, turned toward Yolande, reflected the meaning of Yolande's words: what a crazy girl Cress is. Maribeth, on the arm of Yolande's chair, was

411

openly laughing. Only Corny, in a white dress that made her look all the plumper, appeared sympathetic, thinking, Cress believed, there except for the grace of God go I.

"This boy," Yolande went on, "was a complete and absolute stranger to me. But after he left, do you know what Cress said to me?"

They most certainly did. Yolande had told them at least twice before, and Cress, seeing that she was going to tell them once again, looked out at the sea and tried, stoically, to count waves. "After he left," Yolande said, her voice as shocked with disbelief as if she had never repeated Cress's words before, "she said, 'Yolande, why didn't you introduce your friend to me?' Can you really believe it?" she asked, hooting with laughter. "Anything so childish? Thinking I wouldn't talk to him if I didn't know him?"

Maribeth, holding her stomach to keep her laughs from shaking her too much, called across to Cress. "Oh, Cress, not really?"

Aunt Iris put down the *Scientific American* and struggled in her slow heavy way up from her chair. Don't defend me, Cress thought, don't say what a good sweet girl I am and make them all hate me.

Aunt Iris didn't. All she said was, "I don't know about you girls, but I'm hungry." And she led them to the dining room.

After supper it was as if the girls had never avoided the word boys, as if the boy who had come up out of the sea had been a sign to them to talk and speculate. They had planned to go to a movie, but they went back to the solarium, instead, and there in the summery darkness, without bothering to turn on the lights, they began to wonder and to gossip.

Cress sat on the hassock which Aunt Iris had used to support her lame leg (Aunt Iris herself had taken the *Scientific American* and gone to her room) and watched the green-silver phosphorescence which occasionally smoked at a wave's tip and, further out, the single bobbing red light of a boat moving slowly across the horizon.

The talk was mostly Yolande's and Maribeth's, with questions now and then from Corny. They talked of what boys were like, *really,* and how they were different from girls, and what they liked in girls, *really.*

"Looks are not so important," Yolande said in her clear contralto, which sounded, Cress thought, like a large bell lightly rung. But it was easy for Yolande with her gypsy princess face to belittle looks.

Maribeth said, "I know. Look at Amanda Peters."

"She's got a wonderful figure," Corny said mournfully.

Cress, hoping a plain fact couldn't be considered naive, said, "Mindy Jackson hasn't got either." And everyone knew Mindy was the most popular girl-with-boys in school.

Mavis, speaking by herself (perhaps Aunt Iris' theory about separation and independence was right) said, "It's a complete mystery."

Yolande corrected her. "It's chemistry," she said, in a dreamy voice, "pure chemistry."

Maribeth agreed. "Either you have it, or you don't."

"Is it all settled when you're born?" Corny asked.

"I expect so, Corny," Yolande answered cheerfully, giving her long earrings a clink, like an echo to the bell of her voice. Then before Maribeth, or anyone else could speak, she broke the spell by flicking on the lamp at her elbow. "It's only eight-thirty," she said. "Let's go to the second show."

They came home from the show, an old Alan Ladd movie, with their eyes full of rippling muscles and smoking guns.

"Anybody sleepy?" Yolande asked. No one was.

"Anyone hungry?" Maribeth wanted to know. Everyone was. Cress stirred up her own special concoction called cocoa-mud: cocoa and sugar with just enough cream to make it spreadable. They ate it on thick slices of heavily buttered French bread and washed it down with Coca-Cola. It was very invigorating and after eating everyone felt peppy.

The twins led them in a drum-majorette routine. Cress did

413

handstands. Yolande sang a French song. They had a contest to see who could drink a whole coke without taking a breath.

At midnight, Aunt Iris, in a flowered challis dressing gown, stepped into the hall that opened into the kitchen and said, "Save something for tomorrow, girls."

In their own room Cress and Mavis sat on their twin Hollywood beds. Cress felt boiling with life, as if there were more blood in her veins than her veins could hold. And only seven blocks away dance bands were playing and cars were drawing up to the curb, laden with people for whom the night was just beginning.

Cress jumped off her twin Hollywood bed and went and stood over Mavis. "Oh, Mavis," she implored, "let's do something. Let's not just sit here moldering. Let's . . ." But she didn't know what let's do. Only let's get up, move, go outside, stay awake, give the world and the night a chance.

But Mavis knew. Perhaps she was not a talker but she knew what to *do*. "Let's go get the Samms' boat," she said, "and row on the bay."

"Yes," Cress said. "Oh yes. That will be perfect. Let's row till sunup."

With Mavis rowing by her side, they cut silently through the jagged, multi-colored spears of light which were reflected onto the water from the pier where the dance band played. There were many boats out, but no one else, it was obvious, was out simply to row, to be abroad in the night. Simply to row? To look at the stars? Oh no! That was not true and Cress knew it.

They were rowing toward someone, rowing toward a voice, a meeting on the water, toward the boy who would present the lovely shell and speak the secret words about the Sunday shine. As soon as she had admitted this, it was time to stop rowing; she felt sleepy and tired. What did she expect? Magic?

But with the "Cornelia" tied up once more, and someone (the dance band had gone home) playing a piano, leaving seemed ignoble. Or at least undaring. (And were they the same?) Was she giving up her search too easily? Had this been a test and was the pattern of her life being decided this minute?

Mavis perhaps did not understand her. Or perhaps did, and offered the best she had. Somewhere, from in or under her white drum-majorette kilt, she brought up a package of cigarettes. Tonight smoking seemed, clearly, the thing to do. Cress walked homeward with Mavis, past the still lit bars and cafés and pool halls, trying to imitate Mavis' nonchalance. It was beyond her, though; she could manage neither the down-drooping cigarette, nor Mavis' practiced majorette flip of her skirt.

However short she came of Mavis, she did not come short enough to completely offset the effect of Mavis' black bangs, brown legs and sashaying white pleats. Maribeth had been more than right. People noticed the twins, even when separated. Boys looked and spoke as they went past and at the corner where they turned right, two boys who had been watching them as they came down the street turned right with them, and falling in behind them, kept pace with them. "Aren't you two girls out pretty late?" they asked.

They were kids, Cress saw, sixteen or seventeen, and they did not attempt to catch up with them and she didn't feel anything but uncomfortable until, as they were leaving the lights of the business district, three more boys joined the queue. Then she was frightened. Mavis was too; she could tell by Mavis' grip on her arm and the increased speed of her walking.

There were two more blocks before they would reach home. And all the time the boys were calling to them, asking their names, where they went to school, what track team they were training for. "What's your best time for the 440, girls?" they asked. "What's that you're wearing for a skirt?" they called to Mavis. And, to Cress, "Hey, sweater girl, turn around."

It was worse than frightening, it was cheap, and Cress's face burned. The boys were gaining on them, coming closer and closer, and one of the boys used a word whose meaning she didn't know but whose sound was ugly.

In the minute before they would have reached the Samms'

house, they were suddenly surrounded. The boys' tone was still joking. One of them, an unlit cigarette in his mouth, said: "Give us a light, will you, girls?" But in spite of the joke, the boys stood in that unyielding circle, close about Cress and Mavis.

Cress, trembling, in a voice that scarcely emerged from her dry throat, said, and was hardly aware of what she said: "Is *that* all you want?"

These words, somehow, gave immediate pause to the joking. Miraculously the circle of boys opened, and the two girls walked through the gate and into the Samms' yard. Once inside the yard, and the gate slammed behind them, they began to run.

Neither spoke until they reached their own room and had that door closed behind them, too. Then Mavis, not in the least winded by the sprinting, said: "I don't want to sleep in the same room with you any more, Cress Delahanty." And having said that, she calmly left. In a few minutes she returned with Avis. "I'm going to sleep with my own twin," she told Cress. "You go on down to Corny's room."

"Mavis," Cress asked, "what's the matter?"

"You know," Mavis said, as she and Avis moved with their duplicating steps across the floor.

Cress, pajamas in hand, went down to Corny's room. There Corny, her round face heavy with doubt, looked at her suspiciously. Cress apologized. "I'm sorry to be disturbing you, Corny. But the twins got homesick for each other."

"No," Corny said. "It wasn't homesickness for each other. It was disgust for you."

"Me?" Cress asked.

"What you said to those boys," Corny explained. "What you asked them."

Cress moved up to the bed and in real amazement said, "But, Corny . . ." Corny cut her short. "And you've been smoking, too. You really reek, Cress. I don't blame Mavis for not wanting to sleep with you. I don't want to either. I don't think Mother would like me to, in fact."

416

Rejection by Corny, who wanted everyone, even stray dogs, to love her, was the final humiliation. Cress, without a further word, went out to the living room. She could sleep on the sofa and in the morning she would hitchhike home. But before she had undone a button Aunt Iris came to the doorway. "What is all this uproar about?" she asked.

"Corny doesn't want to sleep with me," Cress said.

"Why?" Aunt Iris asked.

"She says I reek."

Aunt Iris was beside her now, sniffing. "Reek?" she asked. "What of?"

"Tobacco," Cress said. "Mavis and I went rowing and on the way home we smoked."

"I thought Mavis was the one you were sleeping with anyway, not Corny," Aunt Iris said.

"Mavis doesn't want to sleep with me either," Cress admitted.

"Why?" Aunt Iris asked. "She reeks too, doesn't she?"

"Mavis doesn't mind the tobacco. What she doesn't like is something I said. Anyway, that's what she says."

"To her?"

"No. To some boys."

"What did you say?" Aunt Iris asked.

Cress told her. "You come on down to my room," she told Cress, "and sleep with me. I reek too."

It was a fact. Aunt Iris' room was hazed with smoke. "During the war," Aunt Iris said, "when cigarettes were hard to get, I smoked a corncob pipe. I got to like it, but in a girls' school I had to keep my door locked for fear of shocking someone."

Cress stared at Aunt Iris in astonishment. The idea of Aunt Iris shocking, instead of being shocked, was too great a reversal for her to comprehend so suddenly.

Aunt Iris opened a window, using a magazine to fan out some of the smoke. Then, leaning from the window, she said: "I should've done this earlier. It's a beautiful balmy night. Smell the iodine and salt and the bitter-sweet of the kelp."

She turned from the window. "I tell you what we both need, Cress, since we both reek. A little dip. Ten minutes only. We'll sleep better for it."

Cress said, "My suit's down in the twins' room."

"Suit?" Aunt Iris asked. "What do you need a suit for at this hour of the night?"

Cress didn't know. So she said nothing. "Here," Aunt Iris said, "you can wear this to the water." It was a smock, Cress guessed, or a laboratory coat of the kind doctors wore. She undressed in silence, modestly turned away from Aunt Iris who, when she faced about, had on a white toweling robe.

The air outside was sweet and fresh, even a little sharp. Cress had to slow her steps for Aunt Iris, whose lameness gave her a clumsy laborious gait.

"I never reconcile myself to this," Aunt Iris said, slapping her crippled leg, "never, never."

Cress, trying to equal Aunt Iris' matter-of-factness, asked, "Was it that way—from the beginning?"

"Do you mean was I born with it? No. No. I got this in a most unlikely way, in a cyclone. When I was nineteen. At a dance in a schoolhouse in Kansas. I was the teacher," she said, turning to speak over her shoulder and raising her voice to be heard above the surf. "In a way I was lucky that night, in a way I wasn't. Five people were killed. One of them was the boy I was going to marry that summer. That was my life's bad luck."

They were at the water's edge now and Aunt Iris took off her white robe and threw it back up the beach.

"You couldn't ever love anyone else?" Cress asked, trying to take in the whole of Aunt Iris' life from that long-ago night in Kansas to this moment on the edge of the Pacific.

"Oh yes," Aunt Iris shouted, "I could indeed. But not any of those who were able themselves to love a lame woman." She had stopped to say these words. Now she began to wade slowly out in the water.

Cress threw off her own covering and walked into the water, milky warm after the night air. Ahead of her, ungainly, but

418

steadfast in front of the deepening breakers, was Aunt Iris. "Would you like to go out with me tomorrow?" she called back. "These rock pools here are regular mines for algae."

Hunting algae with Aunt Iris had been the last thing Cress had ever imagined doing on a house party. The last thing she had imagined a house party could be *for*. But as the warm water rose from knee to thigh to waist, and then went sliding shoreward past her, she did not seem to have lost, either the imagined house party, or the imagined boy with the shell and the words about the Sunday shine. She caught up handfuls of water and dashed them across her chest and face.

Aunt Iris was waiting for her and Cress called above the surf, "Oh yes, I do want to go. Please may I?"

Aunt Iris, without answering, faced the open sea again and motioning with one big arm for Cress to follow, dived under the wall of the comber toppling above her. Cress followed, diving less cleanly; but she came up out of the smother in open water, only a little breathless, and swam easily in Aunt Iris' wake.

CHAPTER VIII

T HE interior conversations of Crescent Delahanty started, consciously, the spring she was fifteen. In an April twilight, the delicacy of early evening and early spring mingling, she admitted for the first time that it was impossible to tell other people what they were determined not to believe. But she didn't —couldn't—stop for a minute contradicting their false statements; all she could do was stop doing this out loud. The counter-statements, the explanations, the corrections, continued to be made, though no longer audibly. That spring she abandoned forever the belief which, in spite of setbacks, had persisted through childhood, that to be understood one has only to tell the truth. There were some truths which some people— particularly parents—simply could not swallow. Particularly about their own children. They just couldn't and it was useless to try to make them.

She was at the dining-room table memorizing geometry theorems and their proof. The windows were open and the scent of daphne mingled with the smell of a meat loaf baking for dinner. Her mother and her mother's friend, Mrs. Agnew, were visiting in the living room. They kept their voices low, but since the two rooms were separated only by an archway, she couldn't help hearing them. When one word began to be repeated she looked up from her geometry and really listened.

"Boys!" Mrs. Agnew said, using once more the word that had caught her attention. "If any other idea ever enters Joan's head, I don't know it." Joan was Mrs. Agnew's daughter and Cress's friend. She continued, "I don't know what's happened to girls nowadays. When I was fifteen, I didn't know boys existed."

Cress awaited her mother's reply with interest, but Mrs. Delahanty had nothing to say of her own youth. Instead, she said pensively, "I don't suppose we really appreciate how lucky we are with Cress. She's never given us a minute's worry. In that regard, I mean."

"Cress is just like I was," Mrs. Agnew agreed. "Boys don't exist for her."

"I expect that's perhaps carrying it a little too far," Mrs. Delahanty admitted. "But she does have so many other interests. She debates. She plays basketball. And this spring she's mad about track meets."

Mrs. Agnew sighed so strongly the sound carried clear to the dining room. "Well, don't rub it in, Gertrude. Cress is a girl in a thousand. You can tell that just by looking at her. She'll marry late, if at all. Be a career woman of some sort. I can see her all in white, a lady M.D. Devoted to healing. Can't you? There's something so wholesome and out-of-doorsy about Cress. The way she loves plaid, for instance."

Mrs. Delahanty said, "I won't prophesy about the future, Kay, but I do admit it's a pleasure to have the boy business postponed for a while."

Cress closed her geometry book, and began, quite consciously, her interior conversation, a reply it was useless for her to make aloud. Why? Because they really *had* been different when they were fifteen? Because they had some picture of an ideal fifteen-year-old which they wanted her to fit? Because no one *ever* really sees another person? How else did they get this picture of her, the calm outdoor girl in a plaid skirt, the debater and basketball player, the yell leader; the junior M.D.

Oh Mother, oh Mrs. Agnew! Is that what you see? The girl who never thinks about boys? Why I don't ever think about anything *else,* really.

And then, because she was trying to tell the truth, she explained that "really." By "really" I don't mean all the time, but "completely." I think about geometry, of course, but not with all my mind the way I think about boys.

When we moved to Tenant, I was nine years old and in the fifth grade. Do you remember Hubert Fairchild, Mother? The kids called him Bert, but I never did. When I was nine he was fourteen and in the eighth grade, and planning to be a minister. Maybe he was an awful sissy—I don't know. He came to school late, because he'd had typhoid that summer—and his head was shaved because during the fever most of his hair had fallen out. But I thought he was beautiful and spiritual and I loved him.

I loved him so much that I hid my face in my desk and cried and cried. Do you know why, Mother? Because he had been sick and in pain and I hadn't been there to nurse him. All that summer while I'd been carefree, going to the beach and the mountains, *he'd* been suffering. It broke my heart. Really I thought it did. So I cried and cried. I told you about it. You thought I should be a Red Cross nurse because I was so tender-hearted. I told you as clearly as I could, but you wouldn't believe a word I said. I cried and moped and you thought it was sickness and suffering that made me unhappy. It wasn't. It was Hubert.

And now? Debating? Because Calvin Dean was on the team last year. In assembly, do you know why I sit with my arm around the back of the seat of the girl next to me? Because of the boys in the row behind us. To suggest things to them. Yes, I *do*. Don't argue, don't contradict. I *know*. I'm the one who does it. And sometimes when I ride into town with Father at dusk, do you know what I do? I sit close to him so people will perhaps think he's a date. Once, a kid did. He asked me about him the next day. "Who was the guy I saw you out with last night?" he asked.

And track meets? Oh Mother! "Mad about track meets." What do I care now about track meets? All that running and jumping and sawdust pits and high and low hurdles? Nothing, except that he is always there. But if I tell you and Mrs. Agnew, you won't believe it; you'll say I don't know my own mind, or what I'm talking about. You'll say, if you do believe it, it's puppy love and too silly to talk about.

I'm fifteen. I'm in love. I won't tell you a word about it. But don't be dumb, Mrs. Agnew, just because I wear a plaid skirt and am a yell leader. The way I act and the way I feel are two different things. And don't think, Mother, just because he's sick too that I ought to be a Gray Lady or something.

I had heard about him before, but when I saw him I didn't know who he was. He was always at the track meets, dark and slender and burning-faced. He watched everything very intently, not just the boys running, but the movement of the glossy new leaves in the walnut grove next to the track; or a meadow lark on a post. He drank things in, he tipped the cup of seeing until he had the last drop. He had to—because he's dying.

He is Mr. Cornelius. Now you know who he is. He is the father of the Cornelius boys, the track stars. The boys' names are Norman, Wayne, and Lester. They are thirteen, fifteen, and seventeen years old. Mr. Cornelius is thirty-eight. Yes, he *is* one year older than Father. His name is Mark. His wife drives one of the school buses. She is heavy, with short curly hair that sticks out from under a cap like a taxi man wears. Mr. Cornelius lives in a little tent-house outside his own house so that he can have more fresh air. It is in the walnut orchard, halfway between his house and the school grounds.

When I go to the track meets I watch him all the time and by now he knows that I do. He smiles at me, he nods his head. We spoke once. He said, "Do you know my boys?" I said "Yes." He said, "Do you like track meets?" I told him the exact truth. "Yes, but not for the same reason I used to." He knew then; I know he knew. His eyes, they're hazel, deepened and darkened. He said, "What's your name?" I told him. "Crescent Delahanty." He said, "I know your father, Crescent. I like him."

That is all we ever said to each other. But he knows, I know he knows, I love him. I don't know whether he loves me or not but I know I am special for him. There is a special look he has for me, of tenderness, of lovingness.

I don't know why exactly. It's not that I have any illusions about being beautiful or talented or glamorous. Is it that I understand more than anyone else how it is for him to be dying?

Is it worse for him because he sees more than anyone else? And because he was an athlete too? I've heard about it at school, how many records he broke as a boy—so he has to leave swiftness behind and grace and winning? People who have never had those, people who can only half see or half touch or who can only jog-trot, not run, and who never hear meadow larks or music, dying can't be so hard for them. Can it? And I know how hard it is for him to leave these things, because I practice all the time *being* him. I begin when I wake up in the morning by thinking, This may be my last day on earth, because whatever he suffers I want to suffer. I would do anything to save him or to make him happy.

The minute she told herself this, Cress asked herself, "Do you mean it? Would you die for him? Do you love him enough to die for him?" You must stop saying it if it isn't true. You must stop saying you love him, even, if you aren't willing to die for him, because otherwise it's just an infatuation or something. True love would give up its life a thousand times over. Fire, sword, water, torture. Nothing would matter.

She stood up, and her mother called to her: "Cress, if you've finished studying, take your things to your room, will you? It's about time to set the table and Mrs. Agnew's going to stay for dinner."

Cress gathered up her books and papers and stopped in the dining room to greet Mrs. Agnew. She tried to fathom how Mrs. Agnew might have looked as a girl. It was strange how women lost, as they grew up, their own private, special look. She could tell at once what a girl was like—bright or dare-devil, prim or dull—by her looks. Girls flashed signals as to who they were, jumped, screamed, cried: they let you know. But grown-up women like Mrs. Agnew? What could you tell about her? Except that she was grown-up. She was round, she was gray, she was grown-up. She had crawled in under a smooth shell. She had heard her mother ask her father about women who looked like Mrs. Agnew, "What does her husband do?" Trying to get hold of some label which would make her different from other women just like her. Mrs. Agnew's husband was a dentist. That was the most personal thing about Mrs. Agnew.

How different Mr. Cornelius was, how much himself; how many thousand times more he was, in himself, than anything he had done. He had been an athlete, then a telephone linesman, and now he was sick and dying. But he was so much more than these things; he was like a phoenix which rose above all the realities of just existing; he, absent, was as present as Mrs. Agnew could never be. She had to look *through* Mr. Cornelius, he was so much closer and more real than Mrs. Agnew to see Mrs. Agnew at all. Mr. Cornelius who was—

Mrs. Agnew spoke, spoiling this reverie. "Now don't let us two old chatterboxes keep you from your studying, Cress. I was just telling your mother how much I admire it in you. In fact I said you were my ideal schoolgirl."

"Thank you, Mrs. Agnew," Cress said.

CHAPTER IX

MR. AND MRS. DELAHANTY, Cress, and Cress's
friends, Jo Grogan and Bernadine Deevers, sat down
to the Delahanty dinner table on Wednesday evening. The
table was round with a white cloth that dipped at its four corners
to the floor. Mrs. Delahanty, who hadn't even expected Cress
home for dinner, let alone Jo and Bernardine, felt apologetic
about the food which, besides being rather uninviting, was
skimpy in amount: a small salmon loaf, Harvard beets, mashed
potatoes, and for dessert a cabinet pudding which did nothing
to redeem the meal that had gone before. But the girls didn't
seem to know or care what they put in their mouths and she
decided that strawberries and fresh asparagus would have been
wasted on them.

A mockingbird was singing in the orange grove outside the
opened windows and the girls listened, a spoonful of cabinet
pudding lifted to their opened lips—then, as the song ceased,
put the spoons down without having tasted a bite. Mr. and
Mrs. Delahanty had given up trying to carry on a conversation
with them and treated them as so many portraits ranged round
their dining room—"Girls at Dusk," or "Reveries of Youth."
They talked their own talk and let the girls dream their dreams,
wrap their feet around the rungs of their chairs, and listen
(mouths open, eyes closed) to the bird song.

"I saw Doc Mendenhall in town today," Mr. Delahanty said.

Mrs. Delahanty said "Yes?" waiting for whatever it was that
made this fact worth reporting, but Bernadine interrupted his
train of thought, if he had one, by extending her long arms toward the darkening windows and singing very softly, "Oh night
of love, oh beauteous night." Bernadine was barefooted (it was
the spring's great fad at high school) though she was eighteen,
and wore an elaborate blue voile dress which drifted about her

426

like a sky-stained cloud. Bernadine was to be married the day after school was out and sometimes, Mrs. Delahanty felt, overplayed her role of bride-to-be.

It was already, unbelievably, the last week of school which, in Southern California, is the second week in June, a time climatically as well as scholastically neither one thing nor another, neither spring nor summer, neither truly school nor truly vacation. Class routines had been relaxed but not abandoned. Grade-wise, the feeling among the students was that the year was already water over the dam; still they couldn't be positive. Climatically the days started spring-like, damp and gray with threat even of one more unseasonal rain; at 1 P.M. exactly the day did an about-face. The overcast burned away and the tawny grasses, sun-bleached foothills, and smoldering flowers of full summer emerged. It was very confusing after getting up into a dripping cold which made sweaters and open fires necessary, to finish the day barefooted, hot-cheeked, and as naked as possible.

Cress and Jo both wore shorts and halters. Cress had shasta daisies tucked in the V of her halter and Jo Grogan, with those three flame-colored hibiscus in her short dark hair, might have been August itself on any calendar of girls. As the day darkened the white tablecloth grew silvery, the mockingbird retreated deeper into the orchard, and Mrs. Delahanty felt that the whole scene might be unreal, a mirage cast up into the present out of either the past or the future—that girls *had* sat in many a darkening room in years gone by and would so sit in the future; but that "now," the present minute, was unreal.

"Jo," she said briskly, "if you'll put some more custard on your pudding you might be able to eat it."

"I beg your pardon," said Jo. "Were you speaking to me?"

"Never mind," Mrs. Delahanty told her. "I was only urging you to eat."

"Oh food!" said Cress. "Food. Who cares about food?"

"I do," said Bernadine. "Howie adores puddings. Will you copy down this recipe for me, Mrs. Delahanty? I plan to serve

Howie a different pudding every single night for thirty nights. I already have twenty-two recipes."

"Tapioca, jello, and bread," said Jo, sing-songing. "If puddings be the food of love, cook on."

The mockingbird had ceased to sing. The leaves of the bougainvillaea vine which clambered over the dining-room wall rustled faintly. Mrs. Delahanty began taking the spoons from the serving dishes.

Mr. Delahanty remarked in the voice of a man who has had the words in mind for some time, "Doc Mendenhall says that Frank Cornelius had a bad hemorrhage this morning."

Mrs. Delahanty laid the spoons down, clattering. "Oh John!" she said. "I understood he was getting better."

"I don't think he's taken very good care of himself," Mr. Delahanty explained. "You can't throw off t.b. just by wishing. You've got to co-operate, rest, stay put. I've seen Cornelius about town off and on all spring. Baseball, things like that. Staggering around half-alive. I saw him yesterday, sitting along the road out by his place. Today, a hemorrhage. He was asking for . . ."

Cress sprang to her feet, interrupting her father. "You mustn't say that. You have no right to say that." She pulled the daisies from the neck of her halter and passed them from hand to hand distractedly. "You don't have any idea what it's like to be dying. Do you?" she insisted.

Mr. Delahanty agreed instantly. "No, I don't, Crescent. The worst I ever had was a touch of shingles."

"Don't be funny," Cress said, her chin quivering. "Don't be funny about death. How can you understand how terrible it is for Mr. Cornelius to think he may die, no matter how much he takes care of himself? And that if he doesn't go out and see the sunshine and people and trees today he may never see them again. Never, never. And you were never a great athlete like Mr. Cornelius, so it's a thousand times worse for him than it would be for you to stay in bed. And you blame him. You blame him for not giving in. You blame him," she paused, trying to

428

steady her voice. "I hate—I hate *people* who say cruel things like that." She looked at her father and Mr. Delahanty looked back. Then she dropped her daisies onto her plate amidst the uneaten salmon and beets and ran from the room.

Mrs. Delahanty, after the sound of the slammed door had stopped echoing, leaned over and began to gather up the daisies. The two girls excused themselves and left the room.

"What did I say?" Mr. Delahanty asked. "To cause all that?"

Mrs. Delahanty continued without speaking to shake bits of food from the flowers. "Gertrude, did what I said sound cruel and hateful to you?"

"No, John, not to me," she answered. "But then I'm not in love with Mr. Cornelius."

In her bedroom, Cress sat on the floor, her head on the window sill. When she felt an arm about her shoulders, Jo's by the weight and pressure, she said, "Go away, please go away and leave me alone." The arm remained where it was. Jo knew, and so did Bernadine. Not much, because there wasn't much to know, except that she had spoken to Mr. Cornelius exactly twice and that she loved him and would willingly die for him.

There was "not much to know" in what was called the outside world; but inside herself, in her dreams and imaginings there was nothing *but* Mr. Cornelius. In her dreams she and Mr. Cornelius sometimes went away together, Mr. Cornelius saying, "Cress, without knowing it I have been searching for you all of my life. My sickness is no more than the sum of my disappointment, and without you I can never get well."

Sometimes in her dreams Mrs. Cornelius came to her and the gist of what she said was, "My life with Mr. Cornelius has been a failure. He has not many months to live. I do not want to stand between him and his happiness in the little time that is left. Go, with my blessing."

But for the most part Mrs. Cornelius and the Cornelius boys did not exist in her dreams; even the world, as she knew it in what was called "real life," was greatly altered; or, perhaps, simplified. Changed, anyway, so that it consisted of nothing but sunshine, a background of sand or water, and a grassy or sandy bank against which Mr. Cornelius reclined, getting well. And as he got well she waited on him, and talked to him. Sometimes she imagined that Mr. Cornelius kissed her. She had to be careful about these imaginings however. She had never been kissed, family didn't count, of course, and since she supposed that when you were kissed by the man you loved, the sensations were near to swooning, swooning was what she nearly did whenever she had imaginings of this kind.

Most often she simply helped Mr. Cornelius as he reclined in the midst of the sunny simplified landscape, his thin beautiful face becoming tanned and fuller as his health improved. In her dream she picked flowers for Mr. Cornelius, went to the library for him, read to him, smoothed his brow, sometimes kissed him and always, always gazed at him with enraptured eyes. But all the time she was imagining this life with Mr. Cornelius she suffered, because Mr. Cornelius was dying and there was nothing she could do about it; she suffered because she had feelings which she did not know how to express, suffered because she had put the core of her life outside its circumference.

She sat up, and Jo took her arm away. It was still light enough to see Bernadine on the floor leaning against the bed, and Jo by her side. The room was quiet and warm and full of misery.

"There is nothing you can do, Cress," Jo said. "You love him and he is dying. You can't do anything about either one. All you can do is to endure it."

"I can do something," Cress said.

"What?" Jo asked.

"I can go to Mr. Cornelius and tell him I love him."

"Oh no," Bernadine said, very shocked. "You can't do that."

"Why not?" Cress asked.

"You don't know whether he loves you or not."

"What does that have to do with it? I'm not going to him to ask him if he loves me. I'm going to tell him that I love him."

"Is that what you really want to do, Cress?" Jo asked.

"No—if you mean by want to, do I feel good about going. I feel awful about going. It makes me feel sick to my stomach to even think about it. It gives me the shakes."

Jo once again put an arm around Cress's shoulders. "It's a fact," she reported to Bernadine. "She's shaking like a leaf."

"Look, Cress," Bernadine said. "I'm almost married myself. It's just a matter of days. For all practical purposes I *am* married. You must think of Mr. Cornelius, Cress, and what he'd feel. I know if Howie was sick and maybe dying he wouldn't want some other woman coming to his sickbed and saying, 'I love you.' The first thing he'd do, I know, is say to me, 'Bernadine, throw this madwoman out.' And that's exactly what Mr. Cornelius is liable to say to you."

"I know it," Cress said bleakly.

"Well, then?" Bernadine asked, pride of reasoning in her voice. "Are you still going?"

Cress huddled silent, unanswering.

"It's probably not a very kind thing to do," Jo suggested in her deep, thoughtful voice. "Going to see him now when he's so sick."

"Oh I *know* that. If I just asked myself what was kind I would never do it. But what has kindness got to do with love? I'm not doing it to be kind to Mr. Cornelius. I'm doing it because I have to."

"Have to?" Jo reminded her, steadily. "You don't have to. Sit right here. Sit still. By morning everything will be different."

"By morning Mr. Cornelius may be dead."

"Well then," Bernadine said, "all your problems will be over. Mr. Cornelius will be dead and you'll be sad. But you won't have bothered him or made a fool of yourself. And think about Mrs. Cornelius. How's she going to feel about someone barging in on her sick husband, making passionate declarations of love?"

"It wouldn't be passionate. I would just say, very quietly, the minute I got there, 'I love you, Mr. Cornelius.' Then leave."

"Cress," Bernadine said, "what actually do you see yourself

431

doing? You get there, the whole family is around the bed, and doctors and priests too, maybe. What are your plans? To say 'I beg your pardon but I've a little message for Mr. Cornelius'? Then push your way through them all to the bedside, drop on your knee, kiss his wasted hand and say, 'Mr. Cornelius, I love you.' Is that it?"

"Oh, don't heckle her, Bernadine," Jo said.

"What I see myself doing," said Cress, "is telling Mr. Cornelius something I have to tell him."

"How," asked Bernadine, "do you see yourself getting there?" Bernadine had Howie's car while he was in the army and she had driven the girls home from school. "Do you see yourself walking eight miles?"

"If I have to," Cress said.

"O.K.," Bernadine told her. "I'll drive you. And let's go right away and get it over with."

Mr. Cornelius was still living in the small one-room tent-house at the edge of the walnut grove. It was nine o'clock when Bernadine stopped the car in front of the Cornelius ranch. A dim light was burning inside the tent-house, but there was nothing to indicate the presence of the crowd of people she had prophesied. "Here we are," she said, turning off the engine.

Cress wished for any catastrophe, however great, which would prevent her from having to leave the car. She felt real hatred for Bernadine and Jo. Why, if they were convinced that she shouldn't come, hadn't they remained steadfast? What kind of friends were they, to give way to their better judgment so weakly? And what were her parents thinking about? Why had they permitted her to go riding off into the night? To tell a strange man she loved him? True, she hadn't told them where she was going nor that she loved a strange man. But what were parents for if not to understand without being told? She blamed them for her fright and unhappiness.

Still anything that *happened* would be better than continuing to live in a make-believe world in which she only dreamed that she told Mr. Cornelius she loved him. She opened the car door and stepped out into the night air which, after the warmth of the car, was damp and cold against her bare legs and arms.

"Cheerio," said Bernadine quite calmly as she was walking away from the car under the dark canopy of the big trees toward the dimly lighted room. Why was it so hard to do what she had set her heart on doing?

She stood at the screened door looking into the room as into a picture. Why did it seem like a picture? The small number of furnishings? Their neat arrangement, dresser balanced by table, chair by bed? The light falling from a bulb, shaded by blue paper, so that part of the room was in deep shadow? But most of all, was it picture-like because she had imagined the room and Mr. Cornelius for so long, that a frame had grown up about them in her mind? Now, would it be possible to break that frame? She opened the screen door, stepped into the room and became a part of the picture by that easy act.

Mr. Cornelius lay on a high narrow bed. He lay very straight, his head supported by three or four pillows and his hands folded across an ice pack which he held to his chest. His eyes were closed and his face, in spite of his illness, was warm with color. At the sight of him all of Cress's doubts left her. Oh Mr. Cornelius, she thought, I do truly love you and I have come at last to tell you.

Without opening his eyes Mr. Cornelius said, "Joyce, I think I'm going to be sick."

Joyce. Cress was surprised at the name. It seemed too gentle for the bus driver. "It's not Joyce, Mr. Cornelius," Cress said. "It's me."

Then Mr. Cornelius opened his eyes and Cress was enchanted all over again by the enormous blaze of being alive and searching and understanding which she saw there.

"It's Cress," he said, in a very low careful voice, "the track-meet girl." Then he closed his eyes. "I'm going to be sick," he said. "Hand me the basin."

The basin, Cress saw, was an enamel wash bowl on the night

433

stand by the bed. She got it, put it on the bed beside Mr. Cornelius.

"Help me," Mr. Cornelius said and Cress helped him the way her mother had helped her when she was sick after her tonsils were out, by putting an arm around his shoulders and supporting him.

"Don't be scared," Mr. Cornelius whispered. "It's not a hemorrhage. I'm just going to lose my supper."

He did and afterwards he lay back against his pillows for a minute or two, then he reached up his hand and rang the bell which was suspended from the headboard of his bed.

"A glass of water," he told Cress, and Cress was holding it for him to rinse his mouth when Mrs. Cornelius arrived. Mrs. Cornelius paid no more attention to her than if she'd been some kind of device to help Mr. Cornelius—like the ice pack or the bell. She took the glass from Cress's hand, slipped her arm around her husband's shoulders and said, "Frank, Frank. Oh thank God, Frank, no more blood. Just your supper and that doesn't matter. I made you eat too much. This was to be expected. If you can swallow a bite or two later I'll fix you another. How do you feel now, honey?"

Cress had backed away from the bed. Mrs. Cornelius was wearing a housecoat or dressing gown of deep red, lightened by wreaths of tiny yellow and white flowers. She looked like Robert Louis Stevenson's wife, "trusty, dusky, vivid and true with eyes of gold and bramble dew." Her bosom, which had spoiled the lines of her chauffeur's coat, was exactly right for pillowing an invalid's head, and her chestnut hair, curled corkscrew crisp, said "Never give up," as plain as any words, said "Fight on," said "Defy the universe." And all the time she was cradling Mr. Cornelius in her arms, and helping him rinse his mouth she was pressing her cheek to his hair and speaking comforting words through which there ran a mixture of laughing and joking.

"Take this to the bathroom and empty it," she said to Cress when Mr. Cornelius had finished rinsing his mouth. She handed the basin to Cress and nodded toward a door at the back of the room. Cress, ordinarily too squeamish to pull off her own Band-Aids, marched away with it without a word.

When she returned Mr. Cornelius was once more against his pillows and Mrs. Cornelius was wiping his face with a damp cloth.

"Where'd you come from?" she asked Cress as she took the basin from her.

"From out there," Cress said, nodding toward the road. "The girls are waiting for me. In the car," she explained.

Mrs. Cornelius paused in her washing. "What did you come *for?*" she asked.

Cress welcomed the question. It was a wonderful help, like the upward spring of the diving board against her feet when she was reluctant to take off into deep water. Though she no longer had so great a need to say what she had come to say; some change had taken place in her since she had come into the room; what had been locked inside her and had been painful, because unsaid, had somehow, without a word being spoken, gotten itself partially expressed. She was not completely sure how. Nevertheless she had come to speak certain words. They were the answer to Mrs. Cornelius' question. They were *why* she had come.

So, louder than was necessary, and in a voice cracking with strain she said, "I came to tell Mr. Cornelius I loved him." Then she turned, resolutely, and said the words directly to Mr. Cornelius. "Mr. Cornelius, I love you."

At that Mrs. Cornelius laughed, not jeering, not angry, not unbelieving, but in the soft delighted way of a person who has received an unexpected gift.

"Oh, Frankie," she said, running her hand through Mr. Cornelius' thick black hair, "look at what we've got here."

"What *we've* got," was what she'd said as if, Cress thought, I'd said I loved them both. And then, watching Mr. Cornelius reach for his wife's hand, she saw that there was nothing she could give to Mr. Cornelius without giving it also to Mrs. Cornelius. Because they were not two separated people. They were really one, the way the Bible said. It was an astounding discovery. It was almost too much for her. She felt as if her mind, by an infusion of light and warmth, was being forced to expand to accommodate this new idea. And it was an idea which, contrary to all her expectations, she liked. It was exactly what she wanted. Not Mr. Cornelius alone on a stretch of desert sand and she kissing his wasted hand—in spite of her six months' dreaming. What she wanted was Mr. and Mrs. Cornelius. She was so happy for Mrs. Cornelius' presence she almost took and kissed *her* plump brown unwasted hand.

Mrs. Cornelius, however, was continuing her laughing murmur to her husband. "Frankie," she said, "oh Frankie, you old jackanapes. You old irresistible. What's all this talk about being on your last legs? Done for? Caved in? With school girls coming with professions of love? Pretty school girls. Boy, we're not cashing in our checks just yet. Not us. What's your name, dear?" she asked Cress.

Mr. Cornelius answered in his low half-whispering voice. "She's John Delahanty's daughter, Crescent. They call her Cress at school."

"Well," said Mrs. Cornelius. "I've heard the boys mention you. Where'd you see Frank?"

"At a track meet."

"I stared at her some," Mr. Cornelius said. "Reminded me of you at her age. So alive."

"That's what *I* thought about Mr. Cornelius," Cress said.

"Alive?" asked Mrs. Cornelius.

"Oh yes. More than anyone there. More than the boys. I thought his eyes fed on the sights," she said, daring the poetry of her thoughts.

"Fed?" Mrs. Cornelius studied the word then accepted it. "I see what you mean. Now Frank," she said, "will you lie still and take care of yourself? Unknown school girls loving you and wanting you to get well. You do, don't you?" she asked Cress.

"Oh yes," Cress said. "I was willing to die for him."

Her voice evidently convinced Mrs. Cornelius. "Oh Frank," she said, "school girls willing to die for you and you not half trying."

"Mrs. Cornelius," Cress said, wanting, since even partial confession made her feel so much better, to tell everything, "I ought to tell you something else." She stumbled for words. "I ought to tell you what else I planned."

"I bet you planned to run away with Frank and nurse him back to health."

Cress was amazed. "Yes," she said, her face burning with guilt and foolishness, "yes I did. How did you know?"

"Oh Frank, don't it bring it all back to you? No wonder you were reminded of me. *I* was going to run away with the minister," she said turning to Cress. "Save him from his wife and family. And he *was* the most beautiful man in the world, Frank. You can't hold a candle to your father—never could."

Cress wanted to say something, but she couldn't settle on what. She had too many emotions to express. Exhilaration at being released from the isolation of her dreaming; relief to find that other girls had loved secretly too, but most of all joy to have acted, to have made for herself a single undivided world in which to live.

"Oh Mrs. Cornelius," she said, "oh Mrs. Cornelius . . ."

"Cress," asked Mrs. Cornelius, "can you play cards? Or checkers?"

"Yes," Cress said, "I can. I like to."

"And read out loud? Of course you can do that, can't you? Why don't you come read to Frank? And play cards with him? It gets so darn lonesome for him. I work. The boys work, and besides they haven't got enough patience to sit still. And the good people come in and tell Frank how their uncles or mothers passed away with consumption and for him to be resigned. He needs somebody interested in living, not dying. Would you come?"

"Oh yes. If you want me—if he wants me. I could come every day all summer."

"O.K.," Mrs. Cornelius said, "we'll plan on it. Now you'd better run on. Frank's had a bad day. He's worn out."

Cress looked at Mr. Cornelius. His eyes were closed but he opened them at Mrs. Cornelius' words and made a good-by flicker with the lids.

"Good night," Cress said.

Mrs. Cornelius went to the door with her. "We'll count on you," she said once again and put a hand on Cress's shoulder and gave her a kind of humorous loving shake before she turned away.

Cress flew to the car propelled, it seemed, by the beat of her heart as a bird is propelled by the beat of its wings. The walnut leaves were alive and fluttering in the warm air and all about her mockingbirds were singing like nightingales. As she emerged from the grove she saw the June stars big and heavy-looking like June roses. This is the happiest hour of my life, she thought, and she yearned to do something lovely for the girls, something beautiful and memorable; but all she could think of was to ask them to go to town for milk shakes.

"I could stand some food," Bernadine said, "after all that waiting."

"He was sick," Cress explained, "and Mrs. Cornelius and I had to take care of him."

"Mrs. Cornelius? Did she come out?"

"Of course," Cress answered. "Wouldn't you, if Howie was sick?"

Bernadine had no answer to this. She started the car and after they had gone a mile or so Jo asked, "Did you tell him?"

"Of course."

"Does he love you?" Bernadine asked.

Cress felt sorry for Bernadine. "You're a fine one to be getting married," she said. "Of course he doesn't. He loves Joyce."

"Joyce? Who's Joyce?"

"Mrs. Cornelius. I remind him some of her. I adore Mrs. Cornelius and *they* are one person. Mr. and Mrs. Cornelius, I mean. They are truly married. I don't suppose you understand," she said, arrogant with new knowledge, "but what is for the one is for the other. I am going to help her take care of him this summer. Isn't that wonderful? Maybe I can really help him get well. Isn't this the most gloriously beautiful night? Oh, I think it's the most significant night of my life." The two girls were silent, but Cress was too full of her own emotions to notice.

When they went into the soda fountain, she looked at their reflection in the mirror and liked what she saw. The three of them had always been proud of one another. Bernadine had glamour, Jo character, and Cress personality; that was the division they made of themselves. "Look at Bernadine, listen to Cress, and let Jo act," someone had said. Oh, but I've broken through that, Cress thought, I can act, too. She searched for some understanding of the part Mrs. Cornelius had played in that break-through. If she had said, "You wicked girl," or made her feel that loving was a terrible thing? Would she have been pushed back, fearful, into the narrowness of dreaming, and into dreaming's untruths? She didn't know. She couldn't hold her mind to such abstractions.

"What we want," she said to Lester Riggins, the boy at the fountain, "is simply the most stupendous, colossal, overpowering concoction you ever served."

"This a special night?" Lester asked.

"Super-special."

"How come?"

"Bernadine's going to be married."

"Known that for six months."

"Jo's been accepted for Stanford. With special praise."

"Old stuff."

"Then there's me."

"What about you?"

"I'm alive."

"That's different," Lester said. "Why didn't you tell me in the first place? This obviously merits the Riggins' special. Expense any issue?"

"No issue," Cress said.

He brought them something shaped, roughly, like the Eiffel Tower, but more dramatically colored.

"Here it is, girls. Here's to being alive!"

They sank their spoons in it and ate it down, their appetites equal to the whole of it, color, size, sweetness and multiplicity of ingredients.

CHAPTER X

THE steam from the kettle had condensed on the cold window and was running down the glass in tear-like trickles. Outside in the orchard the man from the smudge company was refilling the pots with oil. The greasy smell from last night's burning was still in the air. Mr. Delahanty gazed out at the bleak darkening orange grove; Mrs. Delahanty watched her husband eat, nibbling up to the edges of the toast then stacking the crusts about his tea cup in a neat fence-like arrangement.

"We'll have to call Cress," Mr. Delahanty said, finally. "Your father's likely not to last out the night. She's his only grandchild. She ought to be here."

Mrs. Delahanty pressed her hands to the bones above her eyes. "Cress isn't going to like being called away from college," she said.

"We'll have to call her anyway. It's the only thing to do." Mr. Delahanty swirled the last of his tea around in his cup so as not to miss any sugar.

"Father's liable to lapse into unconsciousness any time," Mrs. Delahanty argued. "Cress'll hate coming and Father won't know whether she's here or not. Why not let her stay at Woolman?"

Neither wanted, in the midst of their sorrow for the good man whose life was ending, to enter into any discussion of Cress. What was the matter with Cress? What had happened to her since she went away to college? She, who had been open and loving? And who now lived inside a world so absolutely fitted to her own size and shape that she felt any intrusion, even that of the death of her own grandfather, to be an unmerited invasion of her privacy. Black magic could not have changed her more quickly and unpleasantly and nothing except magic, it seemed, would give them back their lost daughter.

Mr. Delahanty pushed back his cup and saucer. "Her place is here, Gertrude. I'm going to call her long distance now. She's a bright girl and it's not going to hurt her to miss a few days from classes. What's the dormitory number?"

"I know it, as well as our number," Mrs. Delahanty said. "But at the minute it's gone. It's a sign of my reluctance, I suppose. Wait a minute and I'll look it up."

Mr. Delahanty squeezed out from behind the table. "Don't bother. I can get it."

Mrs. Delahanty watched her husband, his usually square shoulders sagging with weariness, wipe a clear place on the steamy windowpane with his napkin. Some of the green twilight appeared to seep into the warm dingy little kitchen. "I can't ever remember having to smudge before in February. I expect you're right," he added as he went toward the phone. "Cress isn't going to like it."

Cress didn't like it. It was February, the rains had been late and the world was burning with a green fire; a green smoke rolled down the hills and burst shoulder-high in the clover crops that filled the spaces between the trees in the orange orchards. There had been rain earlier in the day and drops still hung from the grass blades, sickle-shaped with their weight. Cress, walking across the campus with Edwin, squatted to look into one of these crystal globes.

"Green from the grass and red from the sun," she told him. "The whole world right there in one raindrop."

"As Blake observed earlier about a grain of sand," said Edwin.

"O.K., show off," Cress told him. "You know it—but I saw it." She took his hand and he pulled her up, swinging her in a semi-circle in front of him. "Down there in the grass the world winked at me."

"Don't be precious, Cress," Edwin said.

"I will," Cress said, "just to tease you. I love to tease you, Edwin."

"Why?" Edwin asked.

"Because you love to have me," Cress said confidently, taking his hand. Being older suited Edwin. She remembered when she had liked him in spite of his looks; but now spindly had become spare, and the opinions, which had once been so embarrassingly unlike anyone else's, were now celebrated at Woolman as being "Edwinian." Yes, Edwin had changed since that day when she had knocked his tooth out trying to rescue him from the mush pot. And had she changed? Did she also look better to Edwin, almost slender now and the freckles not noticeable except at the height of summer? And with her new-found ability for light talk? They were passing beneath the eucalyptus trees and the silver drops, falling as the wind shook the leaves, stung her face, feeling at once both cool and burning. Meadow larks in the fields which edged the campus sang in the quiet way they have after the rain has stopped.

"Oh Edwin," Cress said, "no one in the world loves the meadow lark's song the way I do!"

"It's not a competition," Edwin said, "you against the world in an 'I-love-meadow-larks' contest. Take it easy, kid. Love em as much as in you lieth, and let it go at that."

"No," she said. "I'm determined to overdo it. Listen," she exclaimed, as two birds sang together. "Not grieving, nor amorous, nor lost. Nothing to read into it. Simply music. Like Mozart. Complete. Finished. Oh it is rain to listening ears." She glanced at Edwin to see how he took this rhetoric. He took it calmly. She let go his hand and capered amidst the fallen eucalyptus leaves.

"The gardener thinks you've got St. Vitus' dance," Edwin said.

Old Boat Swain, the college gardener whose name was really Swain, was leaning on his hoe, watching her hopping and strutting. She didn't give a hoot about him or what he thought.

"He's old," she told Edwin. "He doesn't exist." She felt less akin to him than to a bird or toad.

There were lights already burning in the dorm windows. Cress could see Ardis and Nina still at their tables, finishing their Ovid or looking up a final logarithm. But between five and six most of the girls stopped trying to remember which form of the sonnet Milton had used or when the Congress of Vienna had met, and dressed for dinner. They got out of their sweaters and jackets and into their soft bright dresses. She knew just what she was going to wear when she came downstairs at six to meet Edwin—green silk like the merman's wife. They were going to the Poinsettia for dinner, escaping salmon-wiggle night in the college dining room.

"At six," she told him, "I'll fly down the stairs to meet you like a green wave."

"See you in thirty minutes," Edwin said, leaving her at the dorm steps.

The minute she opened the door, she began to hear the dorm sounds and smell the dorm smells—the hiss and rush of the showers, a voice singing, the slap of bare feet down the hall, the telephone ringing. And the smells! Elizabeth Arden and Cashmere Bouquet frothing in the showers; talcum powder falling like snow; *Intoxication* and *Love Me* and *Devon Violet;* rubber-soled sneakers, too, and gym T-shirts still wet with sweat after basketball practice.

But while she was still listening and smelling, Edith shouted from the top of the stairs, "Long distance for you, Cress. Make it snappy."

Cress took the stairs three at a time, picked up the dangling receiver, pressed it to her ear.

"Tenant calling Crescent Delahanty," the operator said. It was her father: "Grandfather is dying, Cress. Catch the 7:30 home. I'll meet you at the depot."

"What's the matter—Cressie?" Edith asked.

"I have to catch the 7:30 Pacific Electric. Grandfather's dying."

"Oh poor Cress," Edith cried and pressed her arm about her.

Cress scarcely heard her. Why were they calling her home to watch Grandpa die, she thought, angrily and rebelliously. An old man, past eighty. He'd never been truly alive for her, never

444

more than a rough, hot hand, a scraggly mustache that repelled her when he kissed her, an old fellow who gathered what he called "likely-looking" stones and kept them washed and polished, to turn over and admire. It was silly and unfair to make so much of his dying.

But before she could say a word, Edith was telling the girls. They were crowding about her. "Don't cry," they said. "We'll pack for you. Be brave, darling Cress. Remember your grandfather has had a long happy life. He wouldn't want you to cry."

"Brave Cress—brave Cress," they said. "Just frozen."

She wasn't frozen. She was determined. She was not going to go. It did not make sense. She went downstairs to meet Edwin as she had planned, in her green silk, ready for dinner at the poinsettia. The girls had told him. "Are you wearing that home?" he asked.

"I'm not going home," she said. "It's silly and useless. I can't help Grandfather. It's just a convention. What *good* can I do him, sitting there at home?"

"He might do you some good," Edwin said. "Had you thought about that?"

"Why, Edwin!" Cress said. "Why, Edwin!" She had the girls tamed, eating out of her hand, and here was Edwin who loved her—he said so, anyway—cold and disapproving. Looking at herself through Edwin's eyes, she hesitated.

"Go on," Edwin said. "Get what you need and I'll drive you to the station."

She packed her overnight bag and went with him; there didn't seem—once she'd had Edwin's view of herself—anything else to do. But once on the train her resentment returned. The Pacific Electric was hot and smelled of metal and dusty plush. It clicked past a rickety Mexican settlement, through La Habra and Brea, where the pool hall signs swung in the night wind off the ocean.

Her father, bareheaded, but in his big sheepskin jacket, met her at the depot. It was after nine, cold and raw.

445

"This is a sorry time, Cress," he said. He put her suitcase in the back of the car and climbed into the driver's seat without opening the door for her.

Cress got in, wrapped her coat tightly about herself. The sky was clear, the wind had died down.

"I don't see any sense in my having to come home," she said at last. "What good can I do Grandpa? If he's dying, how can I help?"

"I was afraid that was the way you might feel about it. So was your mother."

"Oh Mother," Cress burst out. "Recently she's always trying to put me . . ."

Her father cut her off. "That'll be about enough, Cress. Your place is at home and you're coming home and keeping your mouth shut, whatever you think. I don't know what's happened to you recently. If college does this to you, you'd better stay home permanently."

There was nothing more said until they turned up the palm-lined driveway that led to the house. "Here we are," Mr. Delahanty told her.

Mrs. Delahanty met them at the door, tired and haggard in her Indian design bathrobe.

"Cress," she said, "Grandfather's conscious now. I told him you were coming and he's anxious to see you. You'd better go in right away—this might be the last time he'd know you."

Cress was standing by the fireplace holding first one foot then the other toward the fire. "Oh Mother, what am I to say?" she asked. "What can I say? Or does Grandfather just want to see me?"

Her father shook his head as if with pain. "Aren't you sorry your grandfather's dying, Cress? Haven't you any pity in your heart? Don't you understand what death means?"

"He's an old man," Cress said obstinately. "It's what we must expect when we grow old."

"Warm your hands, Cress," her mother said. "Grandfather's throat bothers him and it eases him to have it rubbed. I'll give

446

you the ointment and you can rub it in. You won't need to say anything."

Cress slid out of her coat and went across the hall with her mother to her grandfather's room. His thin old body was hardly visible beneath the covers; his head, with its gray skin and sunken eyes, lay upon the pillow as if bodiless. The night light frosted his white hair, but made black caverns of his closed eyes.

"Father," Mrs. Delahanty said. "Father." But the old man didn't move. There was nothing except the occasional hoarse rasp of an indrawn breath to show that he was alive.

Mrs. Delahanty pulled the cane-bottomed chair a little closer to the bed. "Sit here," she said to Cress, "and rub this into his throat and chest." She opened her father's nightshirt so that an inch or two of bony grizzled chest was bared. "He says that this rubbing relieves him, even if he's asleep or too tired to speak. Rub it in with a slow steady movement." She went out to the living room leaving the door a little ajar.

Cress sat down on the chair and put two squeamish fingers into the jar of gray ointment; but she could see far more sense to this than to any talking or being talked to. If they had brought her home from school because she was needed in helping to care for Grandpa, that she could understand—but not simply to be present at his death. What had death to do with her?

She leaned over him, rubbing, but with eyes shut, dipping her fingers often into the gray grease. The rhythm of the rubbing, the warmth and closeness of the room, after the cold drive, had almost put her to sleep when the old man startled her by lifting a shaking hand to the bunch of yellow violets Edith had pinned to the shoulder of her dress before she left Woolman. She opened her eyes suddenly at his touch, but the old man said nothing, only stroked the violets awkwardly with a trembling forefinger.

Cress unpinned the violets and put them in his hand. "There, Grandpa," she said, "there. They're for you."

The old man's voice was a harsh and faltering whisper and to hear what he said Cress had to lean very close.

"I used to—pick them—on Reservoir Hill. I was always sorry to—plow them up. Still—so sweet. Thanks," he said, "to bring them. To remember. You're like her. Your grandmother," he added after a pause. He closed his eyes, holding the bouquet against his face, letting the wilting blossoms spray across one cheek like a pulled-up sheet of flowering earth. He said one more word, not her name but her grandmother's.

The dikes about Cress's heart broke. "Oh Grandpa, I love you," she said. He heard her. He knew what she said, his fingers returned the pressure of her hand. "You were always so good to me. You were young and you loved flowers." Then she said what was her great discovery. "And you still do. You still love yellow violets, Grandpa, just like me."

At the sound of her uncontrolled crying, Mr. and Mrs. Delahanty came to the door. "What's the matter, Cress?"

Cress turned, lifted a hand toward them. "Why didn't you tell me?" she demanded. And when they didn't answer, she said, "Edwin knew."

Then she dropped her head on to her grandfather's outstretched hand and said something, evidently to him, which neither her father nor her mother understood.

"It's just the same."